INTRODUCTION TO
ENVIRONMENTAL PHYSIOLOGY

Perhaps this Task, which I have propos'd to myself, will incur the Censur of many judicious Men, who may think it an over-hasty, and presumptuous Attempt. . . . . . Although, therefore, I come to the Performance of this Work, with much less Deliberation, and Ability, than the Weightiness of it require; yet, I trust, that the Greatness of the Design itself, on which I am to speak, . . . will serve to make something for my Excuse.

Tho. Sprat
The History of the Royal Society
London, 1722 (3rd Edition)

Introduction To
ENVIRONMENTAL PHYSIOLOGY

Environmental Extremes and Mammalian Survival

G. EDGAR FOLK, JR., PH.D

Professor, Department of Physiology,
University of Iowa
Iowa City, Iowa

With 110 Illustrations

Lea & Febiger   Philadelphia

To my wife, Mary

Preface

This book is primarily concerned with the physiological responses of healthy mammals to natural changes or extremes of the physical environment. The use of the expression "healthy mammal" assumes that a young man who "feels it is too hot to work" is still a normal mammal. Thus, the emphasis on true Pathophysiology has been left to writers of other volumes that might be classified as Medical Biometeorology. The present volume is meant to illuminate one approach to Experimental Biology: that which accepts, describes, and analyzes the state of complex integration between mammalian life and its physical environment. This approach is called "holistic," and it considers plants, animals, and their environment as an entity or bio-ecologic whole, which (as with water) may take on characteristics not found in the components. The need for the study of this *entity* has been emphasized by Rene Dubos;[4] he stressed that much more attention must be given by the scientific community to the response of the total organism to the total environment. Sargent[17a] refers to this view of the entity as a holistic view: "First, we must think of the organism as a whole, not merely as a sum of separate parts (cells, tissues, organs, and systems). The whole organism reacts to environmental impacts, not just a part of the organism. Second, the . . . higher organisms are not free of their *milieu exterieur*. Rather they are cosmic resonators. . . Third, we must have the broadest possible concepts of the surround. While the micro-environment may contain the immediate effector system, that environment is in equilibrium with, or at least affected by, an environment that extends at least to the sun and perhaps even further." This means that we can never isolate an animal from its physical environment, nor can we move it without taking its environment with it. We have only moved a strand of the web or meshwork to a new position.

This relationship between organism and environment is described with a different emphasis by Platt *et al.* "Organisms themselves are relatively transient entities through which materials and energy flow and eventually return to the environment. The organism is at the mercy of the environment."[15]

The concept of time and space and the organism has not yet been mentioned. Some environmental physiologists, or biometeorologists as they are also called, have adopted the concept that functional and structural variations in organisms through time and space can be explained in terms of alterations in the atmospheric environment. According to this concept both genotypic and phenotypic variations arise from variation in the atmospheric environment. Thus for the sake of completeness it should be mentioned that the holistic view includes the concept of evolution as well as the relationship between the organism and the environment at any one moment.

This treatise on Environmental Physiology is intended for graduate students in science who have studied the fundamentals of mammalian physiology. The factors of heat, cold, light, atmospheric pressure, the water environment, and subtle environmental factors are considered, and the fundamental physiological reactions of mammals to these environmental extremes are listed. If inclusion of such a broad field is considered too bold, the following reasons are offered: (1) all physical environ-

7

mental factors must be considered, or else the belief in the holistic view has been contradicted; (2) all known factors are presented, a few just superficially, to provide a check list for the design of experiments, since these factors unnoticed by experimenters and engineers usually influence their results. Perhaps the two conditions most frequently overlooked are changes in hours-of-daylight and in barometric pressure. Yes, this book is meant to cover a broad field. If the graduate student is irritated by the numerous omissions, I have at least succeeded in drawing attention to a fascinating field to be delved into more deeply. If the reader is inspired to active experimentation, then my message has been successfully transmitted. Each chapter emphasizes by example the experimental approach to each area, rather than making polished generalizations about the subject matter.

The book was written in the hope that more graduate students will discover the appeal of this area of study. It does not appear to be a neglected area judging by the number of university courses in Environmental Physiology and Biometeorology; yet a few years ago a check list of fifty-nine monographs used at physiology teaching workshops did not include a single title which directly or indirectly referred to environment as an important factor. It is this neglect which prompted the article by Rene Dubos.

The title of this volume refers to *Mammalian* Environmental Physiology because comparative mammalian physiology has been included where it is concerned with environmental influences. This has been done, in part, for academic interest since many physiologists are fascinated by encyclopedic knowledge, such as the studies of the desert rats which revealed, among other facts, that they can produce the most concentrated mammalian urine known. But comparative mammalian physiology is a tool as well. The use of the comparative approach has been brilliantly demonstrated by Homer Smith in the area of kidney physiology. Yet, at this time, the professional associations of environmental physi-

ologists place most of the emphasis upon human subjects and dogs. This is unfortunate since the physiological success of one mammalian species explains the physiological failure of another. To assist those who wish more background in comparative mammalian physiology, the classification of the 18 orders of mammals is included in the Appendix.

The content of a physiological compendium often requires explanation; for example, I have been asked why the topic of daily (circadian) rhythms is included in a book on environmental physiology. In the first place, daily rhythms are the result of millions of years of the environmental conditioning of daylight and darkness. Secondly, the chapter on rhythms includes measurements from animals exposed to constant light and constant darkness, and even from isolated adrenal glands exposed to these environments; it contains descriptions of the recording of physiological rhythms by radio-telemetry from large arctic mammals maintained in large enclosures in inky darkness for the entire winter, at times at minus 55°F. These examples illustrate the material which led me to believe that daily biological rhythms must be considered an appropriate facet of Environmental Physiology.

Most chapters begin with Environmental Diagrams and also some appropriate condensed physiological information; both are intended for quick reference to values such as: footcandles in bright sunlight, or one of the highest recorded human body temperatures or one of the lowest. Similar figures are found in the *Handbook of Biological Data,* and also in *Temperature: its Measurement and Control in Biology and Medicine,* edited by J. D. Hardy.[9a] An Appendix contains references of several types, i.e., one list includes Ecology textbooks, to encourage the student of Environmental Physiology to familiarize himself with the literature and ideas of a related discipline.

G. Edgar Folk, Jr.
Iowa City, Iowa

Acknowledgements

It is a great pleasure to acknowledge my indebtedness to Professor John H. Welsh of Harvard University, whose inspiration and support have been a major influence on the writing of this book. Some of it was completed during tenure of a Traveling Fellowship of the College of Medicine Fund of the University of Iowa. The warm hospitality of Professors James F. Danielli and John Cloudsley-Thompson of King's College, University of London, was extended to me during this fellowship. The previously unpublished data from my laboratory included in this book were obtained in studies supported by the National Science Foundation; the experiments with human subjects were supported by the Iowa Mental Health Fund, Professor Paul E. Huston, Director. The writing of this book has been influenced by association from 1961 to 1965 with the Arctic Research Laboratory (Barrow) under the hospitality of Dr. Max C. Brewer and Dr. Max Britton, and the Arctic Aeromedical Laboratory (Fairbanks) with Dr. Horace F. Drury and Dr. Eugene Evonuk as hosts. It was my good fortune to be Visiting Research Professor at the Arctic Aeromedical Laboratory in 1964-1965. I am indebted to Professor M. L. Riedesel for reading three of the chapters, and to F. W. Kent and the University Photographic Service for valuable photographic assistance. Many thanks are due to Miss Shirley Lent for typing the entire manuscript and for editorial assistance, and to my wife, Mary Arp Folk, who spent countless hours as editor, and drew or redesigned each illustration. All illustrations from other publications have been redrawn with the permission of the authors and publishers. The Lea & Febiger staff, especially Richard P. Sullivan, John F. Spahr, and Victor J. Boland, have exhibited unfailing enthusiasm and co-operation in the publication of this book.

Contents

WHAT IS
ENVIRONMENTAL PHYSIOLOGY:
HISTORY AND TERMINOLOGY

What Is Environmental Physiology: History and Terminology

Mammalian Environmental Physiology as presented in this book is the study of healthy mammals in relation to their physical environment and as individuals rather than as members of populations and communities. "Environment" refers to the natural physical environment as studied in Geophysics. The word Geophysics is useful since there is some dispute as to just what specific ground is covered by the alternative terms "Meteorology" and "Climatology". Our expression "Environmental Physiology" appears to be what Buettner has called "Quantitative Biometeorology"[1], while for the same area ecologists would use the term "Autecology". Of the three, the most frequently used expression is "Environmental Physiology".

old as a concept but very new as an interdisciplinary science".[19]

The theoretical view of Darwin, found in his *The Origin of Species* stressed the interrelations of life and the physical environment. The study of this area was demarked by Haeckel in 1866, as "Oecology". This science (Ecology) was eventually roughly subdivided for practical reasons into: *Autecology,* the reactions between a species and its physical environment and *Synecology,* the causes behind the successions and fluctuations in plant and animal communities. The latter could be described as the web-of-life concept. The ecologists have evolved many thoughtful and stimulating ideas. The interested student of environmental physiology would do well to

> ENVIRONMENTAL PHYSIOLOGY = Quantitative Biometeorology = AUTECOLOGY

The interest in environmental influences, as implied in all three terms, has its origin in two conspicuous lines of thought: (1) medical, first taught by Hippocrates and (2) theoretical, first taught by Darwin. Hippocrates investigated the effects of weather and climate, and laid down the first set of principles of the man-environment concept. In the hundreds of years intervening, this concept was lost and was replaced by an emphasis upon *the disease* as the object of medical study. Today the holistic view of human health is again popular, which means that the old idea of man-environment interrelation is now being taught. As Sargent remarks, "biometeorology is very

ponder such terms as Biome and Biomass. On the other hand, modern second-thoughts about early ecology are enticingly presented by Ehrlich and Holm.[6]

During the period when the science of Ecology was developing, parallel groups of environmentalists were organizing independently. Some of these maintained an applied or medical interest. Each new area of interest was named by an authority in the field. The nature of the terms reflect an attempt to obtain a new orientation toward climatic effects. This emphasis upon a *point of view*, so often stressed by these authorities in the past, is the very justification for this book on environmental physiology.

The list of terms applied to environmental study-areas is included below because: (1) its length argues that a surprising number of scientists have sought to emphasize that "organisms and environment are one system," and (2) it will act as a checklist of terms for specialty interests in environmental studies:

A. Biological Emphasis:

Environmental Physiology, Biometeorology, Physiological Meteorology, Meteorobiology, Stress Physiology, Physiological Ecology, Bioclimatology, Physiological Climatology, Climatophysiology.

B. Human Emphasis:

Human Biometeorology, Human Climatology, Human Ecology, Climatopathology, Medical Climatology, Climatotherapy, Environmental Hygiene, Industrial Hygiene, and Medical Geography.

Scientists have an innate, if sometimes conflicting, tendency to integrate and systematize, so that a need has grown to condense or give priority within the above list. For a time it appeared as if the terms "Animal Ecology" and "Human Ecology" would suffice. Recently the area of Human Ecology has developed to the extent that its workers integrate appropriate data from the fields of Anthropology, Biology, Economics, Geography, Political Science, Psychology and Sociology; Human Ecology was not intended to include the study of pathological effects from climatic origin. Finally in 1956 an international congress of environmentalists decided to support the term Bioclimatology as first used by Carl Dorno in 1910.[1] A few years later the same group of workers changed the name of their discipline of study, the name of their society, and the name of their journal to *Biometeorology*; the group is now called the International Society of Biometerology.[22] Although this area seems to include all that has previously been demarked as Autecology, the new term is intended to cover the study of Pathophysiology as well as Normal Physiology. As defined by the society, "Biometeorology is the study of the direct and indirect interrelations between the geophysical and geochemical environment and living organisms, plants, animals, and man." The biometeorologist, then, is primarily concerned with the atmospheric environment and its effects on plants and animals. Biometeorology, like its more inclusive parent area Ecology, is an integrative and cross-discipline science. It must synthesize the cooperative data from meteorologist, biologist, and medical scientist. In attempting this it will face challenges and criticisms since some scientists will take extreme views: one group saying that biometeorology is superficial and obvious, and another group saying that integration of data must wait until our knowledge of medicine, biology, and the other sciences is more profound. However, even in scientific work you cannot please everyone. If biometeorologists were not making a conscientious attempt to integrate overlapping fields, there would be criticism for "lack of imagination".

The biometeorologist stresses the use of statistics; he conducts investigations in the field or in the laboratory under as rigidly controlled conditions as possible to describe measurable and reproducible physical, chemical, and biological factors which show a sufficiently high statistical correlation with measurable physiological and pathological processes to suggest a valid 'cause and effect' relationship between organism and environment. To obtain a sample of this philosophy, the student is urged to read the chapter by Sargent, "Biologic Variability and Human Biometeorology" in *Medical Climatology*.[12a]

A suggestion for the breakdown of areas now included under Biometeorology is given in Figure 1. A more detailed explanation of the areas which make up Biometeorology is presented by Tromp,[23] and the graduate opportunities in this field are described by Sargent [18] and Lee.[12]

Comparison of Environmental Physiology and Biometeorology

The study of Environmental Physiology is carried on in experimental chambers so that environmental conditions can be controlled; it is also pursued on the Sahara

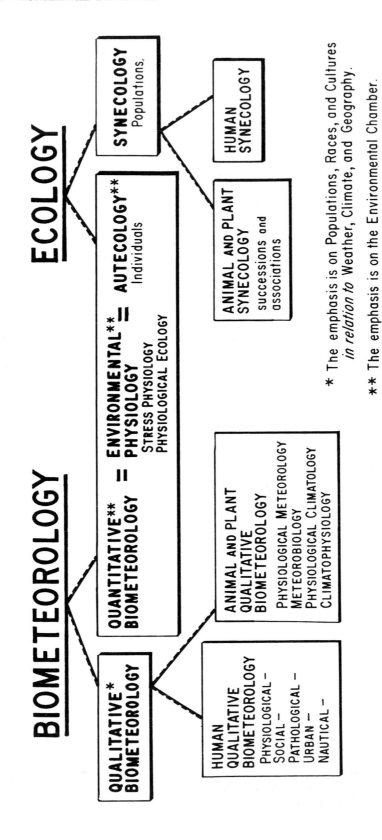

FIGURE 1. *Relationship Between Biometeorology and Ecology.* Environmentalists have organized independently the study-areas listed above to emphasize climatic effects upon animals and plants.

Desert, at the South Pole, and over the side of commercial fishing boats. In respectful deference to the hundreds of investigators who since the 18th century have shivered in cold rooms and baked in hot rooms along with their experimental animals, we must request that this term Environmental Physiology be retained as part of the "classification" of physiology.

This is preparation for the inevitable question from the advanced student as to what sort of scientific verbage he should apply to himself. In the past the professor could say that it did not matter, but today he knows that he himself may get three questionnaires in one week asking him to list the primary, secondary, and tertiary areas of his work and special interests. Thus to fit Environmental Physiology into the picture of Biometeorology is a practical matter. There is no sharp distinction but the working boundaries of the field can be delimited. The environmental physiologist works with individual species in chambers or on animals in the free environment, and attempts to standardize the conditions. He uses the term "ambient conditions" to describe the environment. He is doing what Hatch refers to as "defining the specifics", and is also measuring the excessive stress beyond which the animal can no longer adjust. Where does the biometeorologist raise his voice? When the vocabulary changes to weather, climate, geography, populations, races, and cultures, then one is probably working in the realm of Biometeorology. The biometeorologist as part of his interest synthesizes (or rejects) the data and generalizations of the enviornmental physiologist.* The flow of ideas is reversible—every environmental physiologist should ponder the concepts of the biometeorologist.

We have made a distinction between Biometeorology as a whole and Environmental Physiology (Quantitative Biometeorology); now a more precise definition of the latter is appropriate. Environmental Physiology is the study of animal-environment relationships with particular attention to the effects upon the animal of changes and extremes of the physical environment. The emphasis is upon the analysis of the methods whereby the animal tries to correct by homeokinetic mechanisms any harmful changes in physiological status.

Objectives Defined

The physiological responses of healthy mammals to normal changes or extremes of the physical environment will be considered. Such factors as heat, cold, light and pressure will each be considered separately. Such a treatment is an oversimplification. To be more realistic, note that a single environmental factor is often affected by a related variable: heat exposure may be with high humidity and with or without a wind. This experimental approach of studying single factors is that used in the study of organs: in cardiac research the factors of temperature, blood chemistry, and nerve activity have to be studied individually whereas under "natural" circumstances they act together. In a like manner, light and temperature act together upon the whole organism, but they are first studied separately by the environmental physiologist.

Some environmental responses may be altered quantitatively, as will be shown by describing results from acute, short, and chronic exposure. This approach needs no

---

* Sargent distinguishes between the two approaches as follows: "The work . . . follows two broad avenues. In the one instance the questions are submitted to investigation in a controlled environment . . . one or more environmental factors can be varied at a time and frequently the observations can be expressed in equations. In the other instance, the questions are submitted to investigation in the natural environment; i.e., the weather. Controlled conditions are more difficult to achieve. One frequently has to employ complex statistical procedures to bring out weather effects . . . The biometeorologist who studies weather must have an ecological point of view in order properly to evaluate and interpret his observations. His facts must be scrutinized in such a way that the impact of the total environment is evaluated. Only from this viewpoint can he realistically assign relative significance to weather".[18]

explanation, but material on *animal behavior* will also be included and this needs some defense. Emphasis will be placed upon the sum of the physiological responses of the whole mammal so that in some cases it will be difficult to separate physiological responses from behavioral responses. The difference between these two responses could be better understood by observing the responses of cats and white rats to a cold environment: in the cat the piloerector muscles contract and each hair stands out straight, a physiological response; white rats, as described by Richter,[17] increase their utilization of nesting material (in terms of lengths of ticker-tape) in direct proportion to the decrease in environmental temperature, a behavioral response. The contribution of behavior to temperature regulation is also observed when the "cold mammal" curls itself into a ball, and when the "hot mammal" stretches out to increase surface area. Many such illustrations demonstrate that behavior warrants inclusion in the analyses concerned with Environmental Physiology. A final stated objective of this field of study is to condense appropriate material from Comparative Mammalian Physiology.

Limitations of the Experimental Approach

To record the responses of individual mammals or single species in a single extreme environment may be partially justified by the evidence of observations made in the free environment; frequently a change in one physical factor persists or dominates for long periods. On the other hand the more usual experience of the mammals is to receive a barrage of simultaneous environmental changes including wind, rain, hail, cold, and perhaps a drop in barometric pressure at the same time. In the Kalahari Desert, where the nights are cold and the days are hot, any study of the large mammals would require the assumption that they may be simultaneously heat-acclimatized and cold-acclimatized. Experimental work with environ-

mental factors has usually consisted of oversimplifying the problem by using one or two variables, but a few workers have studied the combined effect of several environmental extremes. These more complex experiments are discussed in the last chapter of this book, but most of the other chapters consider only one environmental variable at a time.

This overemphasis upon the effects of a single environmental factor can be criticized, as can experiments upon individual mammals and individual species. Such an approach contradicts, in a sense that has not been discussed, part of the concept that organisms and environment are one system: namely the obvious fact that animals affect each other. These biotic influences will receive little consideration since our attention is focused upon the responses of individual mammals. A warning is appropriate, however, that biotic factors can profoundly influence the experiments of the environmental physiologist. Many illustrations can be found: the number of rodents reared in a cage affects the time of puberty of the group; several rodents huddled together may have an oxygen consumption which is less than the sum of the oxygen-consumptions of all animals measured separately; if groups of male mice or rats are kept together in cages, we will detect enlargement of the adrenal glands of the low animals in the "peck-order of dominance"[12b] or of a late arrival in the cage, and these individuals may show altered temperature regulation (Fig. 2). The effects due to "number of animals" of the same species has received careful study by ecologists under the name of density-dependent phenomena.

To summarize, in spite of the fact that man does not live in a climatic chamber and the normal life of other mammals is not one of "solitary confinement", still, to define the "specifics" of environmental responses, the physiologist must make many of his studies under controlled but restricted conditions. In the future these workers may be able to compare their laboratory results with more realistic measurements made on free mammals. These

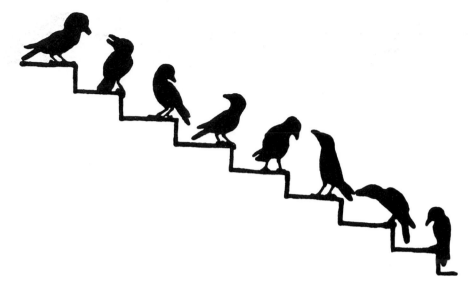

FIGURE 2. *"Pecking Order" as Depicted by Lorenz.* Groups of animals are very apt to set up an order of rank known as the "pecking order". The relationships between each individual and all community members were studied by Lorenz in a flock of semi-tame jackdaws. From Lorenz.[12b]

measurements may even be obtained on many body functions with instruments which record through radio-transmitters.[7, 8]

Natural Physical Environments

What physical environmental factors do the physiologists consider "natural"? This question is not concerned with a division between normal physiological responses and pathology. The physiologist does not attempt to separate himself from data on mammals experiencing environmental-sickness. On the contrary these sicknesses such as heat-stroke or "the bends" delimit range-of-tolerance. It is, however, a question of emphasis in that our primary interest is analysis of any "healthy success" in combating the extreme environment. In cases where climate aggravates a disease or where climate plays a role in treatment of disease, the medical biometeorologists are handling the data. Likewise, specially trained individuals are now available to study problems of toxicology, air pollution, and other divisions of Environmental

Hygiene. If we are looking for a workable dividing line between types of environmentalists, the amount of interest in Pathology does not help, but the use of two classes of physical environments does: 1) natural and 2) artificial. In defining the word *natural environment* a helpful test is the question: does any mammalian species as a *whole* experience a conspicuous physical change due to the addition of this factor? As a working plan we can divide the agents and energies in the environment as follows:

Natural Physical Environments

1. Heat
2. Cold
3. Humidity
4. Water effects on skin
5. Air movement
6. Barometric and deep water pressure
7. Visible light
8. Subtle factors: cosmic radiations, atmospheric electricity and terrestrial magnetism
9. Ultraviolet light
10. Substratum
11. Dust

Artificial Physical Environments

1. Atmospheric pollution from industry: smog; toxic factors in water.
2. High levels of gases: carbon dioxide, ozone
3. Mechanical Factors: noise, ultrasonics, infrasonics, motion sickness
4. Ionizing Radiation: isotopes, x-rays
5. Allergy producing aerosols (a special factor for about 10–20% of human subjects)
6. Artificial ionization of air

This classification is practical, but some environments are listed as natural when it is not yet certain whether they have an important influence upon the behavior and health of any mammals. The nutritional factor is not included since it is too complicated a component of the physical environment to be considered in detail; yet it should be pointed out that many experiments have been affected by seasonal fluctuations in dietary preference, calories consumed, and vitamin content and acidity of foods. The last topics on the "Natural" list: ultraviolet light, subtratum, and dust will not be given detailed consideration. They represent conspicuous factors associated with anatomical adaptations which developed during what evolutionists call "adaptive radiation" of mammals. It is obvious that cattle have defenses against sunburn from ultraviolet light; the specializations for living on a rocky substratum (mountain goats and sheep), compared with those for fertile moist soil, are mostly associated with coordination. As for wind-blown dust, it is evident that this too can control the distribution of mammals, unless they have adaptations to combat it. Attention must now be turned from the environment to the animals themselves, as we ask how they respond to extremes of the natural environments.

Cannon's Emergency Syndrome and the General Adaptation Syndrome

The responses of mammals to changes in factors such as heat, cold and altitude will be discussed. An acute or sudden exposure to one, of these environmental extremes is apt to cause a rapid response referred to as Cannon's Emergency Syndrome, or the "flee, fright, or fight" syndrome. The Emergency Syndrome is usually dramatically revealed to a person who has nearly had a violent or traumatic accident. One to two minutes later the knees of the individual may shake violently, with an accompanying overall weakness. The delayed response is considered evidence for the endocrine component of the syndrome. The importance of this response in Environmental Physiology is illustrated by exposing to extreme cold a cat with the sympathetic nerve chain removed on one side. In the cold room the hair is not erected to increase insulation on the side without a sympathetic nerve chain. If the sympathetic chains are removed on both sides, the cat is completely unable to tolerate cold exposure.

The General Adaptation Syndrome of Selye,[21] also confusingly called the "Stress Syndrome", occurs when there is gradual or prolonged exposure to some of the extremes of the physical environment; it is also induced by other factors such as: (a) internally introduced agents typified by toxins, or (b) by holding a low position in the "peck-order of dominance" in an animal population. The Adaptation Syndrome is recognized by a series of physiological changes of which the most typical are in the adrenal glands. If exposure to an extreme environment is prolonged, there is a gradual increase in weight of the adrenal glands; then there is a successive loss of lipid in the adrenal cortex, followed by a regain of the control level of lipid in the enlarged gland. Selye defines the new condition as a "state manifested by a specific syndrome which consists of all non-specifically induced changes within a biological system." It has been difficult to detect in human subjects those changes which are characteristic of the General Adaptation Syndrome in lower mammals. It is partly for this reason that physiologists have had to use an additional expression to describe adjustments of all animals to environmental changes. Their

Table 1. Conventional Uses of Terms for Acclimatization Responses As Published in the 20th Century

Dates	Uses or Definitions	References
	ACCLIMATIZATION	
1945–1952	A series of titles on acquired acclimatization to cold of various species of mammals: Frazier (1945), Horvath (1947), Adolph (1950), Glazer (1950), Carlson (1951), Sellers (1951), Dugal (1952).	Quoted from Burton & Edholm (1955, p. 195)
1955	"Acclimatization To Cold": Chapter 10	Burton & Edholm (1955)
1938	". . . the major step in (heat) acclimatization was accomplished before reaching Boulder City or at any rate within 24 hours of arrival."	Dill (1938)
1950	"Working ability of Bantu mineworkers with reference to acclimatization to hot humid conditions".	Weiner (1950)
1938	"(in this respect) Hall was unable to detect any changes in the blood of the members of our party during acclimatization, even at 20,000 feet."	Dill (1938)
1955	"Effects of oxygen on acclimatized men at high altitudes".	Pugh (1955)
	An earlier example (1878): "This would explain, not (only) the acclimatization of the individual, but that of the race."	Bert (1878) quoted by Dill (1938)

conventional term has been *acclimatization,* since the term "Adaptation Syndrome" does not appear to apply to man and since there are many expressions of special types of acclimatization which are not part of the Adaptation Syndrome. An example of these special acclimatization effects is the change, after prolonged exposure to high altitude, in red cell count from about 5 million/mm³ to 8 million/mm³.

Acclimatization and the Rules for Uniform Terminology

The concept of acclimatization has been studied by physiologists for many years, and use of the term became common in physiological titles after 1944 (Table 1). Recently their use of the term "acclimatization" has been challenged. Since the present book is entirely concerned with response to extreme environments, it is obviously necessary to take care in deciding what the basic expression will be to describe the changed state of adjustment of a mammal after exposure to an extreme environment.

One group of biologists has defined acclimatization as: "The adjustment or increase of tolerance shown by a species *in the course of several generations* in a changed environment." These workers, especially Sealander,[20] Heistand,[11] and the Committee on Nomenclature of the American Ecological Society, have been making a conscientious and commendable effort to place the vocabulary of their special fields on a precise and exact basis. Difficulty has arisen because they were unaware that simultaneous attempts by other biologists to standardize terminology have resulted in opposing definitions. Look at the predicament we are in now! Hart in 1950, experimenting on deer mice in the cold, stated: "Acclimatization: the changes in the responses of the organism produced by continued alterations in the environment". A year later another author, also experimenting on deer mice in the cold, stated: "The term acclimatization should be reserved for long term adjustments which involve evolutionary changes over generations as the result of selection by the environment." [20] These opposite uses of these terms demonstrate that biologists must try to attain more uniformity in designating major areas of study. If they do not, graduate students and other workers of the next ten years will be more confused than ever and will probably invent a vocabulary of their own. To attain uniformity, the rules for selecting and using a scientific term should be:

1. Priority of publication should be honored in the customary fashion by exact citations and discussions. Arbitrary definitions without citations are harmful.

2. If two accepted synonyms occur for a single phenomenon, and one of these synonyms has several other meanings, its use should be abandoned in favor of the term which has only a single meaning.

The first rule speaks for itself. The second rule can be illustrated by discussing the usage in this book of three important expressions: 24-hour rhythms, general adaptation syndrome, and acclimatization. The first example concerns giving up the conventional term "diurnal rhythm" in favor of its synonym *24-hour rhythm*. This was done by vote of the Society for Biological Rhythms because "diurnal" has two meanings: (1) day-active and (2) 24-hour. "Diurnal" had to be defined each time it was used, but "24-hour" is self-defining. A more accurate term than 24-hour is now used, *circadian*. The reason will be explained in Chapter 3.

The second example of accepted synonyms concerns the dual terminology *Stress Syndrome* and *General Adaptation Syndrome*. The former has been abandoned by most physiologists because "stress" is customarily thought of as "a condition of the atmospheric environment which provokes a physiological response (a strain)." Examples are heat and cold stress. "General Adaptation Syndrome" refers to *reactions* of the organism (distress), while "stress" refers to the environmental condition *inducing* this reaction. We speak of environmental stresses and physiological strains.

The third example of dual terminology, *adaptation* vs. *acclimatization,* has already received some discussion. Three authors seem to suggest (Table 2) that the term "acclimatization" be reserved for adjustments which are inherited. Such an inheritance has usually been called an ex-

Table 2. Recent and Changed Terminology for Acclimatization Responses With Meaning Contrary to Conventional Use

Dates	Uses or Definitions	References
	ACCLIMATIZATION	
1951	The term acclimatization . . . "should be reserved for long term adjustments which involve evolutionary changes over generations as the result of selection by the environment." No supporting reference given.	Sealander (1951)
1952	Acclimatization is the adjustment or increase of tolerance shown by a species in the course of several generations in a changed environment . . . (Committee of Nomenclature of the Ecological Society of America).	Eggleton (1952)
1955	The writers considered *acclimatization* to mean physiological adjustments for long periods involving evolutionary changes.	Heistand *et al.* (1955)

Table 3. Early Published Usages of Terms Related to Acclimatization Responses

Material condensed from: *A New English Dictionary* 1888
J. A. H. Murray, Editor
1: 57 (Oxford)

Dates	Uses or Definitions

ACCLIMATIZATION, ACCLIMATIZE

Acclimatize: a more recent and common adaptation of the French word "Acclimater".

1830–1881	"This acclimatization has been the result of natural selection . . ." (1830); "(I) have become acclimatized" (1836); "The Sardinians, now acclimatized" (1855); "(the new) settlers easily acclimatized to the new locality" (1862); ". . . a series of acclimatizable animals" (1860); "the turkey was one of our best acclimalisations." (1864); "(I) get readily acclimatized to unfamiliar surroundings" (1876); "(He) cannot acclimatize himself . . ." (1877); ". . . attempts to acclimatise particularly useful species" (1880); ". . . successful attempts of acclimatisation of domestic species" (1880); "an acclimatised grey parrot is hardy." (1881).
1878	Definition (Bartley): "Acclimatization is accommodation to new climatic conditions with the intervention of man in this accommodation."
1888	Definition (Murray): "Acclimatization, like acclimation, is the process of being habituated or inured to a new climate, or to one not natural."

ample of an "adaptation," except by these three authors. It is first necessary to ask whether their definition, which follows, stands the test of priority of publication: "acclimatization is the adjustment shown by a species in the course of several generations." To answer this dilemma the sources studied were *A New English Dictionary* [14] and the often quoted article by Monge: "Life In the Andes and Chronic Mountain Sickness".[13] *A New English Dictionary* was published by a committee of scholars and scientists in 1888, who documented their definitions with quotations from published articles of well-known authors. These quotations have been shortened for inclusion in Table 3. This evidence shows that the word "acclimatization" was not, in practice, restricted to cases where several generations were involved. It was used both to indicate change in the lifetime of an individual, as well as changes over a number of generations. Both usages are confirmed in the classic paper by Monge on acclimatization to high altitude. His paper states that a person who has high altitude sickness

may adjust sufficiently (after months or years) and then *the person* may be said to be acclimatized. This is implicit in his lines: "When the adaptation malady is over, acclimatization supervenes: so-called chronic mountain sickness has been cured." To differentiate the two usages Monge called one "acquired acclimatization" and the other "congenital or ancestral acclimatization". However, it should be pointed out that usually when Monge used the term he meant the ancestral acclimatization evident in the "climatophysiological variety of the human race" which lives at high altitude. Thus, evidence is still lacking to *restrict* the term acclimatization to changes over several generations. There is no reason for physiologists to give up the term, and it would be an excellent one to retain because the stem "climate" connotes those experimental atmospheric conditions of extreme heat, cold, and high altitude.

Acclimate

Recently there has been increased use

Table 4. Acclimate, Acclimation
From Murray's Dictionary (1888)

Dates	Uses or Definitions

ACCLIMATE, ACCLIMATION

	Acclimate: the earliest English term to be derived from the French word "Acclimater".
1792–1872	". . . where the Arbutus is so acclimated that it seems indigenous." (1792); "(I) could temper my acclimation" (1853); "(I) am acclimated to such incidents" (1856); ". . . with deer acclimation is easy" (1859); ". . . idea of acclimating the eland" (1855); ". . . acclimatation of silkworms . . ." (1863); ". . . acclimatation of pheasants . . ." (1859); ". . . (low mortality) among acclimated New Orleanists" (1862); "(this man) is well acclimated . . ." (1872).
1878	Definition (Bartley): "Acclimation is the spontaneous and natural accommodation to new climatic conditions."
1888	Definition (Murray): "Acclimation is the process of being habituated or inured to a new climate, or to one not natural."

of the word "acclimate." A survey of its very early use (and thus the priority of publication) is given in Table 4. Comparing in this table the history of the use of acclimate with acclimatize, we find very little difference.

A System of Terms for Responses to Extreme Environments

A revised and new system of use of terms is justified if it is needed and if precisely described in the literature. Just such a necessary revision has been developed over many years by Hart [10] and Dill,[2] with a recent contribution by Eagan.[5] All of the new terms or uses, as far as I can determine, fit the rule of "priority of publication." Use of the term *acclimatization* has been strengthened; a new use for the term *acclimate* has been formalized; a new term *habituate* has been introduced; and the principles or biological processes involved with all three terms are now grouped under one generic term: *adaptation*. The early use and the later history of this last term justifies our use of it today in more than an evolutionary sense. As stated by Prosser:[2,16] "Adaptation is a word which has numerous meanings in biology. It broadly relates differences within and between organisms to environmental varia-

tion. For some biologists, adaptation refers to genetically determined, usually morphological, characters by which an animal or plant is fitted for its environment. For physiologists, the term refers to environmentally determined as well as to genetic variations. We shall use "physiological adaptation" to mean any property of an organism which favors survival in a specific environment, particularly a stressful one." A biological era has begun in which we refer to *adaptational physiology* with subdivisions of meaning according to time, place, and degree of environmental stress. Physiological adaptations are all those changes in the physiological responses and the morphologies of organisms which result from changes in environment. Subdivisions as listed by Eagan are:

(1) *"genetic"* adaptation—used for alterations which favor survival of a species or of a strain in a particular environment, which alterations have become part of the genetic heritage of the particular species or strain. This is the same as acclimatization of the race.

(2) *acclimatization*—the functional compensation over a period of days to weeks in response to a complex of environmental factors, as in seasonal or climatic changes.

(3) *acclimation*—the functional compensation over a period of days to weeks in response to a single environmental factor *only*, as in controlled experiments.

(4) *habituation:* a separate section is found below on this topic.

An impressive crystalization of these terms is found in the *Handbook of Physiology,* Section Four, entitled: "Adaptation to the Environment." Most of this volume of 1056 pages is concerned with acclimatizations. Another group of workers sought a precise system of terminology, yet still made an error: a large international symposium (Leiden, 1962) was titled "International Symposium on Temperature Acclimation." Many papers were concerned with measurements on men in the free environment, and thus, acclimatization. The title of a similar symposium in the future would undoubtedly be: "Temperature Adaptation."

Habituation

Several studies on habituation in thermal physiology have been done by Glaser.[9] It is defined as "the process of forming into a habit or accustoming"; this implies that it "depends on the mind, that it is reversible and that it may involve the diminution of normal responses or sensations." In the session on Motivation, Learning and Behaviour at the 1962 Federation Meetings, Doty[3] gave a comprehensive background for the understanding of habituation. Eagan[5] suggests two types:

(1) *specific habituation*—"specific to a particular repeated stimulus and specific to the part of the body which has been repeatedly stimulated; this is a diminution in sensation associated with the particular stimulus; an example is a progressive diminution in cold pain associated with repeated severe cooling of a particular finger."

(2) *general habituation*—"a change in the psychological 'set' of the organism relevant to the repeated stimulus and the conditions incidental to its application; the result is a diminution in a physiological effector response to the stimulus; an example would be a reduced vasoconstrictor outflow to all of the periphery during cold exposure of any of the fingers although only one particular finger was repeatedly cooled over several days."

We will now turn our attention in the following chapters to individual examples of acclimatization and acclimation.

THE INFLUENCE OF

VISIBLE LIGHT RADIATIONS

THE LIGHT ENVIRONMENT

> **Some radiations which are non-thermally effective:**
>
> Ultra Violet
> X-ray   and   Visible Radiations
> Cosmic

Radiation Wavelengths

Electro Magnetic Waves   (Å units)

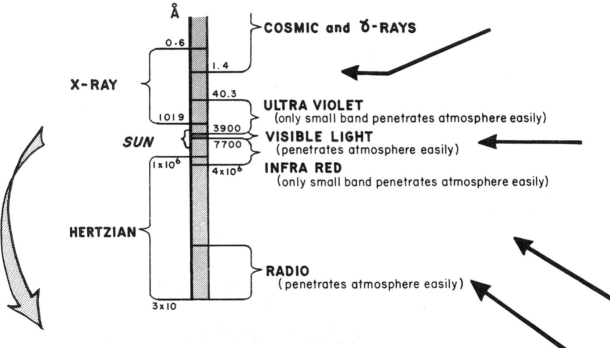

COSMIC and γ-RAYS

X-RAY

0.6
1.4
40.3
1019

SUN

ULTRA VIOLET
(only small band penetrates atmosphere easily)

3900
7700

VISIBLE LIGHT
(penetrates atmosphere easily)

1x10⁶   4x10⁶

INFRA RED
(only small band penetrates atmosphere easily)

HERTZIAN

RADIO
(penetrates atmosphere easily)

3x10

Visible Light and Part of Ultra Violet (enlarged)

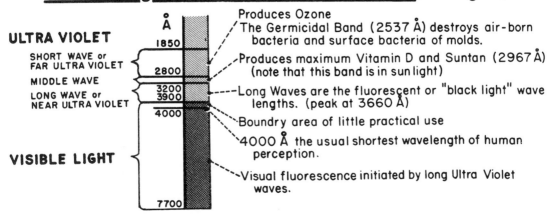

ULTRA VIOLET

SHORT WAVE or
FAR ULTRA VIOLET

MIDDLE WAVE

LONG WAVE or
NEAR ULTRA VIOLET

VISIBLE LIGHT

Å
1850
2800
3200
3900
4000

7700

Produces Ozone
The Germicidal Band (2537 Å) destroys air-born bacteria and surface bacteria of molds.

Produces maximum Vitamin D and Suntan (2967Å)
(note that this band is in sun light)

Long Waves are the fluorescent or "black light" wave lengths. (peak at 3660 Å)

Boundry area of little practical use

4000 Å the usual shortest wavelength of human perception.

Visual fluorescence initiated by long Ultra Violet waves.

THE PHYSIOLOGICAL EFFECTS OF LIGHT

X-RAY. Safe dose is average exposure of 5 roentgens per year. A natural source in space, but an artificial problem below the atmosphere.

VISIBLE LIGHT transfers energy onto single atoms.

VISIBLE LIGHT changes protoplasmic viscosity, causes phototropism, changes electrical charge of protoplasm, alters permeability and protoplasmic streaming, affects colloidal behavior of proteins, and energizes photosynthesis.

VISIBLE LIGHT stimulates special tissue if responsive (photoreceptors), resulting in vision. This is a special quality as a visible form of energy.

VISIBLE LIGHT rejuvinates microorganisms which have been injured by ultraviolet (photorecovery).

VISIBLE LIGHT acts (mostly on retina) upon the pituitary-hypothalamus areas to: (1) control skin color of amphibia and fish; (2) control or induce 24-hour rhythms in mammals and other vertebrates; (3) induce biochemical and behavioral changes (photoperiodism) in mammals and other vertebrates.

INFRA-RED. Human skin reflects 43% and absorbs 57% of solar radiation. Long-wave, nonpenetrating infrared radiation is almost totally absorbed at the surface of the skin.

RADIO. No known physiological effects.

DAILY, GEOGRAPHICAL & SEASONAL VARIATION IN SUNLIGHT ENVIRONMENT
(if unclouded sky)

(A) Daily - In Shade

MIDSUMMER { under North Temperate Evergreen Forest
under Tropical Rain Forest
under 100 meters of Ocean Water

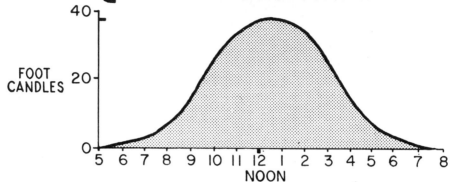

FOOT CANDLES

NOON

(B) Daily - In Direct Sunlight
North Temperate Area

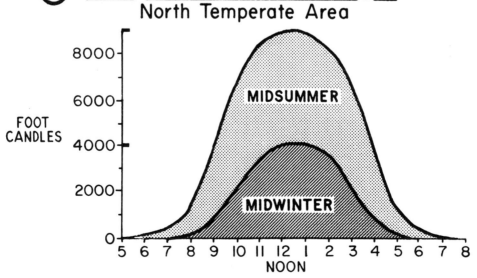

FOOT CANDLES

MIDSUMMER

MIDWINTER

NOON

The above is approximate. Total sun hours may vary from year to year more than 16% due to clouds.

C Geographical

The daily radiative solar intensity upon a horizontal surface at sea level.

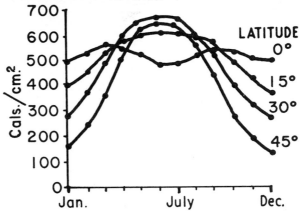

D Extreme Seasonal
ARCTIC & ANTARCTIC

There are *3 arctic* cities of 10,000 inhabitants in Norway and Sweden alone. Example:

Tromsø, 69°39' N, is 200 miles north of the Arctic Circle, and 1400 miles from the North Pole. *Light variation:*

WINTER	SPRING	SUMMER	AUTUMN
Continuous Darkness	Short days becoming Long days	Continuous Light	Short nights becoming Long nights
Nov. 21 – Jan. 23	Jan. 23 – May 21	May 21 – July 23	July 23 – Nov. 21

THE DEVELOPMENT OF CONTINUOUS DARKNESS

The "Shortest day of the Year" at different latitudes.

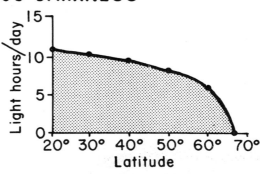

Influence of Visible Light Radiation

The contrast between daylight and darkness provides a daily environmental extreme that usually causes free-mammals to either avoid light, or conceal themselves during darkness. This daily extreme has a geographical amplification near the two Poles where many thousands of people and their domestic animals experience two or more months of continuous light and of continuous darkness (introductory diagram *D, E*). The stages of this change from Equator to 45° of latitude are also shown (introductory diagram *C*). Light to most biologists means "Visible Light," probably because the physiological effects of natural *invisible* light are minor (summarized in introductory diagram *A*).

Terminology

Some essential points about radiant energy of light are: when a molecule (or atom) absorbs a quantum of energy it becomes excited; the absorption of a quantum of light produces only one activated molecule; the energy absorbed may be reradiated at the same wavelength (resonance) or at longer wavelengths (fluorescence), or degraded to heat. Wavelengths of radiations are measured in Å = Ångstrom unit = 10^{-8} cm, a unit of wavelength; $1m\mu = 10\text{Å}$.

When light is responsible for a biological phenomenon, we must first ask whether its action is due to quality of light (wavelength or color), the intensity (actual energy measured in gram-calories or foot-candles), or the duration (length of day-light). Depending upon its type of action, visible light has four direct effects upon mammals: 1) it harms or stimulates all exposed or weakly protected cells, 2) it stimulates photoreceptors, 3) it is responsible for photoperiodism, and 4) it governs 24-hour (circadian) rhythms. The last topic will receive extensive treatment in the next chapter; the present discussion will concern only photoperiodism.

A biological phenomenon demonstrates *photoperiodism* (plants) or *photoperiodicity* (animals) if it changes systematically with either an increase or a decrease in the daily duration of illumination. The most typical effect is found with *some* reproductive cycles. Another type of photoperiodic phenomenon changes with *intensity* of illumination (quantity of energy) instead of with increases or decreases in exposure time. This second effect is particularly evident when some birds or mammals are maintained in continuous light. Their time of starting daily 24-hour sequences of locomotor activity is altered by this environment; the amount of modification depends upon the intensity of light. Examples of the first type, photoperiodic control over the reproduction of some plants and animals, will be discussed first. Plant experiments are included since they serve as a model and were begun long before any animal experiments in this field.

Responses To a Photoperiod (Light and Darkness)

The intensity of light does not always have an effect in photoperiodic control of reproduction, but length of daylight is all-important. Thus a stimulus which is reproducible from year to year is "used" by plants, and they avoid complete dependence upon *sun hours,* which may vary from

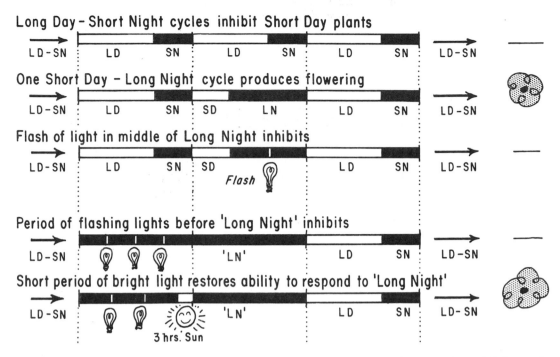

FIGURE 3. *Photoperiod and Short-Day Plants.* The kinetics of the interplay of light and darkness with short-day plants. These experiments on the cocklebur show the persistent after effects of *one long night* of photoperiodic treatment, resulting in subsequent flowering under formerly unfavorable conditions. The single long-night period must be linked with an appropriate preceding period of high intensity light. From Hamner.[42a]

year to year. Early theorizing about the influence of length of daylight began in 1852. By 1912 Ternois had shown that hemp and hops will flower if daylight is shortened to 6 hours. The first two authoritative papers were written by Cajlachjan,[30] and Garner and Allard.[41] Today knowledge of plant photoperiodicity permits the classification: 1) long-day plants which bloom with more than 12 hours of light per day; 2) short-day plants which bloom with less than 12 hours; and 3) plants of wide tolerance with light not a limiting factor. Not only blooming may be controlled by duration of daylight, but also 1) germination of seeds, 2) growth of entire plant, 3) formation of bulbs, 4) shape of plant (rosette or spreading), 5) autumn falling of leaves, and 6) sex of individual plant. The duration of the daylight is not the only factor in both animal and plant photoperiodism, but the *night length* (either alone or with a changed day length) may be important. Evidence is easily obtained by interrupting the dark period by a flash of light. Experiments with the cocklebur showed that after one exposure to a long night (LN) the plants would flower, but a single flash of light in the dark period would inhibit flowering (Fig. 3). In other species the flash of light may promote flowering.[50, 52, 48] This sensitive control over a growth process reminds one of the chemistry of photographic processes. Plant chemistry is certainly involved, since we know that one artificially darkened leaf on a lighted plant can control the flowering that occurs at some distance from the leaf at the end of the stem. Primarily due to the experiments of Hendricks, it can now be said that the initial photo-controls through which changes in light cause plants to respond are known, but the compounds (pigments) and enzymes involved are still to be found. This photo-reaction is described by Hendricks [44] as follows:

tion, and in the analysis of this topic it is reasonable to compare the photoperiodic controls of plants and mammals. At first

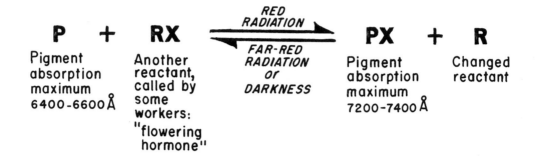

P + RX
Pigment absorption maximum 6400-6600 Å

Another reactant, called by some workers: "flowering hormone"

RED RADIATION
FAR-RED RADIATION or DARKNESS

PX + R
Pigment absorption maximum 7200-7400 Å

Changed reactant

The pigment (P) is now called phytochrome; apparently it is a protein which exists in a growth and flowering inhibiting form which is converted to a non-inhibiting form.

The photoperiodic effects on some birds and some mammals include: 1) the inducing of reproductive condition with an increase or a decrease in daylight hours, 2) migration, 3) seasonal changes in feather or hair coat. Most experimental work has been concerned with reproduc-

this seems to be straining a point, until we realize that the same photochemical-like experiments which were done on plants have been duplicated on some species of birds and sheep. Specifically, some varieties of sheep come into estrus only when the days are short and nights are long, but this effect is prevented by interrupting the night period as described above in plant experiments.[57]

Some mammalian photoperiodic responses experimentally produced are:

SPECIES	RESPONSES	
	Short Days and Long Nights	Long Days and Short Nights
Mink	Mating and delayed implantation	Non-reproductive growth
Northern Weasel	Non-reproductive growth and ermine coat	Mating
Domestic Cat	....	Unseasonal estrus
White Rats on poor diet	....	Higher incidence of mating
Sheep	Mating	Bearing of young (6 months' gestation)
Horse	Non-reproductive growth and winter coat formation	Mating and bearing of young (11 months' gestation)

Further details of other mammalian photoperiodic effects have been reviewed by Farner[34,35] and Hart.[2]

With some mammals the photoperiodic response is independent of temperature (weasel), but with others the response can be prevented by cold (sheep) (Fig. 4). Of

"Many but not all birds are sexually photoperiodic and some respond to factors other than light or in addition to it. Some may be controlled by an inherent rhythm accelerated or retarded by changes in environmental factors, or independent of them." Examples of independent inherent rhythms

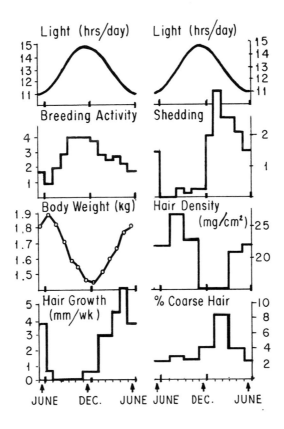

FIGURE 4. *Photoperiod and Seasonal Changes in Ferrets.* Correlation of changes in daylight with those attributes of male ferrets which are governed by daylight. Note that in Australia, day length increases from June to December. From Harvey and Macfarlane.[43a]

course all mammals do not respond to light changes; other environmental factors may trigger growth of reproductive organs and mating. One must also take into account an internal reproductive rhythm, perhaps 12 months in length, which would follow its course even if the physical environment were unchanging. To sum up these factors, we note what Bissonnette[28] has said of birds, which also applies to mammals:

are not difficult to find. One need only keep male and female frogs in hibernation in a refrigerator at 38° F all winter. When spring comes 8 months later, the frogs, still in the constant conditions of the refrigerator, will spawn. Baker and Bird[26] list many species of plants with inherent rhythms, of which the most interesting is a carefully studied specimen of the plant *Breynia cornus*, which exhibited a flowering period about every

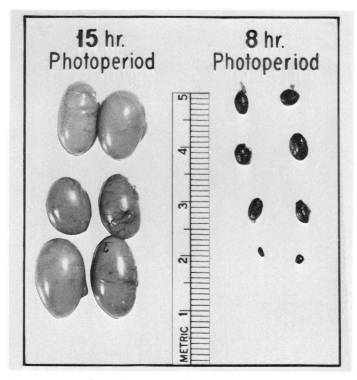

FIGURE 5. *Photoperiod and Starling Reproduction.* The condition of the testes of male starlings after maintaining two groups from December 1st to April 1st under two different photoperiods. The testes of four birds from the short daylight group are shown and three birds from the long daylight group.

5½ months for 11 years. Marshall [51] implies that more birds than mammals have completely freed themselves from external seasonal influences. Out of a large list of examples, the classic example is that of the sooty tern which has a breeding season about every 9 months. On the other hand all higher animals do not possess an internal rhythm associated with the reproductive system. The species of bird with which Farner has developed some of the principles of animal photoperiodicity, the white-crowned sparrow, is among the most completely photoperiodic of any species [36].

When this bird is held on short daily photoperiods of 8 hours or less there is no measurable gonadal development up to at least a year. Wolfson has contributed similar advances using a bird with a stronger internal reproductive rhythm, the slate-colored junco [59] (Fig. 6; See also Fig. 5.)

The numerous photoperiodic responses tabulated earlier are the superficially evident ones. Let us look at some less conspicuous ones which form a chain of events in migratory birds. The following sequence seems to be triggered by light changes: 1) fat is deposited (as much as ⅓ of body weight); 2) the day-active animal becomes nocturnal; 3) migration occurs; 4) breeding occurs; 5) there is a period of molt and inactivity; 6) fat is deposited again; 7) migration occurs. Part of this sequence undoubtedly applies to migratory mammals (sea otters, seals, whales, caribou). In order to investigate the internal mechanism responsible for photoperiodic responses, it must be decided which of these physiological events could be primary (possibly fat-deposition?). This "event" is referred to by Hendricks as the "first-action in the animal arising from a recognized property of the environment." The question also arises whether the hypothetical primary internal

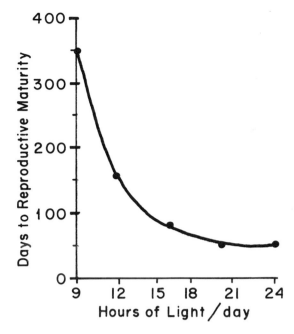

FIGURE 6. *Photoperiod and Rate of Testes Development*. The effect of day length on the growth of the male reproductive organ of migratory birds. The fully functional state for production of mature sperm cells occurs much sooner if the bird is in a long day situation. Adapted from Wolfson.[58]

event alone is light-triggered, or whether the same event is temperature-triggered in non-photoperiodic animals.

The mechanism of animal photoperiodism must be a disturbance of the normal balance of stimuli affecting the hypothalamus-anterior pituitary area.[27] It is not yet certain whether nerve impulses initiated by light, or the direct action of light on cells, is responsible for the accelerated or reduced responses due to changes in light.[49] Probably neither the rods or cones are involved and the photoperiodic control is effected by a low level of radiant energy compared to full daylight. The action spectra usually have maxima in the red-orange. The light-controlled biochemical reactions in animals are completely unknown; clearly the search for them requires first finding how the hypothalamus controls the pituitary through a photoreaction. This photo-

reaction is predicted by Hendricks to be one in which the energy received by a pigment induces the oxidation of another molecule, rather than the reversible reaction found in plants. This oxidation-reaction is the cause of pathological sensitivity to sunlight (klamath weed toxicity in sheep and photosensitization by porphyrins in man). Farner has provided evidence from birds that an essential compound in the response mechanism is formed rapidly in light and disappears slowly in the dark.[33] The supporting data were obtained by dividing the daily photoperiod into a number of short photoperiods. For further information on Photobiology, see Hollaender,[46] Wolfson,[58] and Farner.[34] Particular attention is given by the latter writer to the contribution of the hypothalamus and its portal system to the mechanism of the photoperiodic testicular response. Other recent information centers upon the control of photoperiodism by pineal gland factors.[37, 45, 60]

Is there a photoperiodic effect upon man? Apparently no important effect! Occasional speculation concerning the cause of "spring fever" centers around changes in vasomotor-tone due to temperature effects, rather than possible influence of light. However the cause of the "spring in the step" of the man who starts the day in bright sunlight after a period of cloudy weather, may have its roots in the powerful photoperiodic effects seen in some mammals.

Experimental Continuous Light

In white rats and mice (nocturnal mammals) maintained in continuous light the activity phase of the 24-hour locomotor rhythm continues to be about 9 to 12 hours long, but shows a regular and constant delay in time of starting, so that the activity block travels around the clock.[24, 38, 47] The rate of change of time of activity is faster with an increase in the intensity of the light. When animals in continuous light are then placed in continuous darkness, the daily delay in time of starting ceases. Behavior modification such as this should be called a photoperiodic response. In the studies on rats, the delay resulting from constant light (5.1 foot candles) was ¾

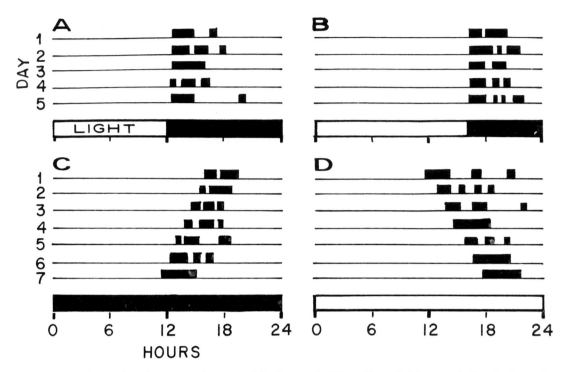

FIGURE 7. *Daily Running Activity Rhythms of White-Footed Mouse.* (A) Rhythm of mouse under short-day photoperiod (12 hours of light). (B) Rhythm of mouse under long-day photoperiod (16 hours of light). (C) Free-running rhythm of mouse under continuous darkness. (D) Rhythm showing Aschoff effect of mouse under continuous light. Adapted from Rawson.[54a]

hour per day and their activity traveled around the clock in 16 days. Day-active rodents have not been satisfactorily tested for their type of response to continuous light, but with day-active birds Aschoff found the opposite of this regular delay in time of starting activity, namely an acceleration. This *early-starting* of activity increased with the intensity of light. The biologists who are interested in photobiology now describe these delays and accelerations of time of activity as applications of Aschoff's Rule, stated as follows: *In continuous light with increasing intensity of illumination, light-active animals increase their spontaneous frequency, while dark-active animals decrease it.*[53] (Fig. 7). Aschoff's Rule does not apply to plants.

Two unexpected applications of the photoperiodic effect on activity were found in rat experiments.[39] In the first case their

activity can be reversed by illuminating at night rather than by day (a convenient procedure if one wants "midnight animals" to experiment with during bankers' hours.) An analysis of the *progress* of the reversal showed that when the light fell on the activity "block" the delay was greater than in the continuous light experiment, but still regular at 3 hours per day, until the block fell in the *new* dark period. In the second case, when a 16-hour light cycle was tried (8—illumination, 8—darkness), again a delay in time of activity was continuous, as if every time 8 hours of light "fell upon" part of the 12 hours of activity, it caused a delay in time of starting.

Natural Continuous Light

Up to this point the use of continuous light in only experimental conditions has

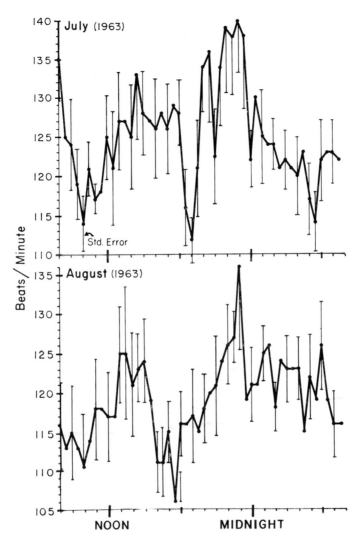

FIGURE 8. *Rhythms of Porcupine in Natural Continuous Light*. Illustration of lack of Aschoff effect under continuous daylight of the Arctic. Peak of heart rate activity would have moved around the clock extinguishing evidence of rhythm in averaged data. Each point is average of 10 days of heart rates. Heart rates by radio-capsule.

been discussed; some years ago [38] it occurred to me that the continuous light (82 days) each summer in the Arctic and Antarctic regions might cause animal activity to change according to Aschoff's Rule. After four summers of study (using radio-telemetry) of arctic ground squirrels and other rodents, foxes, wolverines, and wolves, we reached a tentative conclusion, as did Swade,[56] that natural continuous light does not induce a period consistently longer than 24 hours in arctic mammals.[7, 8, 40] We studied four individuals of each species in most cases. An illustration of data from one of the porcupines is presented, along with the Schuster periodograms which strengthened the conclusion that the activity peak in July was not moving around the clock (Fig. 8, 9). An explanation of this rhythm-stability is too

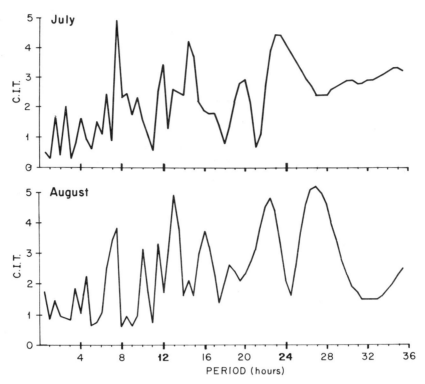

FIGURE 9. *Computer Analysis of Heart Rate Rhythms of Arctic Porcupine.* Each peak of the Schuster periodogram indicates the power of each of the periods which may range from 4 hours to 48. A 10-day consecutive run is barely adequate to demonstrate most 24-hour (circadian) physiological rhythms.

lengthy for consideration in this chapter on the effects of light.

Continuous Darkness

Continuous darkness is not an unbiological environment or a merely experimental environment. Many thousands of people and their domestic animals experience this condition for 2 or 3 months each winter (see introductory diagram D). These domestic animals (dogs, rabbits, cattle, sheep, and reindeer) are provided with little artificial light, and the countless wild animals have practically no light at all (Fig. 10). The term "countless wild animals" appears justified, since it applies to lemmings and ground squirrels, and herds of reindeer, caribou, seals, and muskoxen. According to E. R. Hall,[42] there are roughly the same total number of individuals of land mammals in the Arctic Life-zone as

in *each* of the other five major Life-zones. The question naturally arises whether the temporary lack of a daylight quota has any adverse physiological effect on animals adapted to arctic life. It is of interest that it is useless to ask whether these animals are essentially day-active (diurnal) or night-active (nocturnal) because during some part of the year they are forced to have both of these behavior patterns. The arctic seal, especially in winter, has a challenge to survival, since it must orient in darkness to its breathing hole in the ice, and must locate and catch fish in darkness under the ice. Possibly the arctic seal is assisted by an ability to echolocate its food (*i.e.,* use sonar).[43, 54]

Experimental evidence on the effects of continuous darkness is very fragmentary. A few mammals have been raised in darkness. This caused optic nerve degeneration

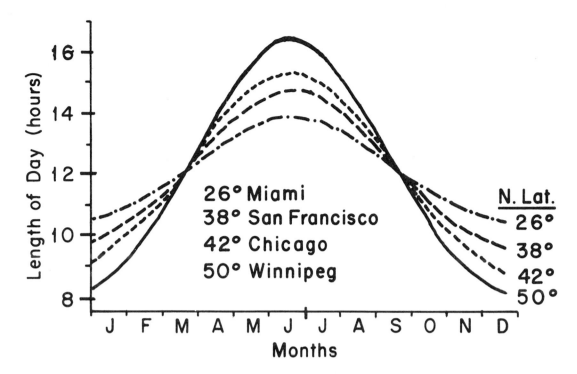

FIGURE 10. *Monthly Photoperiod at Different Latitudes.* Note that all latitudes shown have a 12 hour day simultaneously in spring and fall. From Odum.[52a]

in day-active forms (chimpanzees,[31, 55]), but in nocturnal forms like the rat there has been no effect upon vision. There are of course several dozen species of animals, mostly blind, which have become adapted to life in caves.[29] As far as reproduction is concerned, it is evident that many generations of wild rats breed (too successfully) in sewers, where some of them experience little daylight. Furthermore if given a choice, rats and hamsters usually remain within nest boxes when it is daylight. As for more completely nocturnal rodents (flying squirrels) it is possible that their life span is spent in continuous darkness, except for moonlight. Yet the following laboratory evidence indicates that white rats are adversely influenced by continuous darkness: rats raised in continuous darkness grew more slowly and matured more slowly.[32] This is probably because lactation by the nursing mothers was decreased during this period of continuous darkness.

According to Hendricks[44] there are similar effects of darkness on the seasonal milk yields of cows, expressed as a decrease in winter followed by an increase in the late winter months. As far as mechanism is concerned, there has been little analysis (either physiological or anatomical) of mammals raised in darkness. In one study the thyroid gland was found to be more active in rodents raised in continuous darkness compared to those raised in continuous light. More experimental work should be done using continuous darkness, partly because it would help to define the physiological differences between nocturnal laboratory animals and day-active laboratory animals.

The recording of functions of animals in continuous darkness has been an essential part of the experimental work of biologists interested in biological rhythms of nocturnal animals. In spite of possible detrimental effects of continuous darkness, the use of these environmental conditions has been necessary to test the degree of control of light cycles over biological rhythms. A rhythm which continues in darkness is said to *persist* or to be *free-running*. Experimenters in this field have rarely found adverse effects of continuous darkness. The running of rats in continuous darkness usually increases over control values. Other effects will be described in detail in the chapter on Biological Rhythms.

Chapter Three

BIOLOGICAL RHYTHMS

Chapter Three

Biological Rhythms

The environments of continuous light or continuous darkness would be considered extreme and would demand physiological adjustments no matter whether a mammal experiences them naturally or in an environmental chamber. We must also realize that the light cycle of day and night results in two sets of environmental extremes. The sensitivity of the mammalian retina to light need hardly be stressed (the light of a match can be detected at night for long distances, supposedly at 1 mile). Yet the eye in daylight must frequently tolerate or protect itself from as much as 10,000 foot candles in direct sunlight. Some mammals alleviate this situation by being nocturnal or by staying in forests under deciduous trees, where the mean value of less than 100 foot candles in summer is raised to only 3000 foot candles in winter. Regardless of habitat there has been a powerful daily cycle of light and darkness which has continued to influence the mammalian group since its origin 160 million years ago (end of Triassic). This influence is unlike those of partially localized environments such as temperature, water, or mountains, in that *all* mammals at some time have had to experience the light-darkness extreme. This is one factor of evolutionary pressure which almost all mammals have in common, along with other forms of life including the plant kingdom. The result has been that in some way a phenomenon common to plants and animals has been coupled with the light-darkness cycle. This phenomenon, a composite which we can call "the 24-hour", solar, or circadian biological rhythm, can be detected in the physiology or behavior of most animals and green plants.

Since the daily biological event does not usually begin exactly every 24-hours, today its timing is called circadian, meaning "nearly 24-hour." It is not only coupled with the light-darkness cycle but was probably caused by it.

The circadian (24-hour) rhythm is the most common type of the several biological rhythms, and it will be the only one discussed in full in this chapter. Although the light-darkness cycle is coupled with this rhythm, this cycle is also reinforced by lesser factors such as temperature. For purposes of explanation our attention must be limited to the relationship between light and rhythms, although it is evident that in the free environment in some parts of the globe, the seasonal variation often results in warm long-days contrasted with cold short-days; and the 24-hour period itself may consist of a humid and cold darkness compared with a drier and warmer daylight. The natural occurrences of these multiple factors force the investigator to interpret cautiously the results of single-factor studies from environmental chambers.

The "24-hour" rhythm deserves close inspection and analysis by all students of biological science because it is ubiquitous, and because two important and intriguing biological problems are implicit in all observations of this rhythm: 1) is the periodicity inherited or learned, and 2) why, in most cases, does the rhythm represent a biological process which is independent of temperature? These questions will be considered later. It will first be helpful to examine closely examples of circadian rhythms.

FIGURE 11. *Recording Feeding and Running Activity.* View of four running wheel recorders with running and feeding activity recorded simultaneously on 48-hour kymograph and chart. The principle of the running recorder depends upon a disk with 200 notches; each revolution of the wheel causes a new notch to be engaged on the disk. A complete revolution of the disk causes an up and down stroke of the pen on the chart, signifying 200 revolutions. Movement of the flexible feeding cup was recorded on the smoked drum.

TYPICAL MAMMALIAN CIRCADIAN RHYTHMS

Typical circadian rhythms are found in records of locomotor activity of rodents (Fig. 11). Soon after sunset nocturnal rodents will begin to exercise spontaneously on a running wheel, often running 6 to 10 miles. This running may continue without interruption for food or rest until these exercise bouts have been completed. Some females will cover the astonishing distance of 21 miles in one night. The pattern for a day-active rodent may be the same but reversed to daylight. The time of starting activity is very regular (Figs. 12 and 13).*

If we now direct our attention toward recording other functions, we find that during the period represented by the prolonged running activity (late evening), the resting body temperature or "core temperature" of the resting animal is about 4% higher than resting *daytime* body temperature, and resting *night* heart rate is 5% higher than resting *daytime* heart rate. Similar figures have been obtained for oxygen-consumption, total activity, bladder activity, kidney activity, and many other

* Running wheel records were obtained with recorders loaned from the laboratory of Professor John H. Welsh.

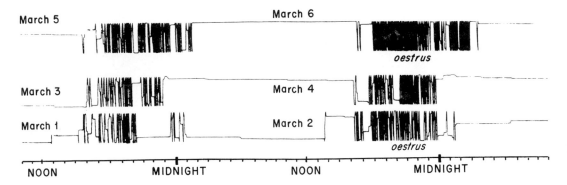

FIGURE 12. *Running Activity of the Rat.* Six-day record on kymograph paper of persistent spontaneous running activity of the white rat. During this period the rat was in a sound-proof room in continuous darkness. Each complete excursion of the pen represents 200 revolutions of the running wheel. The kymograph drum turned once in 48 hours.

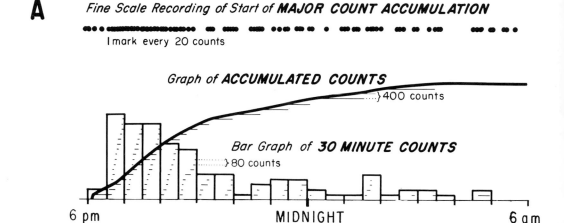

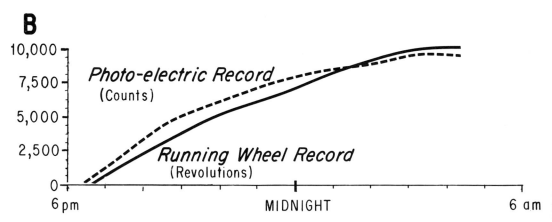

FIGURE 13. *Activity Records From Self-Graphing Recorder.* (A) Hamster activity record using photo-electric-eye drum and self-graphing recorder; the actual record consists of the short parallel dashes. (B) Comparison of recording accumulated movements across photo-electric-eye drum and running activity. (Courtesy of Paul Kim).

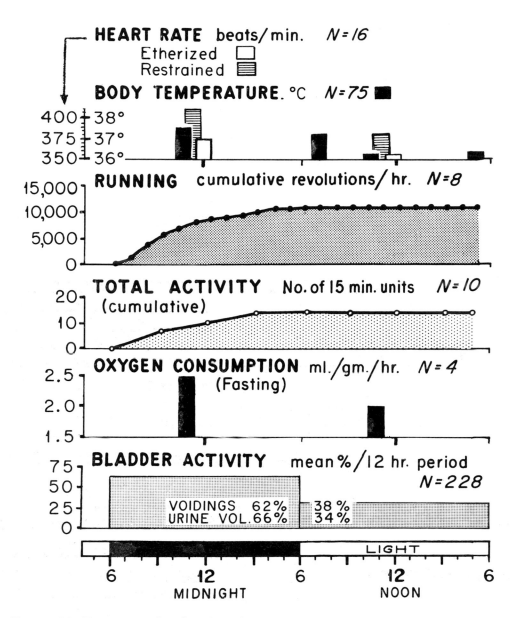

FIGURE 14. *Hamster Daily Physiological Rhythms.* Profile of several types of day-night physiological rhythms which are in phase.

functions and mechanisms. Few simultaneous recordings of different physiological rhythms have been made, yet they prove valuable because there is increasing interest in determining whether "the operating mammalian machine" consists of separate rhythms perhaps slightly out of phase, or closely synchronized rhythms involving the entire physiology of the animal.

Several types of simultaneous rhythms have been compiled in the author's laboratory in different experiments, but by the same workers using one strain of hamster

Table 5: Time Keeping Of Animals And Plants Apparently Without Clues From The Physical Environment*

INTERNAL CLOCK	EXPERIMENTAL PROOF	TEMPERATURE INDEPENDENT **
Welsh '41: CRAYFISH eyes turn light for c. 12 hrs. and dark for c. 12 hrs. in a rhythm over circadian periods.	Constant Darkness (5 months)	6° to 8°C, 21° to 23°C (4 months)
Brown & Webb '48: FIDDLER CRABS turn dark for c. 12 hrs. and light for c. 12 hrs. in a circadian rhythm.	Constant Darkness (2 months)	Over wide temperature range. 6° to 26°C
Brown et al. '53: FIDDLER CRABS show supplemental black pigment with each high tide (50 min. later each day).	Persists in constant laboratory conditions.	Over wide temperature range.
Pittendrigh '54 & *Brett* '55: ADULT FRUIT FLIES do not emerge at random from pupal-cases over a 24-hr. period. They measure time and usually come out between 6 AM - 9 AM, if started in phase with sun.	Constant Darkness	16°, 21°, 26°C
Bateman '55: QUEENSLAND FRUIT FLIES (Dacus) have rhythm as above. Clock set by exposure of parents to light-cycle.	Constant Darkness	....
Bruce & Pittendrigh '56: EUGLENA has rhythm of phototaxis. This means this species must be a "unicellular clock."	Constant Darkness	16.7° to 33°C
Folk '58: GROUND SQUIRRELS in hibernation appear to show regular shallow dormancy during artificial-day (12-hrs.) and deep dormancy in artificial-night.	In most cases individuals awoke in artificial day (for 2 winter seasons).	The combination of regular awakening in light period, and variable length of dormancy (1-18 days) can be understood by postulating a temperature-independent clock, 5°C.
Ball & Dyke '56: Young AVENA SEEDLINGS grow faster during c. 12th hr. and the 36th hr.	Constant Darkness	16° to 28°C
Bünning '56: Leaves of PHASEOLUS BEAN move in a rhythm of 25 hrs.	Constant Darkness	Exceptionally temperature resistant and operates in plants heated almost to lethal temperature.
Menaker, M. '59: Two species of BATS in hibernation showed a daily conspicuous fluctuation in body temperature, a circadian rhythm longer than 24 hrs.	Constant Darkness	At 7.5°C or at 10°C

   ° All references in this Table are found in the book by Cloudsley-Thompson.[76]

   °° Temperatures = the environmental temperatures for each experiment.

Table 6: Vocabulary Of Periodicity*

	Type of Rhythm A	Type of Rhythm B
Examples of: INVERTEBRATE RHYTHMS	Planktonic animals show a vertical migration dependent on responses to changing light intensity. The response does not persist in a constant environment. (Harris and Wolf '55)	Melanopore rhythm of fiddler crab, emergence of Drosophila and activity of millipede all show stable circadian frequency. (Stevens '56, Pittendrigh '56, Cloudsley-Thompson '51)
Examples of: MAMMALIAN RHYTHMS	The white rat has been induced to take on a 16-hr. rhythm, by use of light and heat. (Browman '52)	The white rat and the laboratory mouse seem to show genetically determined stable circadian rhythms. (Aschoff '54 and Folk '56) Some insectivores and some wild mice have apparent inherent rhythms varying from 2½-8 hrs. uninfluenced by light/darkness cycle. (Crowcroft '54)

AUTHORS	TERMS USED TO DESCRIBE THE ABOVE	
Bünning '35	Exonome (German)	Endonome (German)
Welsh '38	Extrinsic rhythms	Persistent rhythms
Park '49	Exogenous rhythms	Inherent (genetical) endogenous rhythms
Kleitman '49	Causal, synchronous, associated or coupled periodicities.	Persistent rhythms
Aschoff '54	Exogenous (exogene)	Endogenous (endogene)
Stevens '57	Environment-dependent frequencies.	Environment-independent frequencies.
Pittendrigh '57	Field rhythms, impressed rhythms, entrained oscillators.	Overt persistent rhythms or Free-running rhythms or self-sustaining oscillators.
Harker '58	Exogenous rhythms	Persistent or Endogenous rhythms

* All references in this Table may be found in the book by Cloudsley-Thompson.[76]

(Fig. 14). The important concept shown in this "profile" is that *two* animals are really being studied: *The Day-Animal* and *The Night-Animal*. The animal is committed to a continuous sequence of Jeckel-Hyde changes throughout its lifetime. This idea must be carried through the interpretation of all circadian rhythms whether they concern the responses of protozoa, or the changing of day-shift industrial workers to a new night-shift program. In the latter case it is especially helpful to think in terms of *The Day-Man* and *The Night-Man*. The meaning of these terms will be discussed in more detail later.

The profile of hamster rhythms shows some interesting and unexpected details which deserve further study. It is important to note that all of these functions persisted (*i.e.*, free-ran) in continuous darkness. Considering some rhythms in more detail, it is apparent that these particular specimens had completed their major running activity by midnight, and other conspicuous locomotor activity by 3 AM This means that 11 PM, a time frequently selected for "midnight" measurements, may be too late to catch the peak of nocturnal physiological activity. Of particular interest are the measurements of kidney function; in spite of the interest in mammalian biological rhythms during the past 60 years, this study on kidney function is practically unique. It is curious that the "night-animal" shows such large differences in locomotor activity (compared to the "day-animal"), but such small (but completely consistent) differences in kidney and bladder function.

In another laboratory Halberg and his students [57] have shown that the peak and trough of 24-hour mitotic activity of cheek pouch and ear epithelium are the reverse of body temperature highs and lows.

TERMINOLOGY

Persistent, Endogenous, Exogenous Rhythms

The typical mammalian rhythms which have been described are synchronized with the powerful solar light-darkness cycle. The first stage in the study of any rhythm is invariably to test for the dependence of the rhythm upon the light cycle, by placing the animal under constant conditions of darkness (or light), temperature, and sound. Using rodents the results of this test show with remarkable clarity that the amplitude and period (length) of the activity rhythm does not depend upon a light-darkness cycle. For many months in continuous darkness nocturnal rodents make activity records which can hardly be distinguished from records made with a light cycle. Pittendrigh refers to such activity rhythms as free-running. The duration of the rhythm in darkness is usually about 23 or 25 hours rather than 24; under these circumstances the designation "circadian" is especially appropriate. It is certainly preferable to the ambiguous term "diurnal".

Some examples of rhythms which continue in constant darkness [76] have been selected from studies on crayfish, crabs, fruit flies, and plants (Table 5). These rhythms continue in constant darkness, yet other workers have found rhythms which do not continue when cyclical environmental conditions are replaced by constant conditions. Various terms have been applied to these two types of rhythms, first by botanists and later by zoologists. To assist students in understanding the literature and to make due allowance for priority of publication, these terms have been compiled in Table 6, with specific invertebrate and mammalian examples. Most investigators use the term "Persistent Rhythm" (i.e., free-running) for any biological periodicity (such as running or body temperature) that continues in a constant environment (light, sound, and temperature cycles are absent). If the rhythm does not persist, it is usually called exogenous; if still present, it is called endogenous. It is conceivable that a mammal may show both exogenous and endogenous rhythms; perhaps its locomotor rhythm ceases in continuous darkness (exogenous), but its biochemical rhythms continue under these circumstances (endogenous).

The testing for persistent rhythms must differ with nocturnal and day-active animals. With nocturnal animals the procedure involves measuring the rhythm in continuous darkness. Usually the rhythm will continue with minor changes in period length (it persists), since darkness is not a positive environmental factor (Fig. 15). This is not so of continuous light, which may affect the animal so that its activity shows a regular and constant amount of alteration which varies with the intensity of the light (see Chapter 2). This effect is said to be an application of Aschoff's Rule. In the light of this alteration of the rhythm, how can day-active mammals be tested? Continuous darkness cannot be used since it alters the activity of such mammals. For example, ground squirrels showing a distinct running pattern of 7 miles daily cease running completely in total darkness. According to Aschoff, the solution is to use

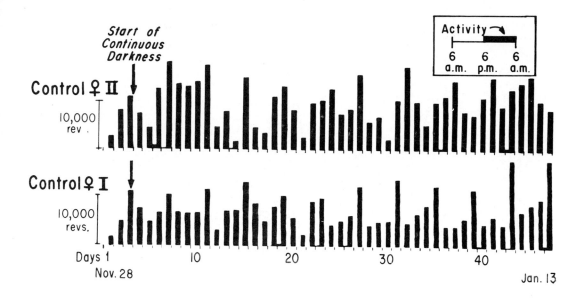

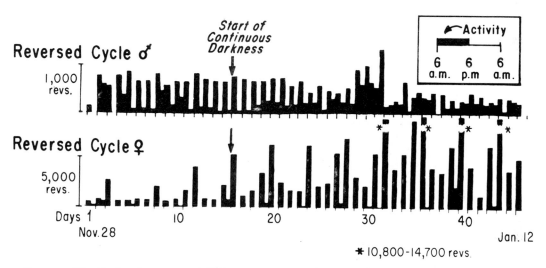

* 10,800-14,700 revs.

FIGURE 15. *Daily Running of White Rats.* Records of 24-hour running during an experiment on "Free-running in Darkness of a Reversed Activity Rhythm". The study was done at the end of a suite of subterranean sound-proof chambers. Charts could record for 60 hours; maintenance activities could not be timegivers since they were carried out at irregular times varying from 36 hours to 60 hours. The activity of two rats had been reversed by artificial light. The first two rats were in one room; the second two in another. Note the regular estrous peaks of the females.

continuous dim light, which alters very little the normal activity pattern of day-active animals.

Another term, "cycle", has gradually attained specific meaning among students of biological rhythms. It is applied to physical phenomena (*i.e.*, seasons, light cycles) and to short term physiological periodicities which have no relation to solar or other cosmic events (*i.e.*, heart cycle and menstrual cycle). How then does one classify

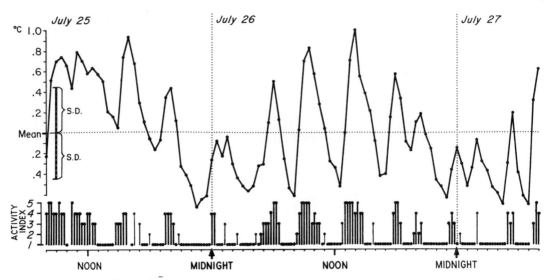

FIGURE 16. *Daily Body Temperatures of Arctic Ground Squirrels.* Circadian body temperature rhythms and activity records by observation; animal was in outdoor enclosure in continuous Arctic daylight. Body temperatures taken by radio-capsule. From Folk and Folk.[8]

the unusual activity rhythms of insectivores and some types of wild mice, which have short endogenous rhythms (2½ to 8 hours) uninfluenced by any light-darkness cycle? Since the entire behavior of the animal is concerned, this situation does not seem comparable to the 4-day estrus cycle of the rat. We will refer to these 2- to 8-hour periodicities as "short endogenous rhythms". An example of a 4-hour rhythm is found in the temperature rhythm of an arctic ground squirrel (Fig. 16).

Insect rhythms seem to be less rigid or fixed than those of mammals. Cloudsley-Thompson has been able to record arrhythmic insects (in terms of activity) of several species, after which he could again induce rhythms of 18 or 24 hours.[76]

TIMEGIVERS AND CLUES

Today, realization of the importance of "timegivers" replaces the earlier and vague belief that the *whole* daylight period was of major importance in determining biological rhythms. The emphasis earlier had been to describe how some mammals show

with inflexible regularity a sequence of approximately 12 hours of activity followed by 12 hours of rest. This was an oversimplification. The important concept is not the length of two units, but that there is a sequence which adds up to 24 hours. The components of the series of events follow each other in a chain-pattern (sleep-feeding-running-defecating-feeding, etc.). Changing the light cycle by 12 hours will cause the entire sequence as a unit to "rotate like a dial" to match the new light cycle. The natural "chain of functions" is not exactly 24 hours, but frequently 23 or 25 hours. Certain events which occur once in 24 hours *set* the rhythm; these events might be: (*a*) the start of a light cycle, (*b*) the end of a light cycle, (*c*) a regular artificial feeding time, or (*d*) the regular noise of other animals in cages. A flash of light at the start and end of a photoperiod will suffice (skeleton photoperiod).[104] Such physical events were given different names by three contemporary workers as follows: Aschoff, "timegivers" (Zeitgeber); Halberg, "synchronizers"; and Cloudsley-Thompson, "clues".[76] Pittendrigh not only stresses the importance of dawn or dusk as timegivers for rhythms, but suggests that experiments, which depend on recordings made when beams of light shine on the animals, may be influenced by the lights as timegivers.[102]

What is the relation between environmental clues and persistent rhythms? Persistent rhythms are detected by removing the known timegivers. Whether some unknown clues are still operating is a question to be discussed later.

The regularity of mammalian behavior in a variable physical environment must now be considered. Daylight is continually fluctuating. Intensity of light varies even at the equator; in the Arctic and Antarctic there is a seasonal variation from constant light to constant darkness; in an area such as southern England the length of daylight varies seasonally from about 8 to about 16 hours. How can any animal in such a changing environment have a regular 24-hour activity pattern? The answer, of course, lies in the "daily-timegiver" (dawn or sunset) which changes the period of the activity pattern by a small amount each day. The fact that the environment does change each day in most parts of the globe shows the importance of thinking of the activity sequence as a dial which is normally and sensitively shifted or readjusted by regular light changes. Light reversal experiments are really not unbiological, but are accelerated cases of a natural process. As for the exact form of the activity pattern, the sequence of events varies from species to species. The hamster has one long main locomotor unit; the guinea pig and mouse have two such periods, one near dawn, the other near dusk.

Symbols for test environments for biological rhythms are now standardized:[103]

L = artificial daylight
D = darkness

If "dawn" is at 800 hours (8 AM) and "sunset" at 2000 hours (8 PM), the conditions are described as: LD 12:12 (8-20). LL designates conditions of constant light; DD, conditions of constant darkness. New symbols should be added to this scheme:

CT = Controlled* Temperature
CS = Controlled Sound
CH = Controlled Humidity

A test environment can be concisely described as follows: (DD, CT, CS) or (LL, CT, CS).

BIOLOGICAL CLOCKS

The usefulness of timegivers to maintain a rhythm close to 24-hours, rather than other potential rhythms such as 23 or 25 hours, may suggest that mammals do not need an internal system of time measurement. Yet between 1940 and 1960 more and more biologists began writing about "biological clocks". This at first appeared to be a term too loosely used, but numerous papers since 1950 have justified the statements: *Many animals can measure time accurately*, or *a clock is an integral part of animal physiology*. One school of thought adds that it is possible that this clock is driven by cosmic periodic events, and that the so-called clock is really a receiving station.

There are two advantages of these clocks for animals in free environments. These are illustrated by experiments listed in Tables 5 and 7, each with a column entitled "Internal Clocks". The advantages, which might also be called "survival values", are:

(A) *To Stand-In For Timegivers*. In the free environment timegivers are not regular, and there is known to be "competition" between them. Sunrise may be completely hidden for a number of days, at that same time the barometer may be unusually high and the environmental temperature may show a large change. When such disturbed environmental conditions occur, the internal clock of the mammal maintains its habitual program. This persistence of regularity is of advantage to the species. Perhaps the necessity for the mechanism can be illuminated thus: the ground squirrel which is off in his burrow sleeping when the rest of the colony is active, may not take part in the breeding activities of the colony!

---

* controlled or "constant" or non-periodic

Table 7: Internal Clocks Revealed By Study Of Sun Navigation And Feeding Conditions*

INTERNAL CLOCK	EXPERIMENTAL PROOF	TEMPERATURE INDEPENDENT
Kramer '57 & Hoffmann '60: BIRDS must know the time of day to do sun navigation, thus they must have an "internal clock." Stars are used for orientation at night (Sauer '57).	Use of outdoor aviaries to produce directed migration in a restricted space.	Not needed by birds.
Grabensberger '34: ANTS can learn a feeding period of 3, 5, 21, 22, 26 or 27 hrs. (persist for 6-9 days after food discontinued).	These ants are arrhythmic (they do not respond to the presence or absence of a light cycle).	*Not* temperature independent. Increased nest temperature causes period of rhythm to shorten.
Ribbans '53: BEES tell time, and can learn to feed at 3 specific times of the day. (Could not learn 19-hour feeding cycle.)	All clues removed by placing bees in salt mine with constant light, humidity, temperature, and atmospheric electricity.	Independent until lowered to 7°C.
Von Frisch '52, Kalmus '56, Lindauer '60. BEES (which are experienced) travel to food at the appropriate angle to the sun, depending totally upon their awareness of the time of day.	Hives and feeding tables were used where there were no landmarks. Bees on feeding table were kept in darkness for 60-120 minutes.	

Sun orientation can also be done by fish[90] and reptiles[85].

* All references in this Table may be found in the book by Cloudsley-Thompson.[76]

(B) *To Assist Orientation.* Birds, fishes,[90] reptiles[85] and numerous invertebrates are known to do sun navigation. Some examples are given in Table 7. They travel to various goals by maintaining an appropriate angle to the sun or to polarized light (when the sun is not visible). They must change this angle according to the time of day. Thus, they must measure or know time accurately, in order to make appropriate corrections. Either with or without a timegiver as a starting point, they appear to measure off time units which we can think of as bird-units, fish-units, bee-units, or spider-units.

Mammals have not been shown to navigate by polarized light, yet this ability is spread over so many other diverse groups that it is unlikely that they are exceptions.

We may also assume that mammals orient themselves, perhaps to recognize their territories or to escape to burrows, by seeing "streaks" of polarized light which change their angle to the observer as the day progresses. That even man can learn to see polarized light, is reported by Waterman. This relationship between biological rhythms and biological clocks is so important that an imaginary experiment will be described to assist the student in understanding sun navigation. Suppose you remain in a constant environment (DD, CT, CS) for 2 days. You are then taken still blindfolded in a boat on the ocean out of sight of land. Your blindfold is removed and you are told to row to shore. You know that shore is "to the west", but if you do not know the time of day (by a good physiological timepiece) then you cannot tell the difference between various positions of the sun such as at 10 AM or 2 PM, and you would not know which direction to go. The experimental animals listed in Table 7 knew the time, even when kept in darkness for several days. Some were studied facing the equator (the sun rose on their left). When released they "knew the time" and went in the right direction from the sun to a goal. Some of them were then taken to the Southern Hemisphere, where the experiment was again done facing the equator.[94] The sun now rose on their right; when released, according to the two investigators, they used the wrong angle to get to the experimental goal. They seemed to use the sun formula of the Northern Hemisphere.

The experiments just discussed (Table 7) were selected to illustrate the biological principle that many animals have a sense of time. Birds, in feeding experiments, have also been shown to have a good sense of time.[93] No feeding experiments with mammals were found in the literature; young research students will find an excellent opportunity to do interesting and simple experiments in this area.

The acceptance of internal biological clocks has developed to the point that Pittendrigh has named three types: [102]

1. *Continuously Consulted Clocks:* The mechanisms used in sun navigation would come under this category, as well as the ability to learn and anticipate feeding periods as shown by bees and ants (Table 7).*

2. *Interval Timers:* When Drosophila are about to leave the pupal case to take adult form, the culture demonstrates awareness of "forbidden periods" for emergence, relative to a light stimulus at egg laying. Most emergence occurs only for a specific 3-hour period out of each 24 hours, according to an internal interval-timer. The adaptive function of this interval-timer is a varia-

tion of what was called previously the function of "standing-in for a time-giver". We might very well call it "Anticipating The Timegiver". As Pittendrigh expresses it: "The advantage of eclosing (hatching from pupal cases) at dawn is clear: this is the time when the evaporating power of the atmosphere is at its lowest. It is what might be called a target-time. The functional problem of restricting eclosion to this recurrent target-time includes the problem of identifying it; but since the fly initiates processes leading to eclosion some hours prior to the act, the identification problem is not the simple one of directly recognizing dawn as the appropriate time. Indeed the real problem is identifying an appropriate point in time some hours before dawn, and this is difficult or impossible to do by the recognition of external cues. In fact it is done *by a time measurement from the previous dawn.*"

3. *Pure Rhythms:* The persistent rhythms of activity, heart rate, and body temperature of hamsters will serve as examples of mammalian pure rhythms.

UBIQUITY OF CIRCADIAN UNITS IN BIOLOGICAL PHENOMENA

A clear-cut circadian activity rhythm associated with a composite group of internal physiological rhythms has been shown in rodents. This composite of rhythms persists in a constant environment (DD or LL, CT, CS). Such rhythms as these have been demonstrated in at least six orders of mammals, in all groups of vertebrates, and in eight phyla of the Animal Kingdom. It is significant that the Protozoa are included in the list (Table 5 and other examples in Pittendrigh [102]). The presence of persistent circadian periodicity in Protozoa (and also in one-celled plants) complicates theorizing about biological clocks. Although we can postulate for the Metazoa that some *organ* acts as a clock to control the entire animal, in the protozoa the mechanism would have to be much simpler. Even then there is the possibility of further breakdown, as indicated by the question of Pittendrigh as to whether these

---

* Some remnant of the time sense is present in man: perhaps the reader has, on some occasion, decided to wake up without an alarm clock an hour before his usual awakening time,—and found that he did wake up exactly at the selected early-rising time.

one-celled organisms *are* a "clock", or *contain* a "clock".

Botanists have contributed much of the early proof of periodic biological occurrences which take place in units of nearly 24-hours, and the environmental independence of these units. Bünning's bean plant (*Phaseolus*)[73] shows a rhythm of leaf movement of 25 hours in constant conditions. It is difficult to relate a rhythm of 25 hours to any periodic cosmic event. In the free environment, the addition of a timegiver converts this inherent rhythm to one near 24 hours. Ball[124] and his students have shown 24-hour rhythms of growth in darkness and of CO_2 production by plant tissues of several species. As many as three consecutive circadian periods could be measured with individual tissue samples. These rhythms needed a brief period of light to initiate them, but the sequence of circadian periods could be started at any time of the day. This last observation, one of the more significant findings of the experiment, shows that cosmic periodic events with a 24-hour frequency could not be the cause of the observed plant rhythms. To summarize, the circadian units in biological functions occur at both the cellular and organ level. The broad distribution throughout the animal and plant kingdom of the same pattern of rhythms as in the mammals shows that these rhythms must be related to the daily revolution of the earth on its axis. Three schools of thought have developed as to the exact nature of the relation to cosmic events.

SCHOOLS OF RHYTHM CAUSATION

Three theories as to the origin of 24-hour rhythms may be found in the literature. They may informally be referred to as: (1) an Imprint Theory, (2) an Inherited 24-Hour-Clock Theory, and (3) a Cosmic Receiving-Station Theory.

The Imprint Theory

The imprint theory,[109] assumes that as animals (and presumably plants) develop from the zygote, they are arrhythmic; they then *learn* what is approximately a 24-hour rhythm from environmental conditioning or from the behavior of parents. This condition is reinforced and made accurate by the environment as the animal develops, so that when tested in a constant environment the rhythm persists. There is not yet sufficient direct evidence to justify discarding this theory for mammals; no mammals have been raised in constant darkness without the possibility of being conditioned by the circadian rhythm of the mother through the placental circulation.

An Inherited Clock Theory

The second theory assumes the presence of an inherited circadian clock (*i.e.*, the rhythm is born, not made). Direct evidence exists using birds as experimental material. Chicks were hatched and raised in a constant dim light and without any known periodic environmental factor. They developed a rhythm of slightly less than 24-hours.[25] If subtle daily environmental factors had been an influence, they would have acted as timegivers and set up a more exact 24-hour rhythm in these birds. Much more evidence has been obtained using invertebrates, many of which show rhythms of approximately 24 hours which were shown to be determined genetically. The clocks of all members of an invertebrate population (raised under constant conditions of darkness and temperature) are not necessarily synchronized, especially if several generations are raised under these conditions. Drosophila clocks could be set in the same phase by a flash of light, acting as a daybreak signal.[72, 101] Pittendrigh has unified the concept of a genetic self-sustaining rhythm by use of an oscillator analogy (or model): "Our working hypothesis, which is wholly consistent with the available facts, assumes that all organisms are capable of time measurements; that their clocks have a common and ancient basic mechanism like the hair spring and balance wheel of diverse human timepieces from wrist watches to clocks; and that this basic element is an oscillatory system with a natural period evolved to match, approximately, the period of those environmental variables that are ecologically significant (day, month, etc.)." In other words Pittendrigh and many other investigators believe that a physiological interval-timer, or innate physiological periodicity of about 24 hours, are as much a fundamental characteristic of animals as certain oft-repeated organ patterns such as nervous systems and brains, or circulatory systems and hearts. This theory of the genetic nature of circadian rhythms depends upon the assumption that in those cases where free-running rhythms have been shown to be in phase with cosmic periodic events such as day and night, the explanation is the presence of inadvertant timegivers from the experimental procedure.

Further experiments on mammals should be done to demonstrate conclusively the genetic nature of circadian rhythms. Many results so far can be interpreted according to the imprint theory. An early attempt was made by Stier [112, 113] to test for the presence of circadian rhythms in white rats raised from birth under constant conditions of darkness and temperature. Only after a period in light following the previous life in darkness did the rats show a 24-hour rhythm. Using the Japanese dancing mouse Wolf [125] tried the same experiment. The young mice developed a circadian rhythm which was not synchronized with external environmental changes. Similar results have been obtained by other investigators who studied rodents blinded at birth. Aschoff [63] raised several generations of mice under constant conditions of temperature and darkness. The *mean* free-running period of their daily rhythms remained at about 23½ hours, even to the last generation of the series, and the *range* of values for these periods with succeeding litters remained approximately the same. The investigator interpreted his results as proving the genetic origin of a natural period on the grounds that if the rhythms were learned, there would be an accumulative error which would cause the third generation to have a period other than 23½ hours. This interpretation and the experiment itself is

so critical to the field of biological rhythms that an alternative interpretation must be offered. Perhaps the experiment merely proves the remarkable susceptibility of young mice to imprinting by adults of a rhythm of nearly 24 hours. Such a possibility is hardly remote when we consider that Lorenz could do the following experiment: [12a] young ducks were hatched by geese; and after a short period they were separated from the geese, and raised by ducks. When the young ducks came to breeding age, they would court and attempt to mate only with geese. The early imprint on the young ducks "that they *are* geese" had survived without reinforcement through the period of growth to sexual maturity. In an experiment where a mother rodent raises her young in constant darkness, is there a regular timegiver approximately once in 24 hours to influence the young as they mature? This timegiver would establish the imprint of circadian periodicity. Such a timegiver exists! It is well known by keepers of rat colonies that mother rats nurse their young almost continuously in daylight, and not only do most of their own feeding at night, but are away from the litter much of this time to carry out other activities. The white crescent-shaped mark on the young rats indicating milk-filled stomachs is not visible most of the night. It is not the length of time that the mother is away that is important but the fact that at a specific time of day she regularly leaves the nest, the nest cools, the young cool, and the stomachs of the young rats are emptied. Records have been made of the regular feeding periods of white rats.[38] In the complete set of records for one of these animals (Fig. 17) obtained with equipment shown in Figure 11, note the regularity of feeding (especially the 4 o'clock "teatime") which might act as timegiver to young rats left in the nest by the mother.

Do any factors exists which would facilitate the synchronization of activities of a litter of young rats or mice according to a single timegiver? Experiments on this problem are nearly nonexistent for mam-

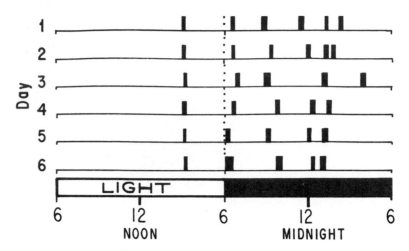

FIGURE 17. *Daily Feeding Records of White Rat.* Tracing of records on smoked kymograph paper of the times of spontaneous feeding activity during an experiment on "The Effect Upon Feeding and Running Activity of Reversal of the Normal Light Cycle". Records obtained as illustrated in Figure 11. Each block is a feeding period. Only control records are pictured (light 6 AM–6 PM). This rat had 5 or 6 feeding periods per day, but some rats have as many as 8 or 10.

mals; for other animals Pittendrigh says "The likelihood that individuals in a population entrain (synchronize) each other in their activity cycles is the . . . first obvious possibility". Two examples will be cited: (1) Stevens[111] reports that in *Uca* the endogenous rhythm is less stable and accurate in isolated individuals than in large groups; (2) Folk[39] studied a reversed cycle female rat (active during solar day) which had persisted in this new activity rhythm as a punctual time-piece in a continuous environment (DD, CT, CS) for 32 days. Two other females in another soundproof chamber persisted in their usual night activity rhythm (DD for 60 days) with great regularity, thus following a time sequence 12 hours different from the first female (Fig. 15). The first female was moved into the room with the other two rats (DD, CT, CS). For 14 days the reversed cycle rat "resisted change" and regularly ran up to 10 thousand revolutions during the period when her two neighbors were resting. Then the single female ran very little or not at all for 4 days and at that point

changed her activity pattern, now running at the same time as the other two females (Fig. 18). This experiment can only be interpreted as evidence of synchronization of rodent activity. Evidence from adult animals may not necessarily apply to baby rats, but no other pertinent information is available.

A way was found to prevent the mother rat from providing timegivers to her nursing young. A litter of rats was raised under constant conditions with a foster mother in addition to the natural mother. The mothers had different daily rhythms; they were exchanged at random times each day, and it was observed that the young had suckled from both mothers equally over each 24-hours. By chance the litter consisted of six males. Their mean weight at weaning was 39 grams compared to the usual mean of 33.6 grams for a litter of this size. After they were 95 days old the three best runners were studied in running recorders in a sub-basement room. The free-running period of the rhythms of these three animals turned out to vary

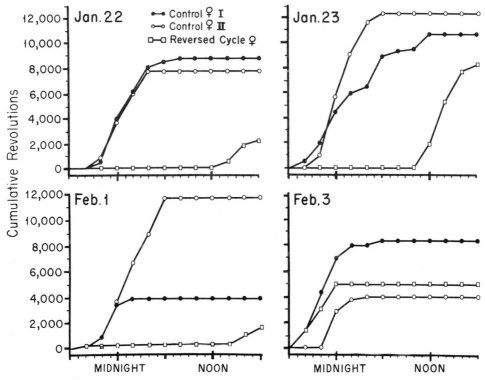

FIGURE 18. *Daily Running Activity of Three Rats.* Graphs of accumulated revolutions obtained during an experiment on "The Influence of the Activity of One Rat Upon That of Another". The entire experiment was in continuous darkness. These graphs show that at first the reversed-cycle rat was uninfluenced by the activity rhythms of control rats I and II. After 2 weeks the reversed-cycle rat took on the activity rhythm of the other two.

from 24.5 to 25 hours. They had one extended period of running (8 to 12 hours) in each of these periods. This evidence appears to support the theory of a genetic 23 to 25-hour rhythm. The behavior of "a mother" during the period of nursing could not have made an imprint. Of course this experimental approach must now be continued backward in the history of the young rodent into the period of gestation, since some periodic factor from the mother acting through the placental circulation of the embryos could act as timegiver. It would not be difficult to prevent all periodic factors from the mother from acting as timegivers to her embryos, but the experiment has not been done.

In summary, the inherited 24-hour clock theory assumes a genetically endowed fundamental pure rhythm with a free-running period of 23 to 25 hours. In the free environment, timegivers set this inherent rhythm at 24 hours, permitting it to be the clock in animal-navigation. Occasionally experimenters can set up abnormal rhythms as small as 16 hours, but these are temporary and the animals revert to the fundamental rhythm when timegivers are removed. Most of the direct evidence supports this theory of inheritance, although few mammals have been studied to test this point. It is doubtful that mammals are an exception to what appears to be the rule.

The Cosmic Receiving-Station Theory

The third theory assumes that animals

and plants respond to periodic cosmic changes other than daylight; that they can act as "cosmic receiving stations" or "cosmic resonators". Some of the periodic cosmic changes or periodic variables include cosmic ray showers, magnetic lines of flux, air ionization, pressure, and humidity. These factors we will call *subtle environmental clues;* Pittendrigh uses *residual periodic variables* (RPV). It is probably these factors which Brown [69] had in mind when he stated that organisms in so-called constant conditions are still receiving some signals from the external physical environment. More specifically he says: "A good working hypothesis for the present appears to be that there exists in organisms an endogenous clock-system which maintains its regular frequencies through some kind of an external pacemaking signal which continues to be effective under what is usually deemed 'constant conditions'." Brown came to this conclusion because of the generalization based on years of experimentation that animals have "the capacity to *reset* persistently the relationship of the endogenous biological cycles to the external solar-day and lunar-day. . . . The organism can adaptively adjust its functional patterns to the highly localized forms of the cycles of light, temperature, and humidity of its specific niche . . ." The key word here is "reset". The question is whether subtle environmental clues can act as timegivers for animals which have lost the normal timegiver (light), when these animals have a marked capacity to reset their inherent 23- to 25-hour rhythm. My statement in an earlier paragraph describes this resetting as turning the dial of the 24-hour rhythm sequence to a new starting point.

What environmental factors are capable of keeping the animal to a 23-, a 24-, or a 25-hour rhythm, or of "turning the dial by several hours" so that the rhythm has a new time of starting? To help answer this question Aschoff has added the rule: "The animal obeys the strongest of the timegivers." It is reasonable to suppose that once a day, several subtle environmental clues, perhaps changes in cosmic ray count, terrestrial magnetism, or air ionization, all come to a peak in phase, and this "bundle" could act as a timegiver. Essentially, then, the behavior of animals demonstrating persistent rhythms (DD, CT, CS) can theoretically be interpreted:

(1) either as following a natural daily period of 23 to 25 hours.

(2) or as accepting as a new timegiver, subtle environmental clues which the animals did not need to respond to before. This second possibility poses an astonishing and stimulating question in the area of sensory physiology.

In order to compare the inherited 24-hour rhythm idea with that which depends on subtle environmental clues, we may now review two observations for and one against the inherited rhythm theory. The first supporting fact is the variability of natural periods (from 23 to 25 hours) from species to species.[102] If species at opposite ends of the 2-hour range were turned-in to replacement timegivers, these would have to be completely different subtle environmental factors which were out of phase with each other; the interpretation of each species having its own inherent period is more acceptable. A second supporting fact is the variability in free-running within the species. There is some evidence that each individual (*i.e.* each mouse) within a species, if studied in isolation, may have its own characteristic free-running period.[102] Two of these periods for two individuals could be different by 1 hour (24.5 to 25.5 hours). Again the interpretation which accepts these rhythms as having natural periods (rather than having cosmic timegivers) is more plausible. Unfortunately the supposed natural periods of very few species or individuals of mammals of the same species have been measured. Many more experiments with larger series of mammals of the same species are needed.*

---

* Such studies are usually made with isolated animals, but if several are kept in the same room, they may all take on the same period perhaps determined by the dominant animal in the "peck order" of the series (see Introduction).

Several series of experiments provide evidence for the theory of subtle environmental clues acting as timegivers. They include: (1) increasing the intensity of the 24-hour cycle of cosmic ray count, using crabs for the experimental material, (2) measuring a persistent cosmic effect when white rat activity changed its daily time of occurrence in regular sequence, (3) finding the effects of a barometric pressure correlate on tissue in a closed system.

The first of these experiments (using cosmic rays) is a rare type in Biology. Until recently very few investigators have looked for possible effects upon animals or tissues of subtle environmental factors, especially where biological rhythms are concerned. There have been attempts to eliminate these factors from experiments, but few have tried to apply them in a 24-hour cycle. Brown did increase cosmic showers on fiddler crabs for 12 hours out of 24 to try to influence the persistent rhythm of chromatophore change. The cosmic showers were produced in this fashion: when a cosmic ray enters the earth's atmosphere, it smashes atoms of gas in air and sends the fragments scattering in all directions, but mostly cascading downwards. The fragments become secondary cosmic rays, striking other atoms of gas until all the energy of the original particles is used up. The secondary cosmic rays reach the earth's surface and if they strike a sheet of lead, they produce more tiny nuclear explosions. This process is called "cascade multiplication". If the lead thickness is about 2 cm or less, the cosmic shower on the "earth" side of the sheet of lead is increased by 50%. If thicker sheets of lead are used, the coincidences per hour of cosmic rays on the earth side are reduced rather than amplified. There is a natural 24-hour variation in cosmic ray count, which Brown simulated and amplified in his experiment. His results showed that small variations in cosmic radiation could produce a physiological alteration within organisms, since the 12-hour period of artificially increased cosmic ray count altered the persistent rhythm of chromatophore change in fiddler crabs:

i.e., the amplitude of the rhythm was increased, with the darkening phase darker and the lightening phase lighter.[68] On the basis of this experiment Brown does not claim that cosmic rays are concerned with biological rhythms, but the physiological evidence implies that in the search for a number of subtle factors which could come to a synchronized peak once in 24 hours and thus act as substitute timegivers, cosmic rays must be included.

Brown's second experiment to show subtle environmental influences depended upon a phenomenon which occurs in rats if they are kept in continuous illumination. The activity phase of the 24-hour rhythm of the rat is 9 to 12 hours in length but shows a regular, constant and definite amount of alteration or delay in time of starting so that the activity block travels around the clock.[62, 38] In Brown's experiment (LL) the amount of activity did not remain constant but increased whenever the activity peak coincided with high tide, or with certain phases of the moon (the reader should note we are still discussing an experiment on a rat not fiddler crabs). These effects are difficult to visualize until the daily amplitude of running is graphed along the same axis as the time of high tide, and the phases of the moon. To summarize, the experiment describes persisting effects of exogenous factors acting upon a moving endogenous rhythm. The influence shown here upon white rats activity can only be said to have a lunar frequency of 27 days. The environmental factor is unidentified.

The third type of experiment on subtle environmental influences by Brown and co-workers involves the use of sections of potatoes, carrots, and seaweed (Fucus) maintained under constant pressure. Oxygen consumption was measured, giving the following results: "Highly significant correlations were shown to exist with barometric pressure and its changes. That barometric pressure is not itself the agent is proven through finding the correlations to persist even in organisms maintained for long periods in constant pressure." It has been learned that the amplitude of daily fluctuations in the metabolism of the potato plant grown for four months under constant conditions, including pressure, was significantly correlated with the amplitude of the concurrent daily cycles of fluctuation in high-energy background radiation. "In view of the existence of clear mean cycles in both barometric pressure and background radiation, it is apparent that the organism has access to external physical signals with good average cycles even under so-called constant conditions." [67] An extension of these experiments has included transporting plant tissues to South America with continuous recording of their oxygen consumption.

Recently Brown and his associates have shown that several species of invertebrates exhibit measurable responses to small changes in such subtle geophysical factors as a very weak magnetic field, an electrostatic field, and gamma radiation.[71] Brown's theory to explain these results is based upon a model called "intraorganismic variable frequency transformation." The physiological basis for the theory is: (1) organisms can reset phase when given a new light cycle, (2) there is in the animal a daily rhythm of responsiveness to illumination and temperature even when exposed to continuous light or constant temperature.[70] Brown assumes the existence of the endogenous rhythm in animals; he then postulates that this rhythm when exposed to constant conditions of conspicuous external factors of the environment (light, temperature) is modified by pervasive environmental factors which do not have a 24-hour period (gamma rays, magnetic flux). His evidence applies to invertebrate rhythms more directly than it does to mammalian.

To summarize, three theories of circadian rhythm-control have been presented:

a. the imprint theory.

b. an inherited clock theory.

c. the cosmic receiving-station theory.

The second theory is generally considered the most acceptable.

ANATOMICAL LOCATION OF THE TIMER

A number of investigators over the years have done experiments which were designed to locate a hypothetical biological clock. One approach is to use operative procedures. Probably the most important results are those where rhythms are *present* after the operations, since the absence of a rhythm in an operated (perhaps sick) mammal is difficult to interpret. Modern experiments in this field are based on a new premise, but partly for historical purposes some experiments with positive results are now listed; the references for each experiment are found in Harker's review:[88]

1. Removal of stomachs: The study of maze and running activity of seven rats from which the stomachs had been removed showed no alteration in activity due to the operation (Tsang 1938).

2. Removal of adrenals: The rhythm of liver storage of glycogen ceases, but the activity rhythm in rats continues (Bacq 1931).

3. Hypopituitary: Genetic hypopituitary mice (dwarf mice) are rhythmic (Osborne 1940).

4. Hypophysectomy: Rats show a 24-hour rhythm after removal of the pituitary (Richter and Wislocki 1930; Levinson, Welsh, and Abromowitz 1941).

5. Removal of thyroid: The 24-hour rhythm of rats is upset but not eliminated (Richter 1933).

6. Lesions in frontal brain tissue and corpus striatum: Some rats retain a rhythm (Beach 1941).

7. Removal of cortex: No loss of 24-hour rhythm in decorticate dogs (Rothmann 1923).

These experiments have been oversimplified almost beyond recognition in this summary; the abstracts do show that at an early stage in the experimental approach to mammalian circadian rhythms, it was evident that the control of these rhythms must be deep-seated and complicated. For this reason it is valuable to refer to animals of simpler architecture than mammals for information on the anatomical location of the biological clock. One experiment on invertebrates demonstrated that a clock can be approximately located but it was a 40 minute timer: Wells [122] showed that the very regular activity of a marine worm is controlled by a discrete portion of the head anatomy. Three-minute bursts of feeding movements (with or without food) and 1-minute rests are followed by locomotion movements every 40 minutes. The physiological clock is the esophagus or even a slice of this structure *in vitro*. The rhythm of this tissue can be likened to the activity of the mammalian heart. Unlike the heart, the rhythm

from the esophagus is transferred through the nervous system to the entire physiology and behavior of the animal. As Wells expressed it: "The oesophagus drives the probosis and the rest of the body." Continuous contributions to these thorough and fundamental experiments have been made by Wells over the past 25 years.

It is evident from the preceding experiments that the thinking of investigators of circadian rhythms after 1923 were similar to that of Wells: the search was for a localized center of control over the circadian rhythm. This point of view was shared in 1957 by Pittendrigh, (who has been one of the American leaders in this field from 1954 to the present time);[103] he suggests that with higher animals the nervous system is all important: "We have

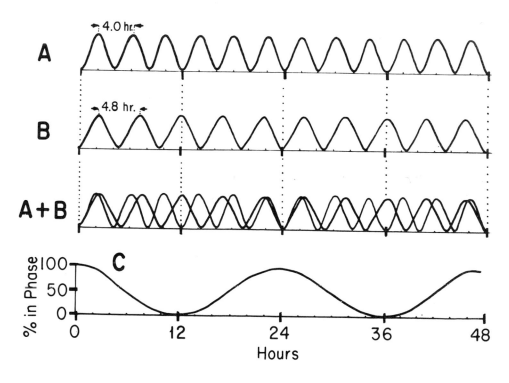

FIGURE 19. *Interaction of Internal Rhythms.* Rhythm *A* shows a period of 4 hours with a frequency of 6 per day. Rhythm *B* has a period of 4.8 hours and a frequency of 5 per day. If the two are superimposed the two rhythms come in phase once every 24 hours. The time of coming-into-phase can be plotted as Rhythm *C*. This is a 24-hour rhythm which has been created from the phase relationships of two rhythms of higher frequency. From Beck.[66]

no doubt that the elaborate chronometers of birds, bees, and crustaceans are all in the nervous system and probably depend on neurological organization for some of their unique complexity." Harker, in her review in 1958, states that the concept of the localized center for the circadian rhythm is an over-simplification: "A new interpretation is proposed, according to which there is a basic 24-hour rhythm present in the cells of all animals and that this rhythm is inherited. . . . The cells of any animal may not all be in phase with one another, and any cell or group of cells may constitute a 'physiological clock' regulating certain activities, although always running to a 24-hour cycle, so that any animal may have a number of clocks all operating at once, either in phase or at variance with each other." Pittendrigh, since 1956, has held essentially the same view as Harker; the reader can look for this in Pittendrigh's papers which are primarily devoted to developing an oscillator model of a circadian rhythm.

Elaborate cellular chronometers are not essential;[91] Bruce and Pittendrigh showed the presence of endogenous rhythms in protozoans,[29a] (Fig. 20), and several workers have described rhythms of oxygen consumption and CO_2 production of plant tissue samples.[124]

Eventually the experimental question was bound to be asked: if there is no apparent central anatomical control of the clock in the mammal, do individual organs have their own clock, or, to paraphrase an expression of Pittendrigh's: *Are* they a clock? A very stimulating but simple experiment by Bunning so excited our curiosity that we have spent the last six years in our laboratory following his lead: he isolated pieces of hamster intestine which then showed circadian rhythms of both tone and amplitude of contraction for three days. We questioned whether isolated rodent organs (adrenal glands and hearts) would show a circadian rhythm of function when these organs were cultured for three to six days. Positive results were obtained as follows:

Tissue	*Measurement*	*Circadian Rhythm*
Hamster adrenal [61] (isolated)	oxygen consumption	60% above and below mean
Hamster adrenal [61] (isolated)	steroid secretion	increase in corticosterone
Rat heart [119] (isolated)	rate of beat	high rate 3 PM to 3 AM
Rat heart cells [119] (cultured)	rate of beat	high rate 8 PM to midnight

These results strikingly support Harker's statement: "An animal may have a number of clocks all operating at once.'

OSCILLATORS AND INTERACTIONS BETWEEN RHYTHMS

The working theory to explain the mechanism of the biological clock as developed by Pittendrigh [103] was mentioned earlier. He described an oscillator model and appropriate related terminology which are adequate for interpretation of all effects studied so far and are useful for speculation of future understanding of circadian rhythms. He suggested that the basic time-measuring element in all biological clocks is an *endogenous self-sustaining oscillation* (ESSO). He recognized that the major operational problem was that of distinguishing a periodicity that *is* ESSO from other cellular periodicities that *are caused by* ESSO. This concept, that animals and plants are composed of interacting oscillators which result in circadian rhythms and ultradian rhythms (2 or more cycles within 24 hours), has received firm acceptance by investigators in the area of biological rhythms.

Biological clocks are probably not definite structures within organs. A clock could be a function that depends on several physiological processes going on in the animal's body; perhaps time measurement depends upon the interaction of several internal rhythms or oscillators. This is a view which has been championed successfully by Halberg.[57] The 24-hour rhythms which we ordinarily observe are called "overt" rhythms by Brown;[69] some workers think of these observations as the "hands of the clock". An observed 24-hour rhythm may be driven by the interaction of other internal rhythms or biological oscillators.[66] Let us suppose that there are two physiological rhythms continuously present in the animal, one with a period of 4 hours and the other with a period of 4.8 hours. (A specific example of the 4-hour physiological rhythm of body temperature in the arctic ground squirrel has been presented earlier.) If the first rhythm is superimposed on the second rhythm, their phase relationships can be diagrammed as seen in Figure 19. At first the two rhythms are out of phase, and they become progressively more out of phase as time passes. At 12 hours they are completely out of phase, then they get closer together until they are again in phase (a beat phenomenon) at 24 hours. The cycle will repeat itself with the rhythms in phase with each other every 24 hours. This relationship can be plotted as a third rhythm (rhythm C in the diagram); one should note that this rhythm shows a circadian period. If the first two rhythms were physiological types involved with body temperature, adrenal activity, heart rate, and kidney function, the rhythm of their phase relationships (rhythm C) could be very important to the measuring systems.

In some way such an interaction probably contributes to the measurement of time; however, two criticisms of this point of view may justifiably be raised: (1) if this interaction-hypothesis is aimed at explaining a 24-hour clock, then the precision of the component ultradian (4 hour, 4.8 hour) rhythms now remains to be explained; (2) isolated individual cells of Metazoans can measure circadian units; thus the postulated A and B rhythms would have to occur at a cellular level.

One writer has suggested that photoperiod comes into this picture if one of the two hypothetical rhythms is found in the brain and is sensitive to light stimuli.[66] The phases of this particular rhythm might be adjusted by photoperiod and this would change the phase relationships between this first rhythm and the second. A change in these two would also change the shape of rhythm C. The consensus of several writers is that a biological clock must be made up of at least two rhythms, because one could not account for all the properties of a clock. If the clock is made up of several rhythms, it is postulated that one at least must be associated with brain function and be sensitive to photoperiod. Yet our recent experiment involving the isolated adrenal glands of the hamster indicates that accurate measurement of time in the mammal does not depend upon the presence in the system of a brain.[61] The brain may be necessary only for sensitivity to photoperiod.

TEMPERATURE INDEPENDENCE OF RHYTHMS

One of the most important characteristics of biological rhythms is temperature independence. Even the mammal may display a wide range of body temperature, so that the hypothetical biochemical clock that it could possess may be "challenged" to measure time at low temperatures. Some mammals have this range of body temperature both in a warm environment and, also, due to going into hibernation. Furthermore in this age of hypothermia as a procedure in human surgery, even human subjects undergo large changes in body temperature. More important than these practical applications are the fundamental implications of this astonishing biological principle. Let us use as an illustration the classic experiment of Welsh [123] who observed that crayfish eyes show a pigment migration which turns them light-colored for about 12 hours and dark-colored for about 12 hours in a persistent circadian rhythm. Let us assume that this rhythm is controlled by the sub-esophageal ganglia. What happens when the crayfish are cooled to 6°C? The cooled clock might run slowly, since ordinarily biochemical reactions in tissue like crayfish brain obey the law of Arrhenius. The eyes of the crayfish should show some prolonged rhythm, perhaps of 30 hours. Instead Welsh found that cooled crayfish (DD) showed the original circadian rhythm throughout the 4-month period of cooling. Although the experiment depended upon test lights, an influence upon the experiment was easily avoided by not using them periodically.

The experiment showed that the control of the crayfish rhythm represented what Brown has called "a biological process independent of temperature." Rhythms are altered or lost when experimental animals have a body temperature below 6°C. When animals in this state warm up, the

rhythms they possess may be out of phase with the solar timetable; then timegivers will gradually synchronize these rhythms with solar events again.

A survey shows that so many biological rhythms are temperature independent that this must be a specific characteristic of endogenous rhythms. Examples of this temperature independence are found in pure rhythms, interval timers, and plant rhythms (Table 5). Typical data showing temperature independence are illustrated by Pittendrigh and Bruce for a rhythm in the one-celled animal, Euglena (Fig. 20).

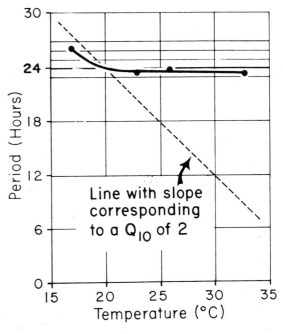

FIGURE 20. *Temperature-Independence in Daily Rhythm of Euglena.* The periods of free-running rhythms of phototaxis in *Euglena gracilis* were recorded at different temperatures. Note that in this experiment a circadian rhythm was demonstrated in a one-celled organism. From Bruce and Pittendrigh.[29a]

Many observations also show that the continuously-consulted clocks of bees are also temperature independent; otherwise they would be useless (Table 7).

Mammalian temperature independent rhythms are illustrated by the regular periodic awakening of ground squirrels from hibernation. In this state (body temperatures often reach 5°C) the animal is not aroused by noise or light.[79] There appears to be a 24-hour rhythm of a shallow and deep hibernation, and the animal usually awakens in artificial daylight. The combination of regular awakening during the illuminated period, a variable length of dormancy periods (1 to 18 days) and a number of other related observations can most easily be understood by postulating a temperature-independent biological clock controlling the state of the animal in hibernation. The ecological significance of the observations can be illustrated by the important rule that the mammalian circadian rhythm (the dial of behavior sequences) can be reversed or "turned" by 12 hours only by a gradual process taking at least 4 days.[38, 87] Thus if a free ground squirrel, a day-active species, were to awaken *at night* from hibernation in the spring, it would probably be incapable of causing its behavior sequence to jump the gap to the day period, until several days had elapsed. Apparently this is usually avoided by the temperature independence of the biological clock during hibernation.[82]

A clear-cut illustration of a mammalian circadian rhythm independent of temperature is found in body temperature records of hibernating bats recorded by Menaker.[99] A simplified graph of one of his illustrations of the temperature of a single myotis is reproduced here (Fig. 21). Recently, also, we have recorded by radio telemetry the heart rates of a marmot

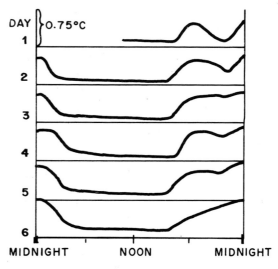

FIGURE 21. *Body Temperatures of Hibernating Bats.* Consecutive records of one hibernating *Myotis lucifugus* show temperature-independence of the daily rhythm. The period of the rhythm is slightly over 24 hours, with a body temperature near 10°C. From Menaker.[99]

spontaneously going into and out of hibernation ten times (see Hibernation chapter). There appeared to be a forbidden time for awakening from hibernation (DD, CT, CS), (Table 7a).

Attempts to explain the temperature independence of biological rhythms cannot be separated from the search for the nature and location of the biological clock. This proposed structure has been described earlier as either a localized structure or a diffuse collection involving many types of tissues. It is of interest that there has been earlier lack of agreement concerning the nature of the causes initiating some spe-

Table 7a. Marmot Hibernation in Darkness

Entering Hibernation	5 AM to 11:30 AM N = 5	5:30 PM to 11:30 PM N = 5
Awakening From Hibernation	4:30 AM to 12:30 PM N = 8	9:30 PM to 11:30 PM N = 2

For other examples see Rawson[105a] and Clayton.[75]

cific physiological processes. A localized origin was postulated by Cannon (1918[74]) to explain thirst in mammals and by Lorand (1912[98]) to explain the aging process in vertebrates. Others now believe in diffuse sources to explain both of these phenomena. In the present case of the biological clock we must look not only for the clock, but also for a structure which by definition also has a very unique biological characteristic, that of temperature independence. This characteristic is so unusual that our credulity is less tried by supposing a discrete localized clock which has a special mechanism to permit performance at low temperatures. If we assume the alternative (a diffuse series of clocks in each animal), there must be a broader distribution than we have supposed of the rare biological material which can display temperature independence. The clock-identification is complicated as usual by the fact that one-celled animals have temperature-independent endogenous rhythms. Further discussion of the one-celled clock is found in Pittendrigh.[102]

Some scanty evidence exists of two types of physiological mechanisms which increase their activity as temperature is lowered: (1) enzymatic activity, and (2) action potentials of brain tissue (EEG). There is not direct evidence of enzymes which increase their activity as temperature is lowered, but Precht[105] has shown that some oxidative enzymes of fish show a decrease in activity after acclimatization to a raised temperature. Presumably these enzymes also show the opposite: an increase in enzymatic activity when temperature is lowered. A clue to this behavior is given by Schwartz[117] who studied enzymes which were activated by heat. This occurred due to the fortuitous coincidence of a heat-stable enzyme and a heat-labile inhibitor. In a similar fashion a temperature-independent biological clock needs only to possess a collection of cold-stable enzymes and cold-labile inhibitors which release more of the enzymes as the temperature is lowered. Bünning[73] provides a slightly different theory: "It is by no means impossible to imagine a chemical mech-

anism that also has no temperature dependence. If part of the mechanism were concerned with supplying a particular substance while a second process destroyed it and both processes were equally temperature dependent, then the substance would accumulate at the same rate irrespective of temperature." Perhaps such enzymes are concerned with the observation of Suda[116] who showed that the EEG of the cat shows an *increase* in amplitude as temperature is lowered from 37° to 24°C.

Two other widely different approaches to explaining temperature independence remain to be discussed. The first is described as part of Pittendrigh's oscillation model of the basic biological rhythm in any animal. He refers to this as an endogenous self-sustaining oscillation (ESSO), but believes that the control or clock presiding over this oscillation is a complex system with constituent oscillatory processes. The control system is not a single temperature insensitive process. Then he explains, "The mutual entrainment (synchronization) of constituent oscillators would result in temperature independence over a limited range provided that key members of the system had reciprocal temperature coefficients." He notes further that temperature has been used to replace light for reversing rhythms by 12 hours. With some theories of temperature compensation, it would be difficult to conceive of a process (the clock) which *responds* to temperature but is also insensitive to temperature. Pittendrigh's argument takes this into account: he describes the clock as a *system* of compensating processes, some of which respond to temperature, while others being resistant to temperature, can restore synchronization.

The second approach to explaining the temperature independence of persisting rhythms concerns the possible response by cold animals to subtle environmental clues. As Brown expressed it: "The main difficulty is to explain how a metabolic clock can maintain such uncanny precision over a temperature range of more than 20°C. An alternative hypothesis which fits all the known facts equally well is that the mechanism is one which can perceive some kind of physical force in the environment hitherto not known to affect living organisms." This hypothesis has been discussed in detail in an earlier section of this chapter. If any physical timegiver other than light affects the cold animal in darkness, there is no reason to suppose it cannot respond to this, since the cold animal still responds to a light cycle. (The rhythm of a cold animal can be reversed by 12 hours by light.) One particular merit to the hypothesis of Brown is that it does not require that any tissue or tissues of the body behave biochemically in an atypical fashion. In other words, this last hypothesis means that the responses of animals with a body temperature of 7°C will be very slow, but they will sluggishly *begin* these responses at times determined by either a light cycle, or a group of subtle environmental timegivers. For further discussion see Sweeney and Hastings.[118]

PROS AND CONS OF MEASURING LOCOMOTOR ACTIVITY

The student of mammalian biological rhythms is faced with deciding which physiological periodicity to measure. Investigators in the field debate the question as to what is the best index to the rhythmical status of the animal (*i.e.*, at just what stage is the animal in its 24-hour sequence of physiological events). The best decision would be to measure three physiological functions continuously or at least as frequently as possible. Practical measurements might be heart rate or body temperature by radio capsule, volume of urine voided, and locomotor activity. Continuous measurements are technically difficult, and many investigators settle upon recording a single function. To select this function it is necessary to compare carefully the advantages of measuring either locomotor activity or internal functions such as body temperature and heart rate. In one sense we are comparing a behavior measurement (locomotor activity) with

physiological measurements. Locomotor activity, as measured by tambour cages, photoelectric cells, or running wheels, records the time of the greatest metabolic expenditure nearly as well as if oxygen-consumption were being recorded. If the activity is measured with running wheels the amplitude of daily running is of interest as a feat of "athletic accomplishment." Activity records (examples typical of the species are given in Fig. 12) frequently prove that the animal does not stop to rest throughout a period of running activity covering 8 or 10 miles. Female white rats in estrus run more intermittently but frequently cover 15 miles in 12 hours. The white rat used as an illustration in Figure 12 would run as far as 21 miles in one night, while Richter and Sloanaker recorded astonishing distances for this same species up to 27 miles, and 38 miles in 24 hours. These efforts are more strenuous than the distances alone represent, since the rats were running uphill on the inclined side of a running wheel. The accomplishment of these short-legged animals compare favorably to that of the best runner of the dogs at the Harvard Fatigue Laboratory. This dog ran in one 17-hour period to 2½ times the height of Mount Everest on an inclined treadmill (reaching the equivalent altitude of 23 km).[76a, 77] While accomplishing this test he ran willingly, covering 125 miles in distance, with a 10-minute break out of each hour for food and rest. The running of rodents on the other hand is entirely spontaneous. The occasional occurrences of these prolonged rodent "marathons" increase our interest in *the running period*, which is but one sequence in the 24-hour series of events.

What is the meaning of this nightly running period? Richter[17] calls it a hunger reaction or regulatory behavior. Random hunger-running, in the free environment, is an important function and increases the probability that the mammal will encounter food. Some mammals in cages run vigorously away from the food which is provided because running is the "correct" sequence in the daily series of events. A test of the hunger reaction was made by Wald and Jackson by simply removing bulk food. Hunger running started at 1000 revolutions a day and increased for each of 6 days by 1000 or 2000 revolutions. As expressed by Wald, "a hungry animal stakes its metabolic reserves against the chance of finding food." However, the amplified hunger reaction, until starvation is near, occurs at the same time of day as the normal hunger running reaction. There is another cause of increased running, which can be called the gonadal-endocrine component superimposed on the basic hunger reaction. One expression of this component is the estrus peak of high running which is observed every 4 or 5 days in the records of female rats and hamsters (Fig. 15). Again the amplified running comes at the usual time in the 24-hour sequence of behavior (Fig. 12). This excessive running increases the probability that the estrus female will cross the path of a male. It is seen in many other mammals such as dogs, horses, and cattle.

One warning about measuring running activity should be introduced here. All rodents are not good runners, and some mammalian species show remarkably little total activity each day. If the animal is quiet for 24 hours, the assumption cannot be made that there is no 24-hour rhythm. A marked biochemical rhythm may still be present.

Now let us compare running activity with other indices which may serve as useful clues to the animal's composite circadian rhythm. These might be physiological measurements such as blood sugar, body temperature, or oxygen consumption. Suppose one selects midnight as the peak of locomotor activity of a nocturnal animal. In between bouts of activity the animal can be removed from the cage and immediately the three physiological measurements can be made. These would be useful indications of the effect of muscular exercise on the three functions. However, the investigator of biological rhythms would not find these data interesting, because he wishes to study the basal state of the animal *at the time* of the habitual large bouts of locomotor activity. This is technically difficult and usually the in-

Table 8. Heart Rate And Body Temperature Before And After Exercise

		HEART RATE Mean beats/minute		BODY TEMPERATURE Mean °C (°F)	
		Before Exercise	After Exercise	Before Exercise	After Exercise
	N =	(4)	(4)	(17)	(17)
	Noon	395	365 **	36.3 (97.3)	38.4 (101.1)
HAMSTERS	Midnight	416	429	37.5 (99.5)	38.7 (101.7)
	Δ	21	64	1.2 (2.2)	0.3 (0.6)
	P. value	....	....	1.0%	1.0%
	N =	(10)	(10)	(10)	(10)
	Noon	71.9	141.9	37.2 (99.0)	38.1 (100.6)
MEN *	Midnight	64.9	137.8	37.1 (98.8)	37.9 (100.2)
	Δ	7.0	4.1	0.1 (0.2)	0.2 (0.4)
	P. value	0.1%	5.0%	1.0%	1.0%

* A few individuals consistently had a reversed rhythm (low in morning, high at night). Their low values are included in the night data, and high values in the noon data.

** Forced exercise caused bradycardia at noontime.

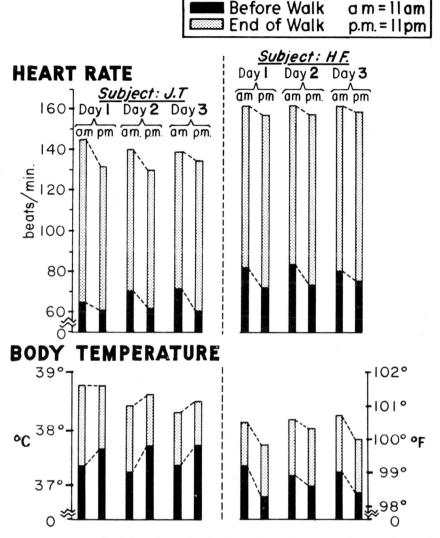

FIGURE 22. *Human Daily Physiological Rhythms After Exercise.* The rhythms of resting heart rate and body temperature are illustrated by graphing values obtained at noon and midnight. The day-night differences are still found after exercise, showing the presence of a day-setting and a night-setting of these physiological factors. Note that the two rhythms of subject J. T. are out of phase (*i.e.*, dissociated). From Timmerman *et al.*[120]

vestigator has to settle for a *resting state* which is still influenced by the specific dynamic activity of food. Even then there may be doubt. For example, if body temperature measurements (resting animal) at noon and midnight differ by 2°C, is the reason because the midnight animal, that may *look* quiet, is not really resting but has tensed his major skeletal muscles?

Years ago this problem was solved by Simpson and Gailbrith, by doing their studies on animals after exercise at noon and midnight. We have used this procedure to reveal in the same individual two component parts: the day-animal and the night-animal, each having completely different "settings" for physiological mechanisms. This procedure can be illustrated with comparative data on body temperature and heart rate obtained from male hamsters and male human subjects (Table 8). Measurements were made both before and after exercise. The hamsters were exercised and the human subjects walked on a motor-driven treadmill at noon and at midnight (Fig. 22). The data from the human subjects were influenced very little by meals, since all recordings were made at equal times after eating. Note that the circadian rhythms persisted after the exercise, an indication that the control of heart rate and body temperature had different "settings" at noon and at midnight.[83, 120]

HUMAN CIRCADIAN RHYTHMS

Ever since early caveman kept fires blazing during the night, man has succeeded in providing himself with approximately 16 hours of daylight and 8 hours of darkness per 24 hours. This has not appeared to make the list of biological rhythms of man particularly different from those of other day-active mammals. It is easier to obtain continuous 24-hour readings from human subjects, with the result that there is a larger volume of data on this "animal". The relative ease of making measurements is counteracted by the variability of each human subject from day to day, and the wide range of results from different subjects (intra- and extra-individual variability). To illustrate the last point consider the homogeneity of body temperatures obtained from 14 hamsters: every animal showed the day-night rhythm. A similar experiment of 10 men showed much variability. Using either body temperature or heart rate as a criterion (standardized, rested, post-absorptive conditions), the series was found to include what Kleitman calls "early-energy" types of individuals. Two subjects showed rhythms the exact reverse of the others (high temperature at midnight). Such variability is common in human experiments on biological rhythms. In order to improve this type of experiment particular attention has to be given to subsidiary

factors such as preconditioning subjects and obtaining background information (individual's history and subjective comments) to aid in interpretation of results.

There are some obvious advantages to man as a subject in biological rhythm experiments. It is no coincidence that many workers who have spent most of a lifetime carrying out such investigations have worked on "mice and men": Kleitman, Halberg, Sollberger, Menzel, Richter, Jores are examples. This point must be made since in this age of molecular biology, fundamental and theoretical experiments on man are becoming unfashionable. In our laboratory we have been interested in looking for a day-night physiological setting in *the whole man*, and for the phase relations of four rhythms, all of which might have separate controls (or clocks), namely the adrenal cortex, the posterior pituitary, the hypothalamus, and some other part of the brain. We wanted to compare the physiological status of a man from 7 AM to 1 PM, with the same man under identical standardized conditions from 7 PM to 1 AM. Reference has been made earlier to the "day animal" and the "night animal," implying a Jeckel-Hyde existence for the animal's daily routine. Actually, we studied three states "in" man: the day-animal, the night (evening) animal, and the sleeping-animal. We tried to eliminate the effects on the experiment of: the observer, meals, exercise, excitement, and sleep. Some details of the experiment and results will now be given: The investigation with 11 control subjects was carried out in an experimental chamber; each test lasted 33 hours or more. Phase relations of heart rates were compared with rhythms of core temperature, rate of urinary flow, and of electrolyte excretion. Data were collected hourly, with the subject reclining for ½ hour (the last 15 minutes in darkness) before the recordings were made. After the recording, the subject could leave the experimental chamber if he chose, although he was rarely inclined to do this. Data accumulated during the first 8 hours in the chamber were not considered suitable for analysis, but this interval provided an opportunity for the subject to become accustomed to the chamber and to get a night of uninterrupted sleep.

A· small radio-capsule, placed in the pocket of the undershirt of the subject, was employed for telemetering of heart rate. One electrode of this capsule was placed above and the other below the heart. Since the antenna was in the experimental chamber, it was only necessary for the subject to walk into the chamber for recording of heart rate to begin. Water was given in equal amounts at hourly intervals. The influence of ingestion of food was studied in a variety of ways, including administration of equal, small amounts of a liquid formula at hourly intervals. In all cases, observations were recorded with the subject awake.

Characteristic phase relations of the four variants were as follows: maximal body temperature, heart rate and rate of excretion of potassium occur between about 5 PM and 9 PM, while the peak in rate of urinary flow occurs slightly later. The great majority of the 11 normal male subjects showed similar physiological rhythms for the four measurements. Of the four variants considered, body temperature demonstrated the clearest sinusoidal curve. A biphasic rhythm of heart rate was sometimes noted. With some subjects, the peak period for each rhythm was usually in the afternoon, although reversed types were encountered with peaks between 7 PM and midnight.[80]

Experiments in which placebo meals were given indicate that the specific dynamic action of food elevates heart rate by about 8% over the values characteristic of the nonpostprandial period, but does not obscure the fundamental rhythm pattern. With some subjects, the basal, resting standardized heart rate in the evening was 25% higher than the same reading in the morning. These differences can be tentatively attributed to two different heart rate control settings.

On several occasions the same subject was studied twice or more, at intervals of 1 day, 1 week or 1 month, and in one case the same subject was studied 1 year later. Individual performance was found to be quite similar in these successive periods of testing.

A totally different approach, an extensive one, is used by Halberg,[86] often involving one or two measurements every 6 hours for several months. We have tried this approach with Rhesus monkeys, only with continuous recording by radio-capsule.[81]

Some interesting generalizations can now be listed based on these experiments and some from other laboratories:

1. In experiments with men living under controlled, standardized conditions, reversed rhythms of several types have been found.

2. Human subjects will "accept" a 21- or 28-hour day more rapidly and completely than laboratory animals (compare Pittendrigh[102]).

3. The sleep rhythm is a *free function* (terminology suggested by Aschoff) in the daily sequence of events which make up a 24-hour composite rhythm. According to P. R. Lewis[97] all 12 subjects on 21-hour days and 27-hour days experience no difficulty in sleeping (*i.e.*, they changed sleep pattern); but especially in the first two weeks most of them had kidneys still on 24-hour time.

4. Human rhythms can be dissociated. Any one of the following in the same individual can be on some abnormal time (such as 21-hours), while all the rest are on 24-hour time: sleep, heart rate, body temperature, water excretion, and potassium excretion. This evidence suggests (at least for man) the presence of separate and simultaneous biological clocks or regulators in the hypothalamus and the adrenal cortex.

Other clear-cut 24-hour rhythms of man[57] are: (1) changes in excretion of 17-ketosteroids with a peak between 7:00 AM and 12:00 noon and a decrease by evening; (2) a minimum count of eosinophil cells in the blood near 9:00 AM with a gradual increase to a maximum after midnight; and (3) a minimum in mitotic activity in the epidermis in the morning, with a maximum in the evening. These are responses that arise from the pituitary body under the control of the hypothalamus.[44] None of these measurements were included in earlier studies of rats which gave evidence contrary to this last statement: the results from the rats showed persistent activity rhythms after hypophysectomy.

Several avenues of study are suggested from the experiments just discussed: (1) More attempts should be made to dissociate rhythms in laboratory animals, as an aid in distinguishing whether the control of rhythms (the biological clock) consists of a few or many mechanisms. (2) Some human subjects are "true or complete adaptors" to artificial times (21-hour days or 27-hour days). If they were turned free of apparent timegivers (alarm clocks, food, muscular activity), would they revert spontaneously to a 24-hour routine?

The effect upon the industrial worker of a change from day shift to night shift represents a practical problem for the student of biological rhythms. Two questions must be asked: (a) how quickly can most human subjects change their conspicuous rhythms by 12 hours; and (b) how complete is the physiological change when the subjects appear to have made a normal adjustment to a night shift? Few controlled studies have been done on this question, although many observations have been made of people actually on the night shift.[106] When workers go on the night shift, social factors keep them from having their usual amount of sleep when they return from working. In rodents the speed of reversal of superficial rhythms has been determined to be about 4 days with ordinary laboratory lighting conditions.[38, 57] The feeding pattern changed simultaneously with locomotor activity. Further experiments will undoubtedly show that it is "harder" to turn the clock backward than forward.

To determine a similar single figure for man would be difficult if we take into account the variability by 4 hours in rhythm types which we demonstrated above. There must be a spectrum of types of response to the change in enforced nocturnal working times. As far as completeness of change is concerned, there is one bit of evidence which must always act as a warning that a supposed reversed-cycle man actually may not have completely replaced his night-physiology by his day-physiology; this evidence is that after 6 weeks of a 21-hour day or 27-hour day, the kidney-rhythms of some of Lewis's subjects were still on a 24-hour basis. There obviously could be a similar resistance to a time-reversal of 12 hours.

Another practical question concerns whether the 4-hour cycle of duty-routine used in some military services, and a similar 8-hour cycle used in other circumstances is an efficient procedure. The system of 8 hours of rest followed by 8 hours of work has been followed in the continuous light of the Arctic,[96] and is now being tested for use in Space Flight. An evaluation of the relation between circadian rhythms and the selection of duty-hours, has been made by Strughold.[114, 115] Many interesting questions remain to be answered such as whether the better space man is the one with the large amplitude or the small amplitude of circadian physiological rhythm.

Other topics concerned with space and trans-globe travel by jet plane [78, 108] must be left to longer reviews of circadian rhythms. The degree of interest in this field is shown by the publication of eight books on circadian rhythms over a period of several years (Bünning;[73] Harker;[89] Cloudsley-Thompson;[76] Menzel;[100] Kleitman;[95] Aschoff;[64] Sollberger,[110] and Reinberg and Ghata.[107] Reviews have also been written by Webb and Brown,[121] Hendricks;[92] and Aschoff.[65] The interested student will also want to refer to three published symposia, edited by Withrow,[57] Foman,[84] and Wolf.[126]

SUMMARY

This chapter on biological rhythms has included abstracts of experimental methods, terminology, and theories of rhythm causation. The discussion of the following topics has been left to longer treatises: (*a*) rhythms other than 24-hour (reproductive, lunar, and annual); (*b*) artificial rhythms produced by drugs, hormones, or light cycles; (*c*) periodic diseases of man. Even the superficial scanning of the field as presented in this chapter should be sufficient to show that the study of circadian rhythms is not a theoretical academic question for a few biologists, but is important to each experimentalist in the designing of all mammalian research plans.

Of the theories of rhythm-causation, most of the support goes to the concept of the inherited circadian clock. This theory assumes a genetically-endowed fundamental pure-rhythm with a natural period of 23 to 25 hours. In the free environment timegivers adjust this inherent rhythm to nearly 24-hours permitting it to be the clock in animal-navigation. The timegiver is ordinarily a conspicuous daily event such as dawn or sunset. Perhaps some individuals of a species can respond to timegivers more subtle than light; these might be several cosmic physical cycles which are synchronized so that they come to a single peak with a frequency different from 24 hours.

The descriptions of animal experiments other than mammalian shows that too little work has been done on mammals and many more experiments are needed on common laboratory rodents. Too many assumptions *about* mammals have been based upon experiments on worms, arthropods and birds. Future work could include studies on day-active mammals, the effects of raising mammals in darkness, the measurements of several simultaneous 24-hour rhythms (to look for dissociation of rhythms), and the effects of reversed-light and different intensities of light. These experiments should strengthen descriptions of the degree-of-importance of endogenous and exogenous factors in Biological Rhythms. They are both there, but it is not yet entirely clear what part each plays.

Chapter Four

PRINCIPLES OF

TEMPERATURE REGULATION

Chapter Four

Principles of Temperature Regulation

In preparation for considering mammalian responses to extreme heat and cold, we must first review the principles of temperature regulation as they apply to moderate corrective-changes in body temperature of the mammal. These changes may be represented either as large oscillations of body temperature in some mammals which are temperature-labile or as rather minute oscillations in the case of man. Essentially the small corrective-events which keep the constant temperature of man are the responsibility of the hypothalamus which serves as the control tower of the negative feedback circuit. The teaching physiologist looks forward to discussing the role of the hypothalamus in regulation because he has probably been dismantling the mammalian physiological architecture for many weeks for the benefit of his classes, and now he must reassemble it into an integrated functional organism; he may now describe how

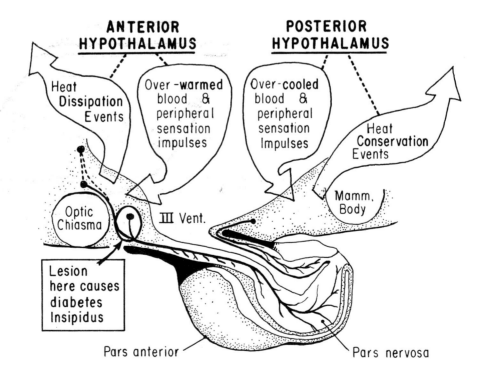

FIGURE 23. *Some Regulatory Events in the Hypothalamus.* The anatomical landmarks near the hypothalamus are shown and also probable physiological processes associated with control of temperature regulation by this structure.

all systems and mechanisms of the mammalian body contribute to temperature regulation. The behavior as well as the physiology of the animal may make a large contribution; for example, it was recorded in an earlier chapter that the wall thickness of the nest of the white rat is directly related to the ambient temperature in which he is maintained. Temperature regulation is an excellent example (as is acid-base balance) of the principle of homeokinesis.* To accomplish this assignment in overall homeokinesis, the hypothalamus must act as an astonishingly accurate thermostat. The reader can imagine moving a sensitive laboratory bath and regulating system into extreme environments; will the thermostat maintain at least the interior of the bath within 0.01°C of the desired temperature? The role of the hypothalamus in regulating body temperature is accomplished by two centers: one in the anterior hypothalamus governs heat dissipating events, and one in the posterior hypothalamus calls on heat conservation events (Fig. 23). The detailed pathways and origins of temperature regulation nerve impulses are the subject of a prolonged classic debate in the tradition of Ludwig and Bowman-Heidenhain. This friendly controversy (guided by J. D. Hardy) will be explained later.

One final point about the temperature regulating center concerns the effect of infections which cause a fever. We say that the temperature regulating center acts like a thermostat, and the pyrogens reset this thermostat at a higher level. The important point is that regulation has not broken down but is being carried out with a new "ceiling". When profound vaso-constriction occurs, the person feels cold, and may shiver. The body temperature rises to this new level of regulation referred to as "having a fever". Once the new ceiling

has been reached, the skin vessels will dilate and the skin of the face will appear flushed. With recovery the temperature falls and profuse sweating may occur to enable heat to be lost rapidly. The action of the drugs called antipyretics is now clear; they reduce the high body temperature of fever by resetting the heat regulating center. Antipyretics have no temperature-regulating effect if the temperature is normal, or if a person is normally heat-exposed.

Only the superficial outline of the principles of temperature regulation can be mentioned here; I recommend extensive chapters in textbooks of medical physiology and Hardy's review [142] of this topic.

PRINCIPLES

Constancy of Body Temperatures

Most mammals are homeothermic which means that they can maintain a relatively constant body temperature which is independent of the environmental temperature. Another convenient term to apply to mammals and birds is "endothermic", meaning that they produce and control their own sources of heat. The remaining vertebrates (fish, frogs, salamanders, reptiles) have body temperatures which fluctuate with changes of the external environment. Such vertebrates are called poikilotherms or ectotherms (external sources of body heat). There are exceptions among the mammals to the rule of maintaining a constant body temperature. The marsupials and monotremes are considered to be thermally unstable,[152] although they are not hibernators (Fig. 24). Some mammals become dormant at certain times, but awaken when a critical body temperature of about 15° to 20°C is reached. Other mammals such as the hazel mouse maintain a critical dormancy (hibernation) until a critical temperature near 0°C is reached; then they rewarm and begin to regulate as homeothermic mammals again. In a later chapter, special attention will be given to the mammals which become dormant.

---

* This is the same as homeostasis; it is the maintenance of constancy of the bodily state, within narrow limits, by a dynamic equilibrium; body temperature (especially in man) is maintained within narrow limits; this also applies to body water, pH, ionic equilibrium, blood pressure and body weight.

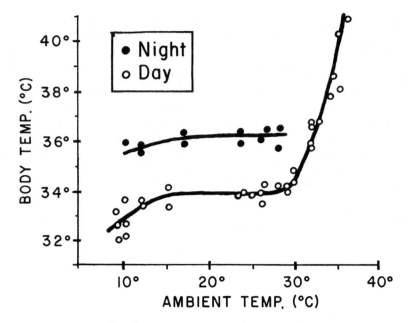

FIGURE 24. *Temperature Regulation of a Heterotherm.* Body temperatures in variable air temperatures in a nocturnally active Central American oppossum, *Metachirus.* From Morrison.[149]

The temperature regulation of small mammals has been analyzed for years; recently many more studies have been made on large mammals. According to Luck and Wright,[147] the core temperature of the rhinoceros varies within a range of 4°C. Cena[133] reports the early morning core temperature of the hippopotamus as ca. 34°C and the afternoon core temperature as ca. 39°C. In water the sublingual temperature dropped from 36° to 25°C. The camel, as part of its temperature regulation mechanism, has a day-night range from 36° to 39°C.[154] One of our captive bears, recorded by implanted radio capsule in the autumn, varied over 24 hours from 36.7° to 38.7°C.[138] Perhaps it is a characteristic of large mammals to have a greater 24-hour body temperature variation than does man.

Variations in Body Temperature in Man

The precision of the accurate hypothalamic-thermostat has had a long history since homeothermism began some 150 million years ago; at that time mammals first evolved from their reptilian ancestors. It should be realized that the mechanisms which the hypothalamus calls upon are not perfect and the body temperature can change within 20 minutes after exposure to extreme environments. Exercise may have a large effect; if a man in poor physical condition begins to do heavy work daily, at first his rectal temperature during exercise may reach 102°F; after a week or so when he achieves good physical condition his exercise temperature might be 100°F which will be maintained as long as he continues daily exercise. Four diagrams illustrate this (Fig. 25); they will give a preview of the type of consideration which will be given in later chapters to the larger responses which are corrective to prevent a thermal run-away in either the cold or the hot direction. Note that the first diagram illustrates two settings of the temperature regulating mechanism, one for the "day man" and one for the "night man". Environ-

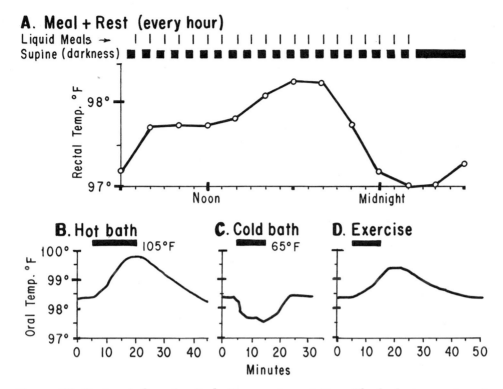

FIGURE 25. *Factors Influencing Body Temperature of Man.* The body temperature is nicely regulated, but exact maintenance is altered by many factors such as hot baths, cold water, and exercise. Also, there is a daily resetting of temperature regulation which persists in a resting individual if the influence of exercise or meals is removed. If standardized exercise is carried out at noon and midnight, the day-night regulation is still apparent in the exercise body temperatures. (in part from Green [139])

mentally caused temperature rises are superimposed upon these settings.

The Measurement of Body Temperature

The standard or basal body temperatures of human subjects of various races will fall within the range of 97° to 99.5°F. Using an accurate thermometer under the tongue, in the axilla, in the groin, or in the rectum, it may take up to 5 minutes before the final temperature equilibrium has been reached. The reading in the axilla is about 0.5°F lower than in the mouth; the reading in the rectum is about 1° to 3°F higher than in the mouth.[155a] In women there are monthly variations; the temperature in the second half of the menstrual cycle is higher than during the first half. For the present discussion we will concern ourselves only with resting body temperatures at a standardized time of the physiological month. This standardized resting body temperature varies over a 24-hour period systematically with the individual. This variation is not due to sleep, activity, or eating, but should be thought of in terms of a change in setting of the thermostat (see preceding section). A statement is frequently found in textbooks that the maximum setting occurs in the evening and a minimum setting in the early hours of the morning. This is an oversimplification since there are actually three patterns of settings. The high setting of the hypothalamic-thermostat may come in the morning, it may be diphasic, or it may be in the evening. Of course the normal routine of activity complicates and sometimes obscures this setting. In resting subjects the setting may account for over 1°F.

Very little is known about the change in hypothalamic setting of mammals other than man; this is because it is difficult to train most mammals to lie down and relax in darkness for 30 minutes before a standardized temperature is taken for each hour of the day. Spontaneous activity of mammals even when they are restrained have made it difficult to study the settings in temperature regulation over a 24-hour period.

The single temperature measurement in mouth or rectum is frequently unsatisfactory, especially for calculations of heat loss from the mammalian body. Experimentally, it has been determined that a useful assessment is the "mean body temperature" which is derived from two sources: (1) numerous skin temperature measurements and (2) a core measurement usually obtained from the rectum. This relationship is usually expressed by the following equation:

tinuously because the probe moves to different locations in the rectum. Dr. Henry C. Bazett, one of the early environmental physiologists, seldom missed an opportunity to instruct budding physiologists that "there are hot and cold areas along the rectum". Accuracy can be improved by using thermistors in the external auditory meatus, if changes in core temperature rather than absolute values are desired.[133a] Radio-telemetry is a tool which is adaptable to continuous recording of temperature; the capsule can be fastened in the axilla of a man, or implanted in the abdominal cavity of an experimental animal. For example, continuous body temperatures (and heart rates) of wolves were recorded in an outdoor enclosure where the air temperature varied down to —45°C.[137] These abdominal temperatures probably come closer to being accurate core temperatures than the mouth or rectal temperatures of these animals would have been.

Thermography

Instead of taking mean skin temperatures with thermocouples or thermistors on many points of the skin, a new technique is to take pictures of the skin with an infrared

Mean body temperature = 0.33 × skin temperature + 0.67 × rectal temperature.

The skin temperatures are weighted, either by the system of Belding[150] or of Ramanathan.[152a] If there are 10 sensing devices (usually thermistors) on the subject's body, the values from the trunk might be weighted 45% while those on the fingers 5% (see Appendix). The average skin temperature for a warm subject is frequently about 33°C, for a cold subject 27°C. However the trunk may be warm while the cold-exposed palm is 5°C. The major difficulty in measuring skin temperature is the conduction of heat from the thermistor down the wire leads. Very thin wire must be used.

The measurement of core temperature in man is difficult to make accurately and con-

camera. There are technical difficulties with using this technique since the studio must be darkened and the temperature of the room should be between 68° and 72°F. This technique was developed by astronomers to take temperature readings of the planets.

Informally the instrument has been called "a camera with an eye for heat"; the resulting picture reproduces a thermal map of the skin. The apparatus scans the skin for about 10 minutes to register the emitted infrared rays. Where blood concentrates close to the surface in veins, infections, or abnormally rapid growths, the skin runs a high temperature and the film shows a light spot. Where there are areas of low metabolism, such as hair or scars or inactive growths close to the surface, the body temperature is slightly lower and the thermogram is proportionately darker. Where an abnormal growth is under the skin the temperature may be indicated as 3°F higher than in a corresponding area of skin on the other side.

This camera has been especially successful in the study of frostbite; the picture demarks several weeks in advance the parts of fingers or toes which will eventually have to be amputated. Temperatures recorded on the film can be read to 0.1°F.[157]

HEAT BALANCE

The body temperature is maintained at a relatively constant level because of the balance which exists between heat production and heat loss. The contributing mechanisms are in Table 8a.

These various factors will be discussed individually in the next three chapters. If there were no heat loss, the factors listed above even in the resting subject would produce sufficient heat to raise the body temperature by 1°C every hour; a 69 kg man produces 70 calories of heat per hour due to the basal metabolism. The temperature rise is expressed in the equation:

The specific heat of the mammal body (70% water) is often considered as 1.0. To be more accurate one may use the value of Pembrey:0.83.[151]

Heat Gained

Heat is gained by the body not only from internal metabolism but also from the external environment, such as desert sand and rock, if they are at a higher temperature than the body. There will also be a small gain of heat from any hot food that is ingested, if it is at a temperature higher than body temperature. On the other hand, if the heat production is insufficient to maintain the body temperature, further metabolism is brought about by the involuntary contraction of the skeletal muscles. A review of three probable types of involuntary contractions has been presented by Haider and Lindsley:[141] body microvibrations, physiological tremors, and shivering. The frequency of all three is often between 7 to 13 cycles/sec. Shivering is believed to be a natural amplification of the continuously present tremor.

The onset of shivering depends upon the integrity or "health" of the temperature regulating mechanism (probably the hypo-

$$\text{Heat Gained (in Cals)} = \text{Mass (in kg)} \times \text{Specific Heat} \times \text{Temperature Change (in °C)}.$$

Table 8a. Heat Balance

FACTORS INCREASING
HEAT PRODUCTION
(over Basal Metabolic Rate)

1. Exercise or shivering
2. Imperceptible tensing of muscles
3. Chemical increase of metabolic rate
4. Specific dynamic action of food
5. Disease (fever)

FACTORS DECREASING HEAT LOSS

1. Shift in blood distribution
2. Decrease in tissue conductance
3. Counter-current heat exchange

FACTORS ENHANCING
HEAT LOSS

1. Sweating
2. Panting
3. Cooler environment
4. Increased skin circulation (vasodilation)
5. Decreased clothing or shorter fur insulation
6. Increased insensible water loss
7. Increased radiating surface
8. Increased air movement (convection)

thalamus) and upon whether the mammal is a hibernator or not. For example, the white rat, when chilled, can rewarm by shivering from a colonic temperature of 23°C and in some cases on down to 16°C but not lower; its shivering mechanism will not function beyond a critical temperature (See Chapter 5). Yet a hamster (a hibernator) may begin to rewarm by shivering with a colonic temperature of 3° to 5°C (for details, see Chapter 7).

Chemical increase of heat production (thermogenesis) is brought about especially by epinephrine, norepinephrine and thyroxin; experimental mammals exposed to cold develop the capability of producing heat, independent of muscle contraction. Curarized, cold-acclimated rats double heat production in a cold room at 5°C with maintenance of rectal temperature. Nonacclimatized rats cannot call upon this mechanism. The important link seems to be norepinephrine liberated from sympathetic nerve endings. This change in the calorigenic effect of norepinephrine has been confirmed in men who are cold-acclimated.[132]

The specific dynamic action (SDA) of food on the basal metabolic rate (BMR) results in a warming effect and is in fact identified by the extra calories produced. It is so long lasting in lower mammals that it creates a technical problem when one wishes to measure their basal oxygen consumption. To illustrate the principle, if a basal human subject drinks 100 grams of glucose, his heat production begins to rise in a few minutes and reaches a peak in 3 hours. The extra heat produced is 25 calories, although the value of the sugar is 370 calories (heat value = 7% of food value). Dietary fat has a relatively slight effect, but protein has a larger effect than carbohydrate (protein heat value = 18% of food calories). Furthermore the protein effect is longer lasting. It is for this reason that only a low protein meal can be permitted the night before the basal metabolic rate is measured. (This must always be measured before 10:00 AM).

Heat Lost

Heat is lost from the mammal by conduction, convection, radiation, and the evaporation of water. A small loss of heat occurs in the expired air which is at body temperature; also, this air is saturated with water vapor. The heat lost by the skin depends partly on the temperature gradient between (1) skin and (2) air and solid objects. The skin temperature is regulated by the blood flow to the skin and by evaporation. With a low peripheral blood flow (vasoconstriction) the skin temperature is low and heat loss to the environment is reduced. With a high peripheral blood flow (vasodilation) the skin temperature approaches the core temperature, and heat loss to the environment is then maximal. To this relationship the cooling power of perspiration is added.

Heat is lost by conduction through physical contact of the animal with objects and substratum. Loss of heat by conduction is minimized by the insulation of fur and clothing. The effectiveness of fur as insulation permits Eskimos and Lapps to tolerate very extreme cold; especially in northwest Greenland they still dress with one layer of fur facing inward, and another layer facing outward.

Convection is similar to conduction in that the heat is transmitted from one molecule to another by physical contact, but in convection the heat is transferred to the air which rises taking the heat with it. Cooler air comes in to take its place. Radiation is the loss of heat by electromagnetic infrared waves. The frequency of infrared is slightly less than visible red, and the radiant energy from the mammalian skin varies in wave length from 5 to 20 microns. Such radiation does not heat the air through which it passes.

The amount of heat gained or lost by radiation depends not only on the temperature of an object but also on its color and texture; dark rough surfaces radiate maximally and light shiny surfaces at the same temperature less rapidly. The human skin acts as a black body radiator irrespective

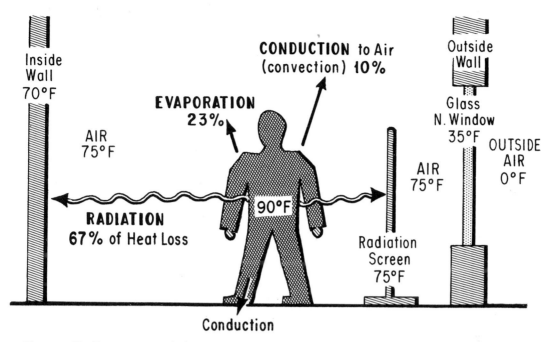

FIGURE 26. *Partitioning of Avenues of Heat Loss From Man.* Note that at air temperatures of 75°F, radiation is responsible for most of the heat loss. If a person is near a cold window but in warm air, heat loss by radiation is greatly increased. This increased loss is prevented by a thin screen.

of the actual skin color; whether this applies to clothing is controversial. White clothing has been often considered more suitable than black, both in the tropics (less heat gained) and in the Polar regions (less heat lost). Light *weight* clothing does protect against heat reflection and from the direct rays of sun. In army tests the heat gain of clothed test subjects seated in the sun was 120 calories an hour; unclothed, they gained 200 calories an hour.

An application of the contribution of radiation to heat loss is evident when a person sits near a large window on a cold winter day (Fig. 26). If he is lightly clad, he will be cold; if he is unfamiliar with heat-loss factors, he will repeatedly look at the room thermostat. This device and the thermometer on it may both read 75°F and the air and walls may be 75°F, but the glass of the window may actually be 35°F. Heat rays leave the person's body and strike the glass, creating a heat "drain".

One frequently sees patients covered with a single sheet in winter time in the corridor of a hospital near large windows. This window glass too is acting as a heat sink because of radiation from the patient to the cold surface. For the circumstances this amount of insulation is insufficient and may be placing a thermal stress upon the patient.

Heat Lost by Evaporation of Water.

In the mammal group there are three types of skin, each with a different anatomical arrangement for evaporation of water for the dissipation of heat: heavy fur without sweat glands, hairy skin with sweat glands, and smooth, relatively hairless skin with sweat glands. The simplest approach is to describe the types of water loss from man and then to list which of these mechanisms are found in the three classes of mammals. Perspiration from the hairless skin of man is of three types: 1) insensible perspiration (diffusion water); 2) thermal sweat (from eccrine glands); 3) non-thermal sweat (also called palma-sole sweat or emotional sweat).

Insensible perspiration leaves the body at all times unless the ambient humidity is 100% RH. This moisture diffuses through the stratum corneum of the skin, through the pores of the sweat glands, and from the lungs. The existence of this phenomenon of continual evaporation was described by Sanctorius Sanctorius (1561-1636), Professor of Medicine at Padua, Italy. His apparatus consisted of a chair on an iron beam, a fulcrum, and a longer arm of the beam which carried weights. When he measured the weight of a person sitting in the chair he found that all individuals continually decrease in weight. This weight loss of the mammalian body must be partitioned into: 1) the excess weight of the CO_2 expired over the O_2 inspired; 2) the weight lost as the water vapor from the lungs; 3) and loss by diffusion through the skin. The first two factors are subtracted from the total in order to obtain the contribution of the skin to insensible perspiration. The weight lost from the lungs is calculated with the assumption that the expired air is at 91°F and saturated at a cost of 0.035 grams of body water for each liter of air expired when the ambient temperature is 20°F and lower. At 40°F the cost is considered as 0.029 grams.[129] The excess weight in grams of the CO_2 expired is calculated assuming an R.Q. of 0.88 by multiplying the oxygen consumption in liters/hr STP dry by 0.3. Insensible perspiration plays an appreciable part in heat dissipation. This is the only source of evaporative heat loss in subjects which do not have sweat glands. Some of these individuals can tolerate fairly high ambient temperatures depending solely on their insensible perspiration as a means of cooling.[156]

Thermal sweating occurs from the eccrine glands in the skin. These may produce up to 12 liters per day of sweat which is a dilute solution of NaCl (often a 0.4% solution). During tests on human subjects on the desert as much as 4 liters of sweat per hour have been produced, but this production could not be continued for more than an hour or so. The details of the initiation of sweating will be considered in a later chapter.

Non-thermal sweating is of minor importance in the dissipation of heat but of considerable theoretical interest. The associated sweat glands in man are eccrine on the sole of the foot and the palm of the hand, and apocrine in the axilla and pubic regions. Non-thermal sweating also occurs on the forehead. When man is under thermal stress, sweating begins simultaneously over the entire body surface. (For a qualification of this generalization see Hertzman et al.[144]) However, the non-thermal mechanism (sweating on the palms, soles, axillae and forehead) is also triggered when the subject is not under heat stress; it is the "cold sweat" of emotional disturbances. Some individuals have a chronic excess activity of this sweating mechanism with the result that their palms usually feel cool and moist. Paradoxically some subjects exposed unclothed in a cold room demonstrate the active production of beads of non-thermal sweat. Kuno studied the non-thermal mechanism experimentally and could obtain a sudden increase in this form of sweat by giving his subjects problems in arithmetic.[146] He also described the evolutionary significance of non-thermal sweating. To understand this, one should realize that in many mammals the only sweat glands of any sort are found on the pads of the feet. Probably the pads of most mammals contain non-thermal sweat glands; this is a subject which needs investigation. The essential point is that mammals including man produce moisture on the bearing surfaces for grasping and pushing. The importance of this can be demonstrated by the person who attempts to walk up a plank barefooted when the plank surface has been sprinkled with talcum powder; the lack of an adhesive material on the soles makes the task difficult. Kuno points out that another demonstration of the necessity of an adhesive material is seen when a woodsman spits on his hands before grasping an axe; in fact he states that to his knowledge the expression "spit on your hands" is found in most languages. It would seem that the non-thermal sweat mechanism serves in locomotion and as part of the Emergency Syndrome in mammals. The importance of this mechanism to the temperature regulation of man is partly a negative one because the accumulation of moisture in gloves and footgear when man is exposed to extreme cold is undesirable.

Water (which passes through the skin as sweat) has a high heat of vaporization. It was emphasized by Henderson [143] in *The Fitness of the Environment* that this property, plus the property of high heat capacity, gives water a peculiar usefulness in the regulation of body temperature. Heat is required to convert water to water vapor; such heat is referred to as the latent heat of vaporization. The vaporization of 1 ml of water requires 0.58 calories; this is the amount of heat lost when 1 ml of sweat evaporates from the skin. If sweat appears on the surface of the skin in a copious flood, some of it will drip from the body without removing heat by evaporation. Non-thermal sweat and insensible perspiration leave the body at the rate of 900 ml a day in temperate zones. This will result in the loss of 900 x 0.58 = 522 calories of heat per day. The 400 ml of water lost from the lungs each day will dissipate 232 calories.

The vaporization of body water is the only mechanism available for the reduction of body temperature when the environmental temperature is higher than that of the body. Under these conditions heat will be gained by radiation and conduction. The heat lost by the evaporation of perspiration will have to include the heat gained from the environment. There is no heat loss by evaporation if the humidity of the surrounding air is too high. The body can withstand very high environmental temperatures if the air is dry; ambient temperatures well below body temperature may be uncomfortable if the humidity is high. These principles will be considered in detail in separate chapters involving temperature adaptations.

Evaporative Cooling in Dog and Elephant. The avenues of heat loss in a small mammal like the dog, or a large mammal like the elephant, are somewhat different from those in man. The dog largely depends upon radiation and convection because it does not call upon functional sweat glands except on the pads of the feet. Even radiation and convection is not efficient through the heavy winter fur of the sled dog. This reasoning is based on Belding's work with arctic clothing;[128] probably the fur of the sled dog blocks 75% of the potential heat loss by radiation and convection. The dog does use evaporative cooling by panting; rapid shallow breathing moves the air rapidly over the moist tongue and air passages, and the blood flowing through this area is cooled. One is reminded of this mechanism by watching a sled dog team (perhaps consisting of 12 dogs)arrive from a continuous forced-run of 30 miles, traveling at about 15 mph; it is hard to imagine just where the dogs had formerly stored and carried such long, extended tongues (Fig. 27). According to Dill,[134] this panting does affect acid-base balance: "In some extreme instances the combined carbon dioxide of the blood of the dogs was reduced to less than one-fourth its usual value, and a very alkaline state was established. A man would find such a degree of overventilation very unpleasant—he would be dizzy and might experience tetanic cramps." The normal rate of respiration in a dog is about 15 to 30 breaths per minute, but in panting this rate rises to over 300 per minute. At the same time, the respiration becomes very shallow, thus cutting down the loss of CO_2 from the lungs and blood. Cattle and sheep both pant and sweat; these mechanisms are not as effective as the sweating of man and the panting of the dog.

Like the dog, the elephant does not have sweat glands. The present day elephant species do not have hair, so radiation and convection are not blocked. However, the extinct arctic species of elephants did have wool and hair. Heat dissipation from such Arctic animals when exercising on warm days must have been difficult because of their relatively small radiating surface and

Figure 27. *Sled Dogs Completing 30-Mile Run.* The extended tongues for evaporative cooling are evident in these sled dogs which have run without a rest for 30 miles in heavy winter coats at temperatures below 0°F.

abundant insulation. As for evaporative cooling, Kuno [146] contributes the following: elephants in the Tokyo zoo on a hot day sprinkled water on their backs and sides to obtain evaporative cooling. When he removed water, they collected saliva from their mouths and sprayed this on their backs. This is not a particularly unusual example since a number of species of small mammals have been observed to lick their fur thoroughly when exposed to heat.

Heat Loss at Different Ambient Temperatures. The relative effectiveness of the three avenues of heat loss in human subjects changes with different physical environments. Some figures for the partitioning of heat loss at various temperatures were obtained by Hardy, who at that time

was at the Russell Sage Institute of Pathology. The following percent contributions to heat loss might be called common values for a nude subject when there is a constant low air-movement:

Room Temperature	Radiation	Convection	Evaporation
Comfortable (25°C)	67%	10%	23%
Warm (30°C)	41%	33%	26%
Hot (35°C)	4%	6%	90%

There is nothing unusual or unpredictable about the interrelationship of these three physical factors at different room temperatures.

CONCEPTS

Temperature Equilibrium

Body temperature is a function of two processes: heat gain and heat loss. Nelson et al.[150] in 1947 quantified this relationship in the following formula, which later came to be called the "Fort Knox equation":

$$M + S + (-) E \pm C \pm R \pm W = 0$$

(all terms in cal/m²/hr)

where M = metabolic heat production, S = stored heat, E = heat lost by evaporation, C = heat lost or gained by convection, R = heat lost or gained by radiation, W = heat lost or gained from water taken. Any complete study of body temperature regulation must consider all of these parameters. M can be measured accurately, either directly by calorimetry or indirectly by respiratory gas exchange; M is always positive. S cannot be measured easily, nor is there agreement on a formula for its calculation in animals other than man. It requires estimates of surface area and "mean body temperature" which are inaccurately known. Total E can only be measured under controlled conditions, and respiratory E can be estimated roughly only by knowledge of fat catabolism; E is usually negative. Convection and Radiation are rarely known accurately, but calculations can be made assuming an emissivity, or by difference when other variables have been measured; they may be positive or negative. W, if present, can be known with ease. The equation is often written without S. When this is so, in many instances of temporary lack of equilibrium, this equation does not read zero. For example, in vigorous exercise, metabolism for a time exceeds the loss of heat by evaporation, convection, and radiation, then it becomes positive. On the other hand it has a negative value when, on exposure to cold, heat loss is great and the compensatory increase in metabolism is inadequate or delayed.

The equation may also be written:

Total Heat Loss = $M \pm C \pm R \pm S - E$.

Riedesel, for his work with small mammals, approximates the above equation as follows, although constants are subject to verification by experimentation:[153]

$$C = 0.5 \sqrt{V} (t_f - t_a)$$

Where V = air velocity, ft/min

t_f = temperature of fur, °C

t_a = temperature of air, °C

$$R = 5.7 (t_f - t_g)$$

Where t_f = temperature of fur, °C

t_g = temperature in a black can 7.5 cm x 3 cm

$$E = 1.4 V^{0.37} (P_f - P_a)$$

Where P_f = vapor pressure of wetted fur (saturated, air at temperature of fur)

P_a = vapor pressure of room air

Evaporation is also the weight change of animal which neither urinated nor defecated during the time of the test.

$$S = 0.83 (0.65 t_r + 0.35 t_s)$$

Where t_r = temperature of rectum, °C

t_s = temperature of skin, °C

Zone of Thermal Neutrality

This zone is the ambient temperature at which warming and cooling of the body is least difficult (in a physiological sense). An unclothed man at rest and in a post-absorptive state is at equilibrium between 25° to 27°C (77° to 80°F). He loses to the environment heat from his resting metabolism (BMR) except for normal storage, without calling on reserve heat loss functions. He would not be able however to handle exercise effects or food effects without these reserve functions. Ordinarily we set a room thermostat at about 75°F; if the room were left at 80°F, clothing and mild muscular movements would make the factor *M* larger and the factors *C* and *R* smaller. According to Hafez,[140] it is popular to state that within the Zone of Thermal Neutrality almost all thermal regulation in homeotherms is by physical mechanisms. Outside this zone the adjustments become exclusively physiological. The physiological mech-

anisms involve muscular, cardiovascular and metabolic changes, while the physical mechanisms involve involuntary activation of somatic reflexes and voluntary behavioral adjustments. The behavioral adjustments include postural changes, changes in food intake and water consumption, day active and nocturnal patterns of activity, as well as special parental behavior. The behavioral changes are controlled by the central nervous system and the hypothalamus. Examples of behavioral adjustments for heat loss by the use of posture are seen in bare-skinned mammals such as pigs and buffaloes. They frequent wet spots, or dig up soil to get to the cooler subsoil, then turn to expose their moist side to the air. Posture is also used by the raccoon in hot weather; in the central United States they have, even in mid-summer, long hair on the back and sides. They lie on their backs and stretch all four legs, attempting to expose the very short hair of the belly. By this means there is some reduction in the

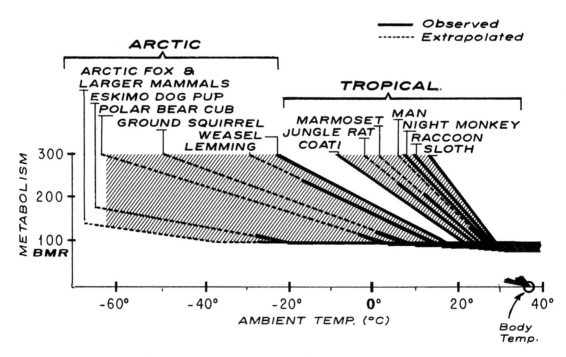

FIGURE 28. *Critical Temperatures of Mammals.* Resting metabolism of arctic and tropical mammals as a function of air temperature. Solid lines represent measurements, broken lines are extrapolations. Critical temperatures are found at points where metabolism graph intercepts standard value. From Scholander *et al.*[155]

insulation of the body. The stretched position increases surface area for evaporation, convection, and radiation. Sleeping children are apt to curl themselves into a ball, or spread-eagle, depending upon the ambient temperature.

Some environmentalists object to the concept of a "Zone of Thermal Neutrality" and prefer to think in terms of "critical air temperature." This is defined as the lowest ambient temperature at which a mammal or bird can maintain its body temperature at the basal metabolic rate. This is 25° to 27°C in unclothed man [135] and in many tropical species of mammals. It may be as low as —40°C in some arctic species and is a fundamental measure of the overall climatic thermal adaptation (Fig. 28).[152] Prosser [152] states that animals with a low critical temperature tend to have a lower slope of the metabolism-temperature curve and for a number of mammals these curves extrap-

olate back to body temperature. The slopes for hibernators tend to be steeper than for non-hibernators. Prosser also makes the point that critical temperatures of some mammals change with season. We do not know if this applies to animals living in a constant environment near the equator. Nor have mammals which increase their insulation in winter been compared in winter and summer without their insulation. Water emersion raises the critical temperature. A recent list of determinations in air are given in Table 9; all figures refer to *lower* critical air temperatures in summer.

Some investigators refer also to the upper critical temperature; the range between the upper and lower is the Zone of Thermal Neutrality. Within this range compensations for ambient temperature fluctuations are made without increase in heat production (Fig. 29).

Table 9: Critical Air Temperatures For Mammals [152]

Order: Primates:	man		27° to 28°C
Order: Edentata:	sloth		25° to 27°
Order: Lagomorpha:	rabbit		17°
Order: Rodentia:	ground squirrel		5°
	lemming		20°
	hamster		20°
	red squirrel		20°
	porcupine		7°
	Dipodomys		31°
	Panama mouse		27°
	deer mouse		30°
	rat		25°
Order: Carnivora:	weasel		15°
	harbor seal		$<-10°$
	red fox		8°
	dog (short hair)		25°
Order: Artiodactyla:	pig		0°
	mountain goat		(−30° in winter)
	steer		7° [136]
	sheep (full fleece 12 cm)		0° [136]

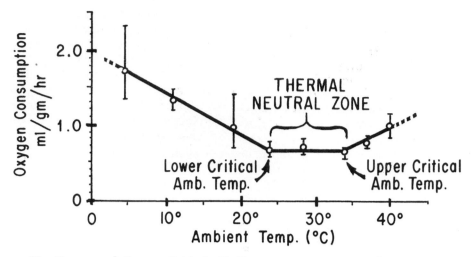

FIGURE 29. *Upper and Lower Critical Air Temperatures of Bats.* The Thermal Neutral Zone of Australian flying foxes (*P. scapulatus*) is shown as determined by oxygen consumption. Each point represents a mean of 3 adults (average weight 362 grams). From Bartholomew *et al.*[127]

The metabolic rate increases as the mammal becomes cold. (Note that the arctic fox does not become "cold" until it is exposed to approximately —40°F). A systematic approach to different mammalian metabolic responses to cold is found in the use of "thermal conductance". This is the term applied to the slope of the chemical heat production curve of homeotherms. Thermal conductance units are volumes of respiratory gas, or heat equivalents (absolute, or expressed per unit of body weight) per unit time per unit temperature. It includes all forms of heat loss by the animal. It is the rate (kcal/day/°C) of heat transfer across the external and internal body surfaces from the animal to the environment, irrespective of means of transfer. Thus, heat dissipated by evaporation of water and heat dissipated by radiation, convection, and conduction are not differentiated in this measurement. For further definitions and examples see Hudson and Brush[145] (1964).

A Classic Debate on Mechanism of Temperature Regulation

We have mentioned that the anterior regions of the hypothalamus are associated with mechanisms responsible for heat loss, whereas it is possible that the posterior hypothalamus regions are associated with heat production mechanisms (Fig. 23). Apparently the hypothalamus (or a place designated as the central thermoceptive area) integrates sensory information derived from three sources: 1) thermal receptors located in the periphery; 2) the thermal-sensitive cells in the hypothalamus and 3) the "core" receptors located deep within the body. There is a friendly controversy between Hardy and Benzinger concerning the degree of influence of the three factors just mentioned.[148] Benzinger once took the view that the first factor, thermal receptors in the periphery, has the major task of control over temperature regulation. Hardy emphasized the importance of the temperature of the blood entering the hypothalamus and the response of thermal sensitive cells there. At the moment, both men hold to "a combination hypothesis". The following experiment of Hardy's will illustrate the types of experiments done: he studied the responses of the conscious dog to local heating of the thermosensitive area of the anterior hypothalamus. The technique consisted of applying radio-frequency energy between two needle electrodes implanted in the pre-optic and super-optic region; the electrode location was confirmed. The hypothalamic temperature was recorded by a thermocouple inside the tip of one needle electrode. When mild heat was applied to the anterior hypothalamus (39°C at the electrodes) the animal became very quiet, lay down, stretched out, and appeared drowsy. When the heat was increased (41°C) the dog sat up, became alert, salivated and began to pant; he continued to pant as long as the central heating was maintained. After 1 hour the heat was turned off and the dog stopped panting; he had lowered (by panting) his core temperature 2°C below the usual body temperature of 38°C; then he began to shiver vigorously. When heat was reapplied to the hypothalamus, the shivering became inhibited and the panting began again. This sequence could be repeated many times. Hardy does not interpret these results as a lack of influence of peripheral stimuli, but rather as evidence that blood temperature acting at the anterior hypothalamus as well as peripheral stimuli can control thermal regulation. An example of Benzinger's work is given in the next chapter.

The physiological debate emphasizes the relative importance in temperature regulation of skin receptors and the two parts of the hypothalamus. As an aftermath of the probing questions introduced by Hardy and Benzinger, there has been more research interest recently in the influence of the thermal state of the skin upon the cen-

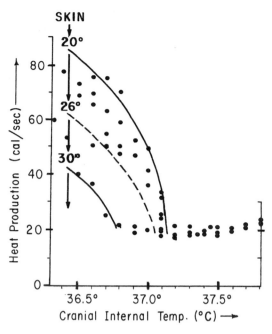

FIGURE 30. *Effect of Skin Temperature and Internal Temperature on Heat Production.* This series of experiments by Benzinger demonstrates that lower internal temperatures are required to initiate a change in heat production when the skin is hot. As internal temperature falls the heat production increases after a critical or set point is reached. However, the extent to which the heat production rises depends on the skin or external temperature. Internal temperature was measured on the tympanum of the ear. From Benzinger.[130]

tral thermoceptive area. The thermoceptive area is said to be altered by each variable condition of peripheral input; the result is a shift in threshold for initial response of the central area, or a shift in set point. Thus a lower body temperature is required to initiate a change in heat production when the skin is hot. Carlson[132] likens this mechanism to a thermostat that turns off the furnace when the outside temperature is warm and allows the temperature of the house to fall below the level it maintains on a cold day (Fig. 30).

SUMMARY

We have considered the means whereby corrections are made by homeostatic mechanisms to obtain a relatively constant body temperature. A related principle should be stated: that mammals adapt the rate of heat production and heat loss to the environmental temperature independently of available energy supply; probably the reverse is true: that variation in energy consumed is a regulatory function modified as rate of use demands.

The means of increasing heat production which were discussed in this chapter include shivering, thermogenesis, fever, and SDA; the heat loss mechanisms discussed were sweating, panting, and radiation. Some of the tools for the study of temperature regulation were described, as well as the concept of thermal neutral zone and critical air temperature.

In the next chapter, special factors decreasing heat loss, and adaptations for cold environments will be considered.

RESPONSES TO

A COLD ENVIRONMENT

THE COLD ENVIRONMENT

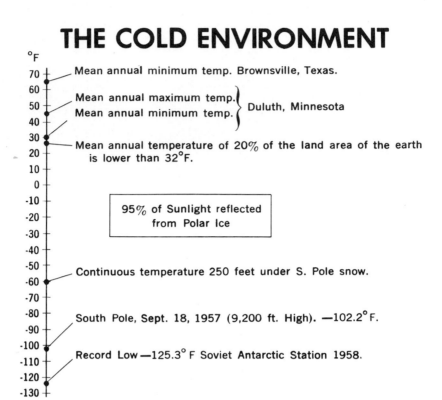

°F
70 — Mean annual minimum temp. Brownsville, Texas.
60
50 — Mean annual maximum temp.
Mean annual minimum temp. } Duluth, Minnesota
40
30 — Mean annual temperature of 20% of the land area of the earth
20   is lower than 32°F.
10
0
-10
-20   95% of Sunlight reflected
-30   from Polar Ice
-40
-50 — Continuous temperature 250 feet under S. Pole snow.
-60
-70
-80 — South Pole, Sept. 18, 1957 (9,200 ft. High). —102.2°F.
-90
-100
-110 — Record Low —125.3°F Soviet Antarctic Station 1958.
-120
-130

WIND CHILL CHART

Equivalent Temperatures in terms of 0 mph (in °F)

LOCAL (Actual) TEMPERATURE	WIND VELOCITY				
0 mph	5 mph	15 mph	25 mph	35 mph	45 mph
32°F	29°	13°	3°	— 1°	— 3°
23°F	20°	— 1°	—10°	—15°	—18°
14°F	10°	—13°	—24°	—29°	—32°
5°F	1°	—25°	—38°	—43°	—46°
—4°F	—9°	—37°	—50°	—52°	—60°

COLD INDUCED CORE TEMPERATURES

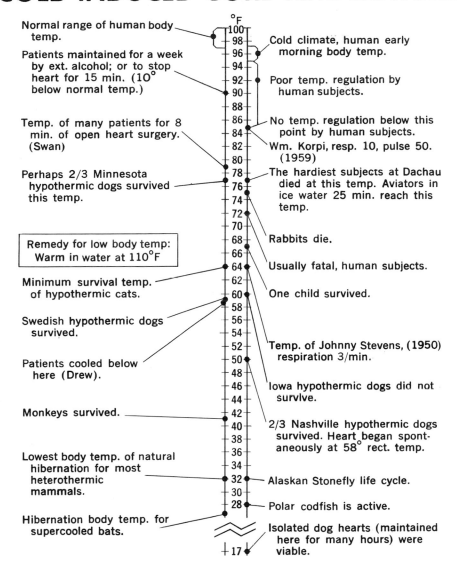

Normal range of human body temp.

Patients maintained for a week by ext. alcohol; or to stop heart for 15 min. (10° below normal temp.)

Temp. of many patients for 8 min. of open heart surgery. (Swan)

Perhaps 2/3 Minnesota hypothermic dogs survived this temp.

Remedy for low body temp: Warm in water at 110°F

Minimum survival temp. of hypothermic cats.

Swedish hypothermic dogs survived.

Patients cooled below here (Drew).

Monkeys survived.

Lowest body temp. of natural hibernation for most heterothermic mammals.

Hibernation body temp. for supercooled bats.

°F
100
98
96
94
92
90
88
86
84
82
80
78
76
74
72
70
68
66
64
62
60
58
56
54
52
50
48
46
44
42
40
38
36
34
32
30
28
+17

Cold climate, human early morning body temp.

Poor temp. regulation by human subjects.

No temp. regulation below this point by human subjects.

Wm. Korpi, resp. 10, pulse 50. (1959)

The hardiest subjects at Dachau died at this temp. Aviators in ice water 25 min. reach this temp.

Rabbits die.

Usually fatal, human subjects.

One child survived.

Temp. of Johnny Stevens, (1950) respiration 3/min.

Iowa hypothermic dogs did not survive.

2/3 Nashville hypothermic dogs survived. Heart began spontaneously at 58° rect. temp.

Alaskan Stonefly life cycle.

Polar codfish is active.

Isolated dog hearts (maintained here for many hours) were viable.

Chapter Five

Responses to a Cold Environment

In this day of heated cars and American houses maintained at 75°F, the average person in the United States and Canada is not aware that his total physiological-reserves for combatting cold may suddenly be drawn upon. In spite of the comfort and convenience-engineering of this age, each year some individuals die of cold exposure. Several examples follow: in August recently a university professor and his daughter were trapped overnight in their car by a heavy snowstorm on a main highway of Wyoming; the car was completely covered by drifts. On the Maine turnpike, I was one of over 1,000 people stranded for 24 hours when a sudden blizzard made it impossible for cars to move; during that period there was a great deal of bitter discomfort although no lives were lost. From 1955 to 1965, 500 cases of severe frostbite were treated by Mills [241] in Anchorage, Alaska. The number of admissions for cold injury at the Cleveland, Ohio, General Hospital from 1950 to 1963 averaged 7 per year,[241] and this state in no sense can be considered an extremely cold part of the United States. The environment of Fairbanks, Alaska during the winter of 1964-1965 illustrates the barrier that the weather can present to the travel of the wage earners of this shopping center for 60,000 people: for 17 days the official *maximum* temperature was —40°F or lower. Temperatures of —60°F were common. A typical case of injury was a woman who stalled her car and walked for 15 minutes with her legs covered only with silk stockings; as a result she spent a month in the hospital with frostbitten legs. Cold weather is not a private concession for Alaska; in 1954, —70°F was recorded in Montana.

Considering lower mammals, the tolerance to prolonged extreme cold presents more of a physiological challenge to a few subarctic animals than to most. Many mammals (even foxes and wolves) can seek protection under the snow or in dens. This does not apply to some winter residents such as moose, caribou, Canada jays and chickadees, which have not been known to seek enclosed shelter. The temperature regulation of herbivores standing (and sometimes marooned) in deep snow at —60°F requires unusual adaptations; with a core temperature fixed at 100°F, these animals must find enough food to hold this temperature when the environmental temperature is as much as 150°F lower. Yet these animals are abundant: in the Fairbanks area (record low at Tanana —76°F) and in the bitter windy cold of the Richardson Highway area, there are estimated to be 130,000 caribou * in winter and as many moose. Many of the caribou migrate on to Yukon Territory where —70°F is not uncommon and North America's lowest temperature (—81°F) was recorded. Even more remarkable is the existance of small birds at these temperatures. Both the mammals and the birds have a short daylight period for feeding during the cold season (3 hours and 40 minutes of sunlight on December 21 at Fairbanks), and so even the "collecting of calories" is curtailed. In the winter of 1964-1965, Anna Larson, a bio-

---

* The 1964 estimate for Alaska revealed nine herds: Arctic herd 300,000 head; Alaska Peninsula 10,000; Porcupine River 140,000;; Steese Forty-Mile 20,000 to 40,000; Nelchina 80,000; Delta 5,000; McKinley Park 14,000; Mulchatna River 2,000; Wrangell 3,000 to 5,000. Total: 585,000 caribou.

chemist at Arctic Aeromedical Laboratory, observed a pair of chickadees coming regularly to a feeding station to peck at ice-hard peanut butter when the temperature was —50°F. On a day when the thermometer was near —60°F, only one appeared. "It did not fly well, was very sluggish, and had frost on its feathers." The next day at —50°F, the same pair of birds were back. The handicap to this species of a large surface area-to-mass ratio must require special cold-climate adaptations as yet undescribed. W. Dawson [175] does suggest that these small birds must seek overhead cover as a radiation screen because the "ceiling" temperature of open winter sky may be as low as —80°F.

There may be animals living in even more extreme cold in Siberia, where there are two official temperatures of —90°F, and one unofficial one of —108°F. It is well to note that a large portion of the globe has a cold climate. The 50°F isotherm defines a region where the average monthly mean temperature even in the warmest season, never rises above 50°F. (An isotherm is a line drawn on a map connecting points of equal temperature). In winter this delimited region experiences temperatures of —60°F. The important point is that this isotherm includes 1/5 of the globe. To describe this area differently, it is claimed that 20% of the land area of the earth (50% of Canada and the Soviet Union) is located in zones where the mean annual temperature is below 30°F. In this region the underlying soil remains perennially frozen (permafrost), while a thin surface layer ("active zone") temporarily thaws during the summer. Several types of cold climates are discussed by Hammel.[2]

Are mammals in the free environment subjected to chronic, or to acute cold exposure? Ordinarily climatic changes are gradual. Is there a precedent for the environmental physiologist when he moves the animal from a warm control temperature directly into cold exposure of 40°F or below freezing? Such experiments are easily justified; for example, the Kalahari Desert in the winter is as hot as 160°F in the day-

time but falls to the freezing point at night.[244] As another case, living organisms (including man) in Browning, Montana, in 1916, experienced in 24 hours a temperature change of 100°F, from 44°F to —56°F. Rapid dry-bulb changes are also common especially in spring in Colorado, and in the Alps.

The degree of cold exposure that man experiences is strongly influenced by cultural habits. Certainly many more British school children are acclimatized to cold in the winter, than are children in the United States. A common winter dressing-room temperature for British children of university-educated parents is 50°F, while this room temperature in the United States is nearer 75°F. Burton states that the office air temperature for civil servants in winter in England is 50° to 60°F.[167]

TYPES OF COLD EXPOSURE

You often hear a physiologist say that his animals have been "exposed to cold". This expression is inadequate for two reasons, first there are several types of "cold air", and secondly the cold-exposed animal does not necessarily experience a low temperature. The secondary factors which must be considered are the amount of moisture in the air, the amount of air movement, and the duration of the exposure to cold. It has been pointed out by a number of authors that wet cold has more meaning near 0°C than at much colder temperatures. It has been difficult to make specific measurements to explain the supposed difference in response to wet cold. Part of the impression by human subjects that wet cold is more unpleasant than dry cold may be based upon sensation alone. Also it may be that the stratum corneum of the skin actually does conduct heat differently or does trap a different layer of air insulation at different degrees of humidity. For further consideration the reader is referred to Woodcock,[243] and Burton and Edholm.[168]

Describing conduction of heat in different wind velocities is more straight-

WIND CHILL INDEX

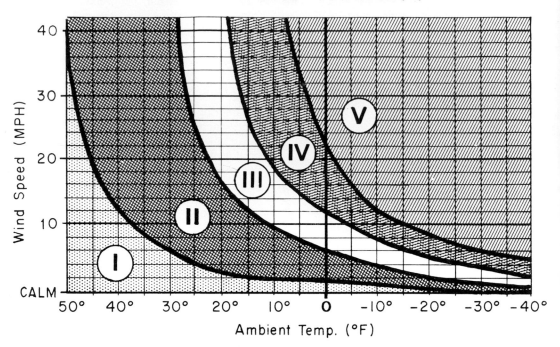

I Comfort with normal precautions.

II Very cold, travel becomes uncomfortable on overcast days.

III Bitterly cold, travel becomes uncomfortable even on clear sunny days.

IV Freezing of human flesh begins, depending upon degree of activity, amount of solar radiation, and character of skin and circulation. Travel and life in temporary shelter becomes disagreeable.

V Survival efforts are required. Exposed flesh will freeze in less than one minute.

FIGURE 31. *Wind Chill Index.* A chart used by the armed forces to make decisions about activities and clothing in very cold weather. It is presented here because of the useful numerical index from I to V.

forward than explaining wet-cold. By means of physical models it has been possible to show different amounts of heat transfer with different wind velocities. The introductory diagrams of this chapter include a Wind Chill Chart in which different local (actual) temperatures can be converted to equivalent temperature due to the effects of various wind velocities. For example, if the local temperature is

23°F and the wind is 25 mph, the person loses heat as if the dry-bulb were —10°F. A variety of charts have been issued by the armed services to express the combination of wind and dry-bulb temperature.[239] Many of these charts have made use of an index of I to V so that very extreme conditions unsuitable for travel can be indicated by a specific wind chill number. These charts consist of several families of hyperbolic curves because the higher wind velocities are more effective than the lower ones; for example, reading off values from Figure 31, an individual at 30°F with a wind velocity of 36 mph may experience a drop in air temperature of 3°F which may change comfort from "very cold" to "bitterly cold". If the person is at 30°F, at 6 mph it will take a drop of 30°F before his subjective reaction would change from very cold to bitterly cold.

The degree or intensity of the exposure to cold must next be considered. A number of qualitative terms have been used, but there is no agreement as to their meaning in terms of time and dry-bulb temperature. A frequent classification is "acute", which means short and severe; "chronic", which indicates long-continued and usually mild; "moderate" duration as opposed to "long-term or seasonal"; and finally "multi-seasonal". In much of the literature on the physiology of cold, the investigators have not indicated in what category they consider their particular cold exposure to fall. It will not be possible to consider examples in each of these categories, but the terms will be utilized from time to time.

The final problem concerned with describing cold-exposure is that often the animal is in the cold but does not experience it. The early experiments attempting to show acclimatization to cold in man gave negative results because the men had adequate insulation, and the skin cooling on face and extremities was inadequate to produce any lasting physiological effects. There is a tendency today to describe much of the exposure to cold of men in the Arctic and Antarctic as being chronic and moderate. Lewis and Masterton [212] have recently presented figures which indicate that the skin temperature (the microclimate) of men under their arctic clothing while working on some of the expeditions was the same as that of men working in the temperate zones with very light insulation. This is only one side of the picture because it is certainly evident that many men on such expeditions have had severe frostbite of the face and hands; Pugh points out that one can ordinarily, in a group of men, recognize the men who have been on Polar expeditions because of their permanently reddened faces. At any rate, it is constantly necessary to ask the question whether the animal or the man does experience the cold in which it is exposed; for example, if the arctic fox (in winter coat) is exposed at —40°F, it shows no increase in resting metabolism. Much colder temperatures must be used in order to introduce the experience of cold to this species.

NEWTON'S LAW OF COOLING

Many of the examples of physiological responses to cold, which will be presented, are concerned with acute cold exposure. Since the heat exchange under these circumstances is quite conspicuous, consideration must first be given to the physical interaction between the warm, living mass of protoplasm and the air around it with its deficit of heat. The convenient physical description is found in Newton's Law of Cooling. This law may be written as a simple proportion in which heat loss per minute is directly proportional to the body surface and the difference between the temperature of the body core and that of the environment, and inversely proportional to the thickness of the body shell; i.e., heat flows from the body core to the external environment at a rate which increases with the surface area and the temperature drop between core and exterior, and which decreases with greater thickness of the barrier between core and exterior.

INSULATION

One of the most important factors in the control of heat exchange is the barrier between the core of the animal and the external environment. How is this measured? Two descriptive units have been devised by Burton and Edholm [168] called the "Met" and the "Clo". These have been defined as follows: resting man produces about 50 kcal/m²/hr. This unit is called 1 Met. When such a person is sitting at rest in an air temperature of 21°C, in turbulent air of 10 cm/minute, with a relative humidity less than 50%, the insulation can be calculated. This is done by

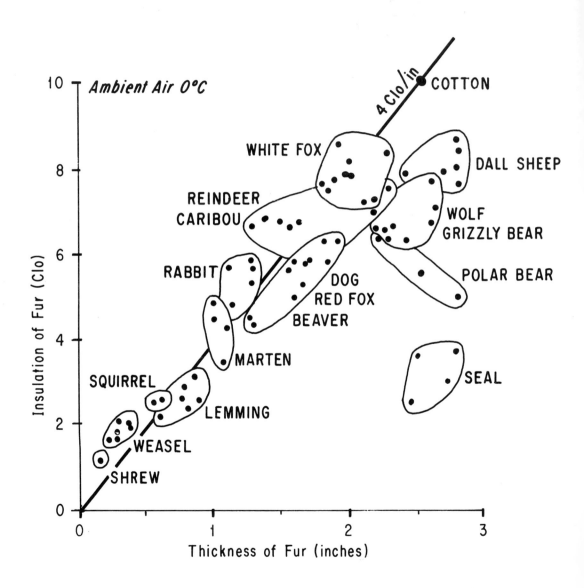

FIGURE 32. *Insulation Value of Winter Fur.* The insulation of variable thickness of fur is compared with the artificial insulation of a black surface and cotton. Measurements were made with a hot-plate guard ring kept at 37°C with the outside air at 0°C. From Scholander *et al.*[228]

subtracting the evaporative heat loss of 25% amounting to 13 kcal/m²/hr. If the body temperature is to remain constant the rest of the heat, 38 kcal/m²/hr, must be offset by insulation which in man amounts to a light business suit.[168] This insulation is called 1 Clo unit and it has been corrected for the insulation of the layer of *still* air next to the clothing surface (0.8 Clo); in a high wind the insulation of the air next to the clothing is 0.2 Clo. Clo units are always measured by physiological means, and they can be calculated for the clothing of men and the fur of animals. For example, a heavy arctic uniform provides about 5 Clo and the fur of the arctic fox provides about 8 Clo (insulation of still air not included). Scholander et al.[228] has expressed the relationship between thickness and Clo value graphically with a scale extending from the fur of the shrew, consisting of a fraction of an inch in thickness, and ending with the ordinary sheep which has nearly 3 inches of thickness. His graph describes a slope of 3.7 Clo/inch of insulation (Fig. 32).

The relation between surface area and mass plays an important part in the effectiveness of insulation. With small objects with a large surface-to-mass ratio, such as the shrew or the fingers of children, to add insulation may actually increase the heat loss. This effect was learned many years ago by heating engineers who found that they could not insulate small pipes. Likewise a thin glove on the fingers of a child may increase heat loss from the fingers. This indicates why a much thicker fur would not benefit the smallest of mammals, the shrew (and they would trip on the fur). These same relationships apply when heavy insulation is added to the hands of men.[168] The problem of "small cylinders" does not apply to the whole body of man. In this case to provide more than 6 Clo units would fail only because it would impair the mobility of the man.

The insulation outside the skin of men and arctic animals creates a physiological paradox when these mammals must exercise in the cold. Only the problem will be described here; the physiological solutions will be described under the section entitled "Physiology of the Sled Dog". If men dressed in a typical arctic protective unit of 3 Clo undertake heavy exercise, they become a tropical man in arctic clothing. With this description in mind it is not difficult to understand why a soldier (a newcomer) was brought to the Fort Wainwright Hospital in a state of collapse during the 1965 Operation Polar Siege; he had been pulling sleds and chopping timber under conditions where the temperature was —40°. The diagnosis at the hospital was heat stroke. He had been so alarmed at the thought of working in the cold that he had piled on every item of insulation he could borrow. Under these conditions some subjects will sweat 350 gm/hr, others 725 gm/hr. The efficiency of such sweating may amount to only 40%. The answer for man, of course, is to ventilate the clothing and take off layers of insulation while working. This is not possible for horses and ponies with heavy winter insulation or for sled dogs. The biological problem evident here will be considered in a later section.

There are two physiological insulative mechanisms which have not yet been considered; these are vasomotor function in the skin and the contribution of subcutaneous adipose tissue. Some animals combine these factors with fur. Seals must have insulation in addition to skin because even in wintertime they come out of the water to rest on ice. Mammals which remain under water, such as whales and porpoises, use only the subcutaneous fat called blubber for insulation. The usefulness of subcutaneous fat to man is detectable in channel swimmers where fat appears to be preferentially layed down in subcutaneous areas rather than in the deep fat depots.[224]

Changes in vasomotor function have the effect of altering the barrier to heat exchange between the core of the body and the exterior. This vasomotor effect (peripheral vasodilation and contriction) will be considered in the next section.

RESPONSES TO ACUTE COLD EXPOSURE

It will be convenient to consider the situation of an underclothed man or a short-haired dog exposed in a coldroom to —20°F and a wind velocity of 5 mph. Within a very few moments the following events will take place: *1*) there will be cutaneous vasoconstriction: this will permit the temperature of the skin and deeper layers under the skin to cool and the surface-to-environment heat-loss will be lowered; in a sense this means the effective thickness of the body shell is increased and this decreases conductivity from the interior. Essentially this is accomplished by a shift of blood from the shell area to the core area. This means there must be an increase of blood in the viscera. *2*) There is a paradoxical increase in heart rate which is very evident in experiments with man,[233] with cats,[214] and with rodents.[213] This response is paradoxical because of the massive vasoconstriction. This increase in heart rate is also found in the cold-pressor test. According to Glaser and Whittow,[191] the systolic blood pressure will rise approximately 18%, the diastolic blood pressure will rise about 33% and the heart rate 14%. A typical case will show a rise from 70 beats per minute to 80 beats per minute. *3*) There will be an acceleration of pulmonary respiration. *4*) Pilo-erection in the skin will show itself as so-called goose pimples in the skin of man and by the erection of hair in the skin of the dog, a factor tending to increase insulation. *5*) This vasoconstriction in man may reduce heat loss by 1/6 to 1/3. *6*) There will be release of norepinephrine at the muscle beds and of epinephrine from the adrenal medulla. All items so far are the familiar signs of sympathetic nervous discharge. Within minutes this syndrome will be followed by neurohumoral activation of the hypothalamus bringing about the release of anterior pituitary hormones, especially those stimulating the thyroid and adrenal cortex. *7*) All of the above result from stimulation of skin cold-receptors which bring about reflex responses all tending to conserve heat. *8*) The next event will be an increased electrical activity in skeletal muscle which will gradually lead to full development of a shivering response. With most subjects, this shivering will begin as soon as the lightly-clad subject is exposed to cold. In some subjects who are especially heavily built and have a subcutaneous fat layer, they still do not shiver after 20 minutes of exposure without clothing. *9*) As a result of shivering, the metabolic rate will increase in both the man and the dog, 3- or 4-fold. *10*) The extent of this increase in metabolism should be found in the extreme limits of the critical temperature curve. *11*) There will be occasional bouts of vasodilation which will increase the temperature of the skin. This process is referred to as cold vasodilation or "Lewis's hunting reaction".[211] The phenomenon is most conspicuous on the palm of the hand and on the fingers and toes, and it is also observed in the arteriovenous anastomoses in the ears of mammals.[188] *12*) Both of the mammals in the case history under discussion may assume a position that will reduce their surface area; this is done by tucking the legs and assuming a ball position. *13*) As a result of the shivering, the body temperature may increase 0.6° to 0.8°C during 20 minutes of shivering. The skin temperature on the chest however may be as low as 8° to 10°C during maximal shivering. *14*) When the subjects leave the coldroom there may be a loss in core temperature to as low as 35°C. This lowering of the core temperature will happen with both vasoconstriction or with vasodilation of the skin. It must be due to lack of metabolic heat when cold blood is still being returned to the core from the periphery.

Shivering

Shivering stimuli arrive from receptors in the skin; the act of shivering depends upon the integrity of the posterior hypothalamus. Hemingway [198] has also shown recently that a region between the posterior hypothalamus and the midbrain in the vicinity of the nucleus of the Field of Forrel must be intact in order that shivering may occur. The shivering stimuli originate from receptors in the skin; by cooling the blood and keeping the skin warm these receptors in the skin can be circumvented. In such an experiment shivering can be prevented completely. The ·function of shivering is to add to heat production (it also adds to heat loss); it provides improved protection of core heat by enlarging the thermogenesis to include the muscle mass of the animal. By this means the temperature of the muscles is raised to approach that of the core. Because the work-function of this muscle contraction is zero, shivering is a very economical thermogenerator.

The onset of shivering has been used as a very effective test of ability to resist cooling. An unusual example is the work of Hong on the diving women of Korea (the Ama).[204] He used as a criteria the critical water temperature at which 50% of the subjects shivered. This 50% critical water temperature varied from 31.1°C in males to 29.9°C in non-diving females and 28.2°C in the divers. These figures illustrate not only the threshold temperature that activates receptors in the skin, but also acclimatization in individuals who lead an outdoor life. Figure 33 shows the water-bath temperatures and the number of subjects. We say in this case the shivering threshold is considerably elevated in the divers as compared to the rest of the subjects. (The threshold is "raised" because as tolerance increases you raise the threshold; if tolerance is lowered the threshold is lowered.)

As stated earlier, man can raise his heat production 3- to 4-fold by shivering and raise core temperature over 0.5°C. This shivering may be prolonged for a considerable time and even during sleep. In recent experiments, Rodahl, at the Lankaneau Hospital, studied men exposed to moderate cold with little insulation for 9 days and 9 nights; the subjects shivered moderately day and night for the entire period.[240] At times when the subjects slept, they stopped shivering and their body temperatures sometimes dropped as low as 34°C. In spite of this shivering, toe temperature sometimes fell to 8°C, which was the same as the room temperature.

Apparently all experimental and wild-caught animals shiver as effectively as does man. In routine experiments the dog shows a 3- to 4-fold increase in metabolism when shivering. This shivering can be prevented by light administration of ether or other anesthetics; hypothermia cannot be induced in experimental animals until shivering is prevented by these means. Shivering is particularly effective in the wild Norway rat which has been known to increase its heat production 5- or 6-fold.

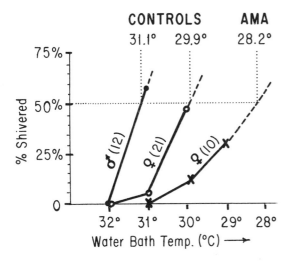

FIGURE 33. *Shivering Threshold of Korean Diving Women.* The diving women (Ama) become cold-acclimatized in winter and shiver at a lower temperature than non-divers and men. From Hong.[204]

RESPONSES TO CHRONIC COLD EXPOSURE

Non-Shivering Thermogenesis

Beginning with the work of Claude Bernard in 1859 [164] studies have shown that the liver and abdominal viscera contribute heat to the cold-exposed animal. It is this mechanism that becomes more efficient in the rat exposed continuously to cold at 5°C for 2 to 3 weeks. At the end of this period, shivering disappears so that it cannot be detected by electromyography; however, total metabolism remains elevated by about 80% and body temperature is held near normal. If these animals are removed to a warm environment (30°C) most workers report that the metabolism of the rats remains for some time 15 to 20% higher than that of warm-acclimated rats. In another type of experiment, if shivering is blocked by curare and the animals are then exposed to cold, cold-acclimated animals show a rise in oxygen consumption which is sustained, while controls fail to maintain an adequate level of oxygen consumption and become hypothermic. The

acclimated animals maintain both rectal and skin temperature near normal.

Acclimation in the White Rat

The first factor of cold acclimation is the non-shivering thermogenesis described above (Fig. 34). This is followed by a rise in total daily food consumption. Initially, there is a transient decrease in body weight followed in the young adult by resumption of growth within a week. There is hypertrophy of thyroid and adrenal cortex as well as heart, kidney, liver and digestive tract. The masses of these organs increase relative to both those of the controls and to the respective body weights of the two groups.[233] These increases occur at the expense of skeletal muscle growth which becomes reduced, relative to controls. The oxygen consumption of each of

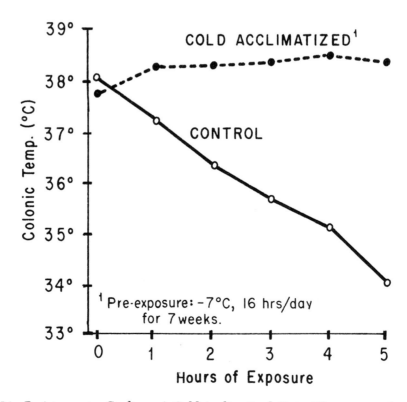

FIGURE 34. *Resistance to Cooling of Cold-Acclimatized Rats.* The mean colonic temperature of 12 rats exposed to −15°C. Note that the experimental rats were pre-acclimatized at a warmer temperature than the cold-stress temperature. From Blair.[166]

these tissues is also increased. Thus, the net effect of the product of oxygen consumption per unit weight X relative organ mass is apparently to shift themogenesis in the direction of visceral regions.[233] With acclimation to cold, heat production by the core region may become more important than that of the surrounding carcass or shell. These changes are not restricted to the rat; Farrand noted the same changes in the cold-acclimated hamster and also described a shift in body water.[186] Added to the above list of organ changes is the marked hypertrophy observed in the brown adipose tissue, also referred to as the interscapular hibernation gland. This tissue is highly vascular and has a high metabolic rate resulting in considerable heat production. Because of a 2-fold increase in respiration and a 2.5-fold increase in mass

as acclimation progresses, this organ (in the 45-day acclimated rat) accounts for an absolute heat evolution of no less than 5 times that achieved in the control. This local supply of heat may be conveyed directly to the posterior regions of the brain.

Recent information from another laboratory has added more information on the capability of producing heat independently of muscle contraction. As mentioned above, Carlson[132] found that curarized cold-acclimated rats double the heat production when exposed to 5°C while maintaining rectal temperature; in his experiments this capability did not exist in the non-acclimated animal. The important factor associated with this non-shivering thermogenesis seems to be norepinephrine liberated

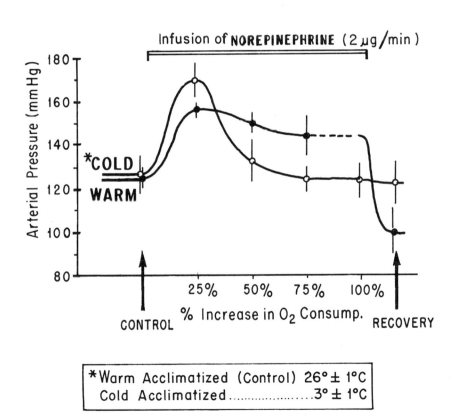

FIGURE 35. *Responsiveness of Cold-Acclimatized Rats to Norepinephrine.* Cold-stressed rats can be distinguished by a rapid and temporary response to norepinephrine. Controls respond less and return to normal slowly. From Evonuk and Hannon.[185]

from sympathetic nerve endings (Fig. 35 and 36). This change in the calorigenic effect of norepinephrine has been confirmed in men who are cold-acclimated.

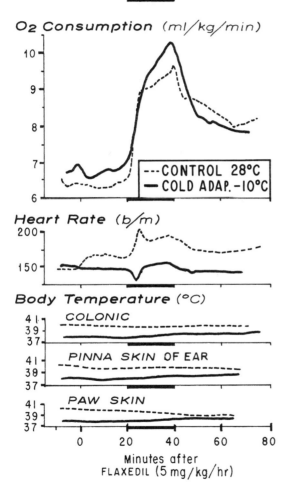

FIGURE 36. *Responses of Cold-Acclimatized Dogs to Norepinephrine.* In most physiological functions the responses to norepinephrine of cold-acclimatized dogs are the opposite to those of control dogs. This was not the case with oxygen consumption; there was a similar response in both groups although a higher amplitude in the cold-exposed dogs. From Nagasaka and Carlson.[220]

The enhanced metabolism described here may be just great enough to increase heat content sufficiently to cause shifts in the peripheral circulation so that hands are more comfortable during cold-exposure.

Terms to Describe Responses to Chronic Cold-Exposure

The long-term responses to cold of man during prolonged exposure will next be discussed. These responses differ in various ethnic groups, and the variations will be individually illustrated. The terms which will be applied have been discussed in the first chapter. They are *acclimation:* studies in cold chambers; *acclimatization:* studies in the outdoor environment; *habituation:* responses explained in terms of the nervous systems, not in terms of physiological thermal differences; and finally *genetic adaptations:* a conditioning cold-stress is not needed to induce these responses. In the following discussion the term acclimatization will be used at first because most of the observations to be considered were made in the outdoor environment. Later, a careful distinction will be drawn between different responses of experimental animals in cold chambers and in the outdoor environment. The essential question concerned with acclimatization to cold is whether there is improved comfort for man as the exposure continues over days and weeks. A systematic approach requires that standardized tests be used to determine whether a changed response can be measured. We have already described the shivering test used by Hong with the diving women of Korea. A second and straightforward test is the immersion of fingers or of hands in ice water (Fig. 37). The third test, one developed by Hammel, we will call a "cold-bed test"; it consists in having subjects sleep overnight in a cold environment with inadequate insulation.[195]

Responses to Cold in Man

Europeans: Examples of Acclimatization When subjects were exposed by Davis

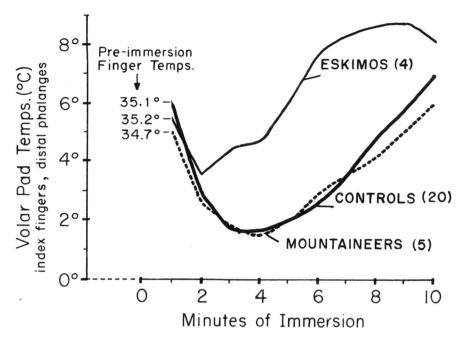

FIGURE 37. *Vascular Responses to Ice-Water Emersion.* The response-to-cold of finger vessels of Eskimos is different from those of other outdoor people. Eskimos retain warmer fingers which will assist dexterity. From Eagan.[5]

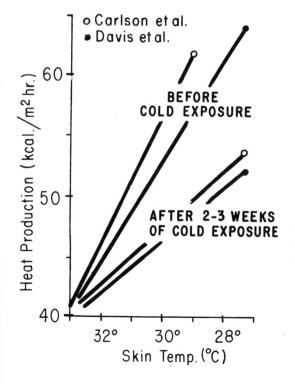

FIGURE 38. *Heat Production of Men Before and After Cold Exposure.* Cold-acclimatized subjects had a lower heat production than controls in a cold test. The graphs above are remarkable because the results were so similar when obtained independently in two different laboratories. From Carlson.[132]

for 8 hours per day at 12.5°C over a 32-day period, the time of initiation of shivering and the total metabolic heat production showed a rapid fall over the first 10 days.[132] A striking example of this reduction in heat production obtained in another laboratory also is illustrated in Figure 38. The next illustration of acclimatization was shown by the cold-bed test. As preliminary background one should note that individuals (especially residents of the United States) working in an indoor environment usually prefer to sleep with a warm body shell, a warm body core, and with relaxed vasoconstriction. Hammel suggests that all of the skin temperature is above 33°C.[194] What is the effect of living outdoors for 6 weeks, sleeping essentially naked in thin sleeping bags in 0°C weather? The unacclimatized person of European stock will be unable to sleep because of constant shivering and a declining skin temperature of the extremities (Fig. 37). With acclimatization, the metabolism is elevated by non-shivering thermogenesis, and skin temperatures are maintained during this cold-bed test. Subjects also learn to sleep when shivering is not completely suppressed and when the insulated shell is partially cooled (Rodahl [240]).

We should now look for evidence of acclimatization through increased body insulation. Apparently the only example in Europeans is that of the preferential laying down of subcutaneous fat by channel swimmers described by Pugh and Edholm.[224] Northern Norwegian fishermen, however, show clear evidence for local acclimatization to cold by having warmer finger temperature in ice water.[160]

The metabolic type of acclimatization must be discussed with caution and with frequent use of qualifications; the reason is that a comparison of the basal metabolic rate in summer and in winter, or before and after prolonged cold exposure, is apt to include a change in the amount of exercise and in the amount of protein consumed. In only a few instances have these factors been controlled. An example is described in the next section.

Eskimos: A Possible Case of Adaptation. Many studies have been done comparing thermoregulation in Eskimos and European (control) subjects. The Eskimo natives begin to shiver at the same skin temperature as the Europeans; they begin to perspire at the same skin temperature, and their overall tissue insulation during maximal vasoconstriction is the same. However, the non-shivering metabolism of the Eskimo is 30 to 40% greater than that of controls; furthermore they have a marked ability to withstand hand cooling (Fig. 39). The natives maintained a high rate of blood flow to their fingers during standardized cooling tests both in summer and in winter and after having lived in a temperate climate for several months. In one experiment the metabolism of the Eskimos was higher than that of the controls and evidence was presented that this was not due to diet.[181] Meehan [216] also observed a cold-induced rise in heat production in Eskimos. It is probable then that the Eskimo possesses adaptations to combat cold. Milan suggests that they have smaller "cores" and larger "shells".[196]

Australian Aborigine: A Case of Cold Adaptation. The responses to cold of the Australian Aborigines are strikingly different from those of any other men. We are indebted to Sir Cedric Stanton Hicks for calling to the attention of physiologists this interesting group of stone-age people.[2] They customarily sleep unclothed on the ground at night. The winter night temperatures in central Australia fall to freezing or below, and the night sky radiation temperature is about 20°C lower than air temperature. Occasionally these aborigines build a scanty shelter or sleep between small fires but they are capable of sleeping without protection, lying on the ground under these extreme conditions. These were, of course, the ideal subjects to test with the cold-bed test. Hicks, and later Morrison [219] and then Scholander,[225] found that the metabolism of the natives was not elevated by the cold and that skin temperatures were low. Foot tem-

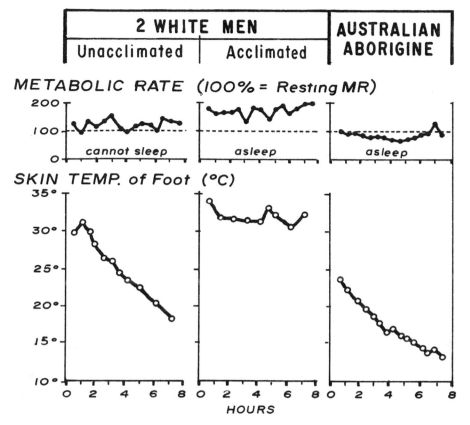

FIGURE 39. *Metabolism and Skin Temperature During Sleep in Cold.* These results showed three patterns: the Australian Bushmen could sleep with a cold skin and cold core; the acclimatized European maintained a warm skin, could sleep, but lost heat due to the warm shell. The unacclimatized white man could not maintain a warm skin and could not sleep. From Scholander.[225]

peratures of the natives were 12° to 15°C. To summarize, the natives increased the insulation of the body shell by vasoconstriction, tolerated moderate hypothermia, and did not elevate the metabolism. These low temperatures are well below the cold pain-threshold of the modern white man.

Further details were obtained when Hammel[2] returned to the native village in the summer to see if the differences observed were inherent or were acclimatizations. By studying the natives from two areas in a refrigerated van in summer, he concluded that the Australian Aborigines have an inborn ability to tolerate greater body cooling without recourse to metabolic compensation; this tolerance could be increased by prolonged exposure to cold.

Therefore this ethnic group demonstrates both genetic adaptation and acclimatization to cold.

Negroes of Africa: Responses Similar to Europeans and Americans. The first Negroid group to be considered are the Bushmen of the Kalahari Desert. They are located on a plateau at altitudes between 3000 and 5000 feet. The night climate is sufficiently cold to act as a stress in winter, as these people go habitually unclothed. While sleeping on the desert, the Bushmen avoid cold exposure by wrapping themselves in cloaks and staying near a fire. The cloaks act as a radiation shield between the skin and the night sky.[244] During tests conducted by Hammel and Hilbes the air temperature went as low as 0°C;

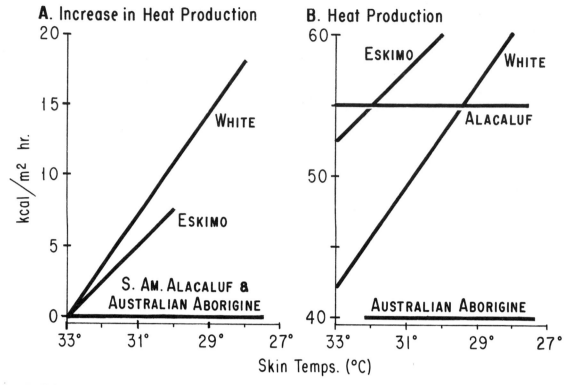

A. Increase in Heat Production

20

15

kcal/m² hr.

WHITE

10

ESKIMO

5

S. AM. ALACALUF &
AUSTRALIAN ABORIGINE

0

33°   31°   29°   27°

B. Heat Production

60

ESKIMO

WHITE

ALACALUF

50

40

AUSTRALIAN ABORIGINE

33°   31°   29°   27°

Skin Temps. (°C)

FIGURE 40. *Response to Cold of Four Ethnic Groups.* Diagram *A* shows the absolute increase in heat production of 4 ethnic types when exposed to cold. When these criteria are used, the white and eskimo seem to respond differently from the South American or Australian Aborigine. Diagram *B* represents the total heat production when men were exposed to cold. With these criteria, there is a marked difference in all 4 groups. From Carlson.[132]

tests of skin, oral temperature, and metabolic responses showed no differences from those of European and American controls.[193, 203] Similar tests, reviewed by Hart,[197] with Negroes in other parts of Africa showed comparable results, with the same responses as white-controls, or only small differences. For example, there were fewer digital rewarming cycles in the fingers of the Negroes than in white subjects. Although there were no differences in temperature regulation, there were racial differences in blood measurements: Negroes had lower plasma volumes and hemoglobin concentration than white subjects. These differences would not be expected to reflect on temperature regulation.

Alacaluf Indians of South Chile: A Case of Habituation. A group of Indians of southern Chile, the Alacaluf, existed as naked people before and since the time of Darwin (1845[173]). At the time he studied them, there were only about 100; these were spread through the archipelago of southern Chile. He saw them at Tierra del Fuego and referred to them as Fuegians. Now, as then, their climate is characterized by cool wet weather, often below freezing. Rainfall is heavy and there is often snow on the ground in winter. These people have little protection from the wind and the rain other than crude huts. They spend much of the day outside gathering food and wood, and they may be soaking wet the entire time. Darwin described his observations of a nude woman in a canoe nursing a baby, also uncovered, while sleet was falling and melting on them both. They now wear enough protection to be described as poorly-clothed, rather than unclothed. When these natives were tested by Elsner,[183] there were slight differences between natives and controls during sleep. It is true that the Alacaluf showed a high metabolism which did not change when they were cooled (Fig. 40); this means that in some respects these natives are like the Australian Aborigine, and they allow their bodies to cool, without a metabolic response. Here the similarity ends because there was no rectal temperature drop in the Alacaluf as there was with the Aborigines. Because of this, one is tempted to decide that in physiological terms the Alacaluf Indians resemble the white controls more than they resemble the Aborigines.

In respect to habituation, the situation is very different. Dr. Elsner observed these people going about barefooted, occasionally walking in snow, and standing in water that was about 8°C. He decided to study the feet of these subjects with foot calorimetry. After appropriate control periods, the feet of the natives were placed in bath calorimeters at a temperature of 5°C; they sat in this fashion for 30 minutes with rather amused expressions, thinking that this was a strange procedure and indicating no signs of discomfort. When the same experiment was done on the members of the expedition, they were in great agony from the cold water. Nevertheless there was little difference between the natives and the controls in the foot heat-loss into the bath water; this indicates that skin temperatures were essentially the same. Elsner considers this experiment a clear case of a very real difference in abilities of two types of people to tolerate cold exposure by habituation.

Other examples of habituation are increasingly prevalent in the literature. Eagan's icewater immersion tests compares fingers which were immersed 6 times per day with fingers of the opposite hand which were not immersed; after 126 days the temperature of the compared fingers did not differ, but there was a marked difference in pain sensation[179] (Fig. 37). Pain was slight for the test fingers, while it was usually severe for the control fingers. This was considered by the investigator as conclusive evidence for a specific habituation to cold pain. Other habituation experiments by Glaser and Griffin[190] showed that the pulse rate response of rats to repeated cooling of the tail decreased as the experiment progressed.

The Diving Women of Korea: A Case of Cold Acclimatization. The recent work of Hong[204] on the women divers or Ama, who harvest plant and animal life from the coastal waters of the Korean Peninsula, has attracted the interest of all environmental physiologists. There are some 30,000 of these divers who are initiated into their profession at age 12 and continue to dive to their late 50's. Despite a large seasonal variation in the temperatures of air and sea water, they engage in their diving work throughout the year; the air temperature approaches 0°C and the water temperature reaches 10°C. During the study by Hong, oral temperatures were taken during all seasons. The greatest reductions were seen in winter oral temperatures which routinely fell to 33°C or less. These subjects experience the most severe form of cold stress that human subjects voluntarily tolerate. It is particularly fascinating to physiologists that the sample of individuals undergoing this severe exposure is large enough for safe generalization; the investigator so often has to be satisfied with data gained from 4 or 5 individuals in a cold chamber.

In this study evidence of acclimatization was sought in the basal metabolic rates of these subjects. The Ama showed a marked seasonal variation, while the nondiving control natives showed a constant BMR throughout the year. The highest metabolic rates of the Ama (35% above normal) were observed in the winter. This increase in metabolic rate cannot be attributed to diet since the analysis of 24-hour urine samples indicated that the excretion of nitrogen was the same in the winter in the Ama and in control subjects. Thus, the elevated BMR of the divers appears to be causally related to the degree of cold stress. According to Hong, these findings represent unequivocal evidence that repeated cold exposure can increase the resting metabolism of human subjects. The findings that the increase in metabolic rate was not due to diet has further support from the evidence that changes in diet in the winter produce small effects upon the basal metabolic rate. Yoshimura [240] studied this in Japanese subjects and found only a 10% increase in the winter due to diet.

The shivering threshold of the Ama indicates a completely different temperature regulation (see earlier section on shivering). There was no difference in threshold in summer and winter and so this observation cannot be considered a part of the evidence for acclimatization.

Tissue insulation was elevated in the winter in the Ama. This was true in spite of comparisons with control subjects possessing equivalent subcutaneous fat layers. Therefore in winter the Ama must have developed vascular acclimatization.

Summary of Responses to Cold in Man. In a recent symposium Hammel [194] classified the types of response to cold: metabolic, insulative, and hypothermic. These types of responses have all been illustrated in the above sections which deal with different geographic groups of mankind. The metabolic acclimatization is typified by that of the Ama; the insulative acclimatization is found in the cold skin of the Australian Aborigines when they sleep at night; the hypothermic responses are also found in the Aborigines, who reduce rectal temperature to 35°C; other metabolic examples are seen in the dexterity-assisting warming of the fingers in ice water by Eskimos. Many of these responses can be interpreted as a lowering of the body thermostat to more economic levels.

There has been some speculation about the advantages of body size and response to cold. Tromp [22] has reviewed the following data: the average weight of Finns is 154 pounds, of Spaniards 132, of Berbers of Algeria 124; in Asia the figures are: North Chinese 142, Annamites 112, Andamese 98 pounds; in Africa, Bushmen of the Kalihari 89. Needless to say, these weight differences are largely due to differences in kind and quantity of food, and to metabolic characteristics, although each of these factors is correlated (either directly or indirectly) with the average temperature condition of the region. There is nothing in the data to contradict a rather interesting and practical hypothesis that an efficient adjustment of animals to cold requires a large body mass. Tromp also suggests that additional requirements are short extremities, much fat, deep vein-routing and high basal metabolism or a combination of these factors.

Long Range Responses

Comparison Between Acclimation and Acclimatization. The technical difference between two types of long range responses to cold has been elucidated by Hart [10] (see Chapter 1). Some of his findings on laboratory cold-exposure will illustrate acclimation. The responses of several species of small mammals were: 1) an increase of heat production while in the thermal neutral condition and 2) better sustained metabolic output of heat in the cold. This acclimation to cold appeared to reach its full expression in white rats after a month and in white mice after several weeks. In a series of 8 species of mammals and 5 species of birds studied by Hart,[10] the increase in resting-rate of metabolism after acclimation was from 0 to 90%. Irving's [2] assessment of this acclimation was: "In spite of the increases in resting metabolism of these animals, their critical temperatures were unchanged except in one case where it rose. The result of acclimation was an apparent decrease of overall insulation and life at a greater metabolic expense."

Now an illustration of acclimatization from Hart's Laboratory will be given: the investigators [200] exposed white rats outdoors in groups of 10 during summer and winter. In contrast to the cold-acclimated rats, the winter rats outdoors had a lower heat production than summer rats outdoors. This was true over a considerable range of exposure temperatures. In keeping with the lower heat production and in contrast to cold-acclimated rats, winter outdoor rats had a greater pelt insulation and lower skin temperatures on the back and tail than summer outdoor rats when measured at the same air temperature. On the other hand, winter outdoor rats had a higher maximal heat production than summer outdoor rats; the winter rats also had a greater cold resistance when tested at —35°C.

Cold Adaptations and Cold Acclimatization. We must now consider in more detail the technique of survival of large arctic mammals. These mammals and birds have greatly extended the thermal limits within which their survival and activity is possible. The poikilotherms (fish, amphibians, reptiles) have not succeeded in extending their survival to temperatures much below freezing. Only among arctic fish do we find that prolonged exposure to cold may lower their lethal limits so that some species may be active when supercooled to levels of —1.7°C. In contrast, arctic mammals may be active indefinitely at temperatures of —40°C and below (Fig. 28). The small arctic mammals make use of the snow layer which shows a steep thermo-gradient. The so-called subnivean layers are relatively warm: Johnson gives figures of 15°F on the ground under 1½ feet of snow when the air temperature was —40° to —50°F.[207] Thus the most interesting arctic adaptations will be found in the large mammals since the small ones seldom venture out on the surface of the snow at temperatures below —20°C.

The challenge of life in what Scholander calls a "heat-hungry" environment has been met in a variety of ways by the evolutionary process; among the adaptations which will be discussed are the cooling of the extremities of large mammals, peripheral nerve conduction at low temperatures and counter-current vascular heat exchange systems. In two sections which will follow, separate consideration will be given to the adaptations of sled dogs and of bare-skinned mammals in the cold. Let us first consider the caribou and moose which undoubtedly spend long hours standing in the extreme winter climate, frequently as cold as —60°F. There are two possibilities for the thermal regulation of these long extremities of the moose as it stands in the "moose-yard": 1) the legs and feet may be warm requiring a large expenditure of energy and fuel on the part of the animal, 2) or these extremities may remain very cold with the requirement that special demands are made on the cellular architecture and function of these extremities. The rule seems to be for arctic animals to solve the problem by cooling the extremities. In the examples to follow, some data from herring gulls will be included with the discussion of mammals because more work has been done on the gulls and their physiological adaptations appear very similar to those of the mammals. Some measurements made by Irving [206] will illustrate: on reindeer, when the air was —31°C the hoof was 9°C and the skin of the smallest diameter of the leg was also 9°C. The rectal temperature was 38°C and the forehead was 36°C. Measurements made on sled dogs at —30°C showed that the pad of the foot was 0°C and the top of the foot was 8°C. As usual with all such animals the body temperature gradient rises sharply once the limb becomes thickly covered with insulation. On the dog the skin at the junction of leg and body on the outside was 35°C.

Turning now to herring gulls, it is remarkable that they can swim with large bare feet in open water and walk on the ice without the webs being frozen white. Irving [206] made measurements of one gull when the air was —16°C. The web varied in temperature from 0° to 4.9°C. The middle of the exposed leg was 7.9°C but the skin under the feathers at the upper thigh varied from 15°C where the feathers began, to 37.8°C a few inches closer to the body. One would suppose that such cooling would reduce the metabolism of these tissues to an ineffectual level, yet in the webs of the feet of these gulls Irving observed active circulation in small vessels (while a thermocouple in the adjacent tissue registered 0°C).

The bare legs of another species of gull (*Larus argentatus*) kept outside during the winter in Boston were studied.[170] The leg tissue temperature was 6°C. Excised tibial nerves from these legs showed responses which were different in the distal and proximal portions; the nerve from the cold bare part of the leg became blocked by cold between 2° to 5°C, while the central part of the nerve from the warm part of the leg under the feathers failed at 8° to 13°C. These results are particularly unusual because they show that parts of cells (the cells are neurons) can be adapted to a relatively cold temperature (2° to 5°C), while at the same time other parts of the same cells will only function at the warmer temperature of 8° to 13°C. Of additional interest was the fact that in summer no part of the nerves from gulls would conduct at the cold temperatures (2° to 5°C). We will call the first type *cold-conduction* and the other *normal-temperature conduction*. When hens were kept in the cold in outdoor runs in winter, and their leg nerves and temperatures were studied in the same way, it was found that their feet were warmer than those of cold-exposed gulls (even summer-gulls). These "winter hens" represent the second possibility which was mentioned as a direction which the arctic mammals could have taken (having warm legs). Excised nerves from the legs of winter cold-exposed hens were sensitive to cold; they demonstrated "normal-temperature conduction." In summary, we can say that the legs of herring gulls possess several interesting adaptations concerned with the use of cold extremities for conservation of heat; also the physiological-behavior of these legs demonstrates acclimatization to cold.

A very similar example of acclimatization to cold of a part of a limb is found in the work of Miller and Irving.[218] They were studying nerve function in several species of Alaskan mammals. The caudal nerves of muskrats were excised; action potentials from these tissues were recorded at temperatures as low as —6°C. Conduction persisted but velocity was reduced 20- to 30-fold. The investigators showed that these nerves were supercooled (by transient increases in temperature at the moment the nerve actually froze). The capability of caudal nerves to conduct in a supercooled state was lost in several muskrats maintained indoors for several months during the winter. Apparently these nerves behave like the tibial nerves of the herring gull. When sciatic nerves from muskrats were compared with caudal nerves, the sciatic nerves would not function at temperatures much below 4°C. This seems appropriate since these nerves are not subjected to the large temperature changes which take place in the tail.

The counter-current vascular heat-exchange system as an adaptation is found in a number of types of mammals extending from the Tropics to the Arctic. In no case is this system better illustrated than in the fin of the porpoise. Scholander[226] asked the question: "what prevents whales in the polar seas from being chilled to death from heat loss through their large thin fins?" The fins which Scholander and Schevill studied included the flippers, the caudal fins, and the dorsal fin. In all cases they found that each major artery was located centrally within a multiple venous channel. No matter what else the function of such an arrangement, these bundles must exchange heat between the arteries and the veins. The system is referred to as an arterial-venous counter-current system, serving for heat preservation. In such an arrangement the warm arterial blood is cooled by the venous blood which has been chilled in the fin (Fig. 41). The result is a steep temperature drop from the body into the appendage; the heat of the arterial blood does not reach the fin but is short-circuited back into the body in the venous system. Body heat is conserved at the expense of keeping the appendage

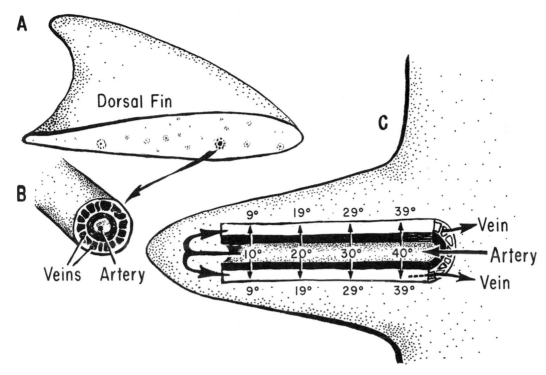

FIGURE 41. *A Mechanism for Rewarming of Blood.* In a series of mammals from man to whales, Scholander has accumulated information on the rewarming of cold venous blood by arterial blood. *A* shows a section of the dorsal fin of a bottlenose porpoise where the veins surround each artery. *B* shows a closeup of the artery surrounded by the multiple venous channel. *C* shows a hypothetical temperature gradient in this concentric counter-current system. From Scholander and Scheville.[226]

cold. There are also separate superficial veins associated with this system; their function might be as follows: if the animal needs maximal heat-conservation, blood circulation through the fins would be slow and the venous return would preferentially pass through the counter-current veins; on the other hand, if maximal cooling as during exercise in warm water is needed, this could be accomplished by a high rate of blood flow through the fins with a venous return through the superficial veins. One author[237] made observations on a dolphin out of water and found that the fins could vary between 25° and 33.5°C, while the core temperature varied only 0.5°C. This appears to be an example of adaptation which is not associated with seasonal acclimatization. It is an adaptation for heat exchange.

The arctic porcupine, as yet unstudied, provides an excellent example of bare flesh being exposed to extreme cold. They walk on the snow on their large, bare, fleshy feet at temperatures from —30° to —40°F; they weigh 15 to 25 pounds and their feet are almost as large as the palm of an adult human hand. They show no apparent concern for the snow, so that their extremities must in some way be protected.

These adaptations and evidences of cold acclimatization illustrate the successful attainment of homeokinesis by small and large arctic animals so that their body

FIGURE 42. *The Arctic Tundra Wolf in Heavy Winter Coat.* (A) These animals chose to sleep outside their shelters even in the coldest winter weather on the shores of the Arctic Ocean at the Arctic Research Laboratory, Point Barrow, Alaska. (B) This arctic wolf is carrying abdominal radio transmitters for body temperature and EKG. Temperatures of −54°F and winds of 25 mph were recorded at his enclosure at Barrow. (Cont. page 119)

FIGURE 42. (Cont.) (C) Few people have seen a *white* arctic wolf. This one in full winter coat was collected by S. D. McDonald on October 14, 1954 on Ellesmere Island. It was mounted by Professor Walter C. Thietje for the University of Iowa Museum. McDonald's notations on the pelt tag read: male; quite fat; stomach contents—remains of wolf (hair, claws, flesh); tape worm.

temperatures are nearly identical with those found in mammals in the tropics. Irving found the mean body temperature for 20 species of mammals in Arctic Alaska was 38.5°C, and for 60 species of mammals from temperate and tropical zones the mean figure was 38°C.[206]

Physiology of the Sled Dog and Wolf. If a biologist is fortunate enough to follow closely, by airplane, a black arctic wolf running in great leaps over the snow of the arctic slope, he will remember it as an unforgettable experience. Of particular interest are the physiological adaptations of this beautiful animal and of sled dogs, many of which are genetically part wolf.[176] Their ability to tolerate cold is excelled only by the arctic fox. With Dr. Max Brewer of the Arctic Research Laboratory, we have maintained groups of wolves at

Point Barrow, Alaska, for several years. During their period of rest, even when the wind chill index is V, these wolves will be sleeping or resting in the exposed part of the pen instead of using warm, dry, protected parts of the enclosures. As the animals get up when approached, their customary bed is evident since their heat has melted a bowl-shaped depression of ice replacing the original fluffy snow (Figs. 42 and 43). If you place the tip of a pencil (for measurement) through the fur of the side of one of these animals, the insulation, irrespective of scattered guard hairs, amounts to 66 mm. This depth of insulation is exceeded only by that of the white arctic Dall sheep, 70 mm. The insulation of sled dogs is similar; it is a common observation of those who chain their dogs to a small kennel that even in

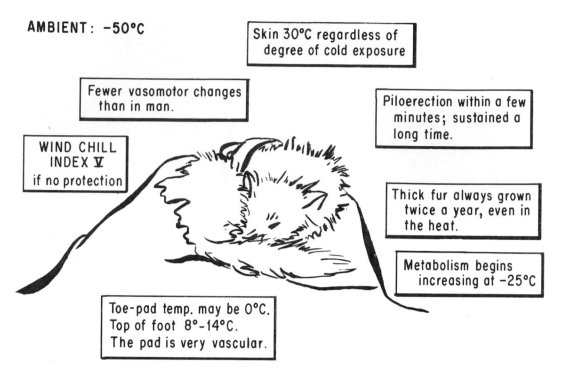

AMBIENT: −50°C

Skin 30°C regardless of degree of cold exposure

Fewer vasomotor changes than in man.

Piloerection within a few minutes; sustained a long time.

WIND CHILL INDEX Ⅴ if no protection

Thick fur always grown twice a year, even in the heat.

Metabolism begins increasing at −25°C

Toe-pad temp. may be 0°C.
Top of foot 8°–14°C.
The pad is very vascular.

FIGURE 43. *Thermal Relations of Sled Dog in Snow Drift.* This diagram illustrates an extreme environmental situation which many sled dogs experience each winter. When chained to small kennels they elect to remain in the snow rather than take shelter even at the coldest temperatures. The foot temperatures were obtained (by Irving) from a dog standing in cold air. Heat loss is reduced because the feet are maintained at such a cold tissue temperature.

the most severe weather these animals curl up in the snow or on top of the kennel rather than inside their shelters. Scholander *et al.*[155] studied the critical temperature of arctic Eskimo dogs, which showed no rise in metabolism at —30°C. Of course dogs are notably different in size and fur depth and it is not surprising that in Philadelphia 3 dogs, which had been living in the laboratory kennel at 27°C, had critical temperatures of about 27°C where their metabolism was elevated by cold.

Acclimatization to Cold in Dogs. Undoubtedly we need only the thickness of the insulation of dogs and wolves to explain their extreme tolerance to cold when lying quietly. It is doubtful that one could demonstrate acclimatization to cold in these

species. A thick fur in sled dogs is always grown twice a year, even in a very warm environment.[217] This is by no means a disadvantage since a heavy fur coat assists mammals to tolerate the heat. Some of the other breeds of dogs appeared to show acclimatization; McMillan[177] states that in his laboratory, and in the laboratories of three other investigators mentioned by Swan, they have lost a great many more dogs from ventricular fibrillation in the summer than in the winter. This evidence in favor of cold or seasonal acclimatization is supported by work from another laboratory[172] indicating that dogs submerged in cold water expired with a rectal temperature of 18.6°C, but the ones which had been acclimated to cold survived to a rectal temperature of 14.9°C.

Sled Dogs, Eskimos and Exercise. The skin

Figure 44. *Working Dogs at the Tip of North America.* These Eskimo huskies are leaving Barrow for a day's work. On that day the temperature was −50°F and the sun was above the horizon for only 30 minutes. The background is the Arctic Ocean.

temperature of dogs exposed to −50°C is a consistant 30°C which is also the skin temperature of arctic foxes and many other arctic mammals upon exposure to cold. Curiously, when these animals are warmed, they still appear to be comfortable when skin temperature is 37°C. One wonders how these active animals can dissipate heat when their metabolism is increased many-fold in exercise. Do dogs and wolves with heavy insulation carry on sustained exercise or is their work performed in short bouts? Dogs with heavy coats still carry on heavy work for native Eskimos and Indians today. The well-known Eskimo guide, Pete Savolik, has estimated that in 1964 there were 500 working sled dogs in the Eskimo village of Barrow. If one walks in mid-winter toward the village, the sustained running of these dogs is evident because one can see the teams fanning out in many directions to accomplish the business of the owners. One seldom sees these dogs walking or trotting; they are invariably at a dead run (Fig. 44). Many long-haired dogs annually compete in sled dog races between Eskimo villages and in the national competitions held in Fairbanks and Anchorage. In the national race these dogs are required to cover 70

miles in 3 days: 20 on day 1, 20 on day 2, and 30 the final day. Some teams had run from their own Eskimo village the day before the races. The winning distances are covered at about 15 miles per hour. How can these animals perform this work while carrying an insulation of approximately 66 mm in thickness? One of the adaptations they have consists of suppression of pilo-erection so that the hair lies very close to the skin. The major heat dissipating system is the tongue which is protruded many inches in most cases, so that panting may take place over the moist surfaces of the pharynx and the tongue (Fig. 45). One wonders if a similar mechanism is necessary with caribou and moose; the problem of dissipating heat is less in these animals because their insulation is only approximately 38 mm in thickness and because their long slender legs, which have scarcely any insulation on them, must serve as a valuable place to shunt the hot blood from the body. Nevertheless the caribou and moose do pant but they do not extend the tongue the way the dog does. The adaptations for dissipating heat by the dog and wolf do not appear adequate to explain the efficiency of the working sled dog. This is particularly the case when we

FIGURE 45. *Alaskan Huskies After a Race*. Sled dogs at end of 30 mile run. The air temperature was −20°F. Even at this temperature, these hardy animals required no protection after their work. The frost indicates the temperature gradient through their fur.

learn that there is less vasodilation in the skin of the dog than in man.[217] We must now consider in finer detail the relationship between the insulation of the dog and the cold environment.

The problem of heat dissipation through insulation is as old as Eskimos in the arctic, and according to Professor W. S. Laughlin they apparently arrived on the scene about 10,000 years ago. The early Eskimo pioneers of America were undoubtedly wearing the same heavy insulation, which was cleverly designed to prevent overheating. As soon as a man in heavy insulation begins to work, because he does not have the same physiology as a dog, he is in the situation of being a tropical man in arctic clothing.[235] There will be heavy sweating under his insulation. This problem is not unknown amongst the mammals

since the horse has very active sweat glands, and some breeds grow extremely heavy insulation in the winter.* Among the many problems the Eskimo had to solve was how to keep from building up a large quantity of wet or frozen insulation. The problem is illustrated by a quotation from a member of Scott's Antarctic expedition; Cherry-Garrard (1948) wrote: ". . . on the most bitter days it seems that we must be sweating; and all of this sweat instead of passing away through the porous wool of our clothing and gradually drying off us, froze and accumulated. It passed just away from our flesh and then became ice. . . .". Does this mean that every time

---

* Some physiologist should study the sweating of Shetland ponies in winter when they are laboring heavily in deep snow.

the Eskimo runs with his dog team his insulation is coated with frost? The answer is that he has evolved two methods to avoid this; he constantly pulls off the outer fur parka so that much of the time his skin is quite cool. More importantly, his clothing is designed with many ventilation areas, gaps, and drawstrings. Those Eskimos, such as the ones in the great barrens of Canada or in Northwest Greenland, who are still wearing the time-honored fur parka instead of Sears, Roebuck flannel shirts, invariably show the bare skin of their backs between pants and parkas when they bend over. Air is constantly being pumped in through either the top or the bottom of the parka and out by some other opening. Other venting areas are indicated in Figure 46. However, the dog and wolf cannot shed their hair during exercise and, in fact, they do accumulate a good deal of frost. It looks as if some remaining mechanism should be present by which we can find more biological adaptability in these species. Part of the answer to this was found in experimental results obtained at the Harvard Fatigue Laboratory: the Clo value of heavy winter insulation was markedly diminished during movement. This was demonstrated with a heated, sealed cylinder covered with wool and pile, which simulated both a man's leg in arctic clothing and a dog's leg covered with fur. The cylinder could be swung to simulate walking movements. The insulation was studied at −18°C, first with the cylinder immobilized, then with it moving at 62 cycles per minute, the approximate frequency of leg movement when walking at 3.5 mph. The Clo value of the insulation when the cylinder was still was 1.7 Clo, and with the cylinder moving was 0.9.[128] This reduction of 47% helps to explain how the dog and wolf can tolerate their heavy insulation when running. In a more recent study it was found that the thermal conductance of pelts was doubled at 20 mph compared to 0 mph.[238]

Now that we have considered some aspects of heat dissipation of sled dogs and fur-clad Eskimos, let us examine further the practical problems of the working sled

FIGURE 46. *Chimney Effect in Eskimo Fur Clothing.* When Eskimo sled dogs exercise, they become a tropical animal in an arctic environment. The Eskimos prevent this effect by designing their fur clothing so that when exercising in extreme cold, vents can be opened permitting maximum ventilation. Only by this means can the accumulation of large quantities of sweat be prevented.

dog. Prolonged hard work (sled pulling) at mild temperatures (about 0°C) causes an increase of only 1° to 1.5°C in the rectal temperature of the average sled dog. At the finish of the Annual North American Sled Dog Championship Race in Fairbanks, Alaska, the average rectal temperature was 39.7°C for 17 dogs in 1963 and 40.1°C for 71 dogs in 1964.[180] The resting temperature of a sled dog is 38.6°C.[206] No differences in the averages of teams were found relating to finishing position in a race. Why is this temperature rise so small? The eating of snow along the sled trail appears to be an important factor in limiting the heat gain of some dog teams. This cannot be the case with all teams because many drivers do not permit dogs to break stride to obtain snow. The advantage of eating snow was studied by C. Eagan et al.[182] by having dogs swallow temperature-sensitive radio capsules (Iowa transmitters [184]) before sled runs; these transmitters (and presumably part of the stomach) cooled below 15°C in some dogs because of snow consumed.[182]

We must now give further consideration to the dog's lower critical temperature, which is made possible by its excellent insulation. As indicated earlier Scholander et al.[155] concluded that the critical temperature of dogs and foxes was between —40° and —50°C, and they calculated that only a 40% increase in their metabolic rate would be needed to maintain body thermal balance at —70°C. Since the winter temperatures in most arctic areas are almost always well within the thermal neutral zone (+30° to —40°C) of sled dogs and foxes, no seasonal variation which might represent acclimatization would be predicted. In an experiment at the Arctic Aeromedical Laboratory (Fairbanks) two investigators decided to test for acclimatization in the sled dog by using daily caloric intake and body weight as criteria of metabolic energy expenditure.[178] The well-insulated sled dog was compared with the poorly-insulated beagle dog. During the period of measurement, the average monthly ambient temperature ranged from 17° to —22°C. The caloric intake of the huskies rose from a midsummer low of 49 kcal/kg/day to a November high of 87 kcal/kg/day. Mid and late winter values averaged about 79 kcal/kg/day. The beagles studied during the summer had minimum values of approximately 85 kcal/kg/day. With the onset of winter the beagles increased their intake to a high of 144 kcal/kg/day in November and 131 kcal/kg/day in March. The relative magnitude of the seasonal changes were quite similar in both groups of dogs, suggesting a paradoxical and unexplained metabolic acclimatization in both instances.

The Physiology of Bare-Skinned Mammals. In an earlier section we have discussed the adaptation of maintaining cold extremities as a response to a cold environment. The cooling of the extremities and the saving of heat by this means has a parallel in another adaptation of arctic animals. This is the maintenance of a cold skin all over the body in mammals which do not have hair. Dr. Irving began to study this type of adaptation with domestic swine maintained at Fairbanks; these animals tolerate the extreme cold down to —50°C with apparent ease. The metabolism of two young pigs was studied to look for the rise in metabolism at some critical cold air temperature; this critical air temperature was 0°C. This appears to be a rather low critical temperature for naked animals. When they were exposed to cold their skin temperature declined steadily until it was as low as 10° or 8°C.

In large hogs the gradient from cold skin to the warm body interior extended by direct measurement as much as 100 mm, varying in depth with the temperature of the air. The skin showed periodic warming and cooling reminiscent of the Lewis waves of vasodilation found in human cold fingers. The evidence that the cold skin is an economic biological adaptation is, as mentioned above, that the critical air temperature is 0°C. Dr. Irving remarks that as a consequence the cost of feeding pigs is not noticeably elevated in the cold Alaskan winter.[2]

Dr. Irving then turned his attention to the study of seals which are comparable in many respects to domestic swine. Out of water their thin hair affords them about 1/10 the insulation of the hair on the caribou, but in water it gives them practically no protection whatsoever because the hair is wetted and the surrounding water is not separated from the skin by as much as a millimeter.* He found that the harp seal, a strictly northern form of seal, showed no increase in metabolic rate when exposed in ice water. Their skin was practically the temperature of the surrounding water, differing by only 0.05°C. Thus in both the swine and the seal, the heat loss from skin to environment is greatly reduced by the cooling of the skin. In man such a cooling at least of the extremities to 0°C could not be tolerated since dexterity is lost at 20°C.

With harbor seals the distribution of the temperature gradient varied with distribution of blood. The seal controlled this in a different fashion when it was in ice water and when it was in warm air; heat was lost from core to surface over a gradient of 40 to 60 mm when the animal was in ice water, but this gradient was scarcely 20 mm deep in warm air. Such a gradient evidently can be compared with the insulation of fur which is found on other animals; just as is the case with pilo-erection of fur, the insulation of the seal and swine can be varied in thickness to match the various media to which the animal is exposed. It is of course the changing vascular bed that brings about this variability.

The temperature regulation of the elephant which is also bare-skinned is entirely suitable to discuss here. Very little information has been obtained. First, one should ask if such a large mammal has a different body temperature from other mammals. A recent study based upon a large series of temperatures of fecal matter immediately after defecation of elephants in the field, and of rectal temperatures of recently-killed elephants has provided a figure of 97.5°F.[169] This mean temperature showed very little variation; this must relate to the functioning of the elephants' testes which are located internally and do not have the benefit of a thermal regulatory scrotum. This body temperature is not particularly unusual; hamsters for example at noontime have a colonic temperature of 97.0°F.[187] Because two species of the elephant group (hairy mammoth and mastodon) lived in the arctic area in quantity, and a similar species, the hairy rhinocerous, was also within this area, it is reasonable to raise the question as to whether the elephant with its bare skin can also tolerate some cold exposure as can pigs. This seems to be a controversial subject; on the one hand, keepers in circuses try not to expose their elephants to temperatures below 70°F, and when it is necessary to move elephants in cold weather they furnish them with blankets. On the other hand, there is some reason to suppose that elephants could resist cold if necessary. The size of the animal alone works in its favor because the surface mass law works here in reverse. As size goes up, the amount of body heat generated goes up as the cube of the dimensions; but the skin, the surface from which this heat is radiated, is raised by the square. While the elephant's body temperature is around 97°F, its skin temperature according to Benedict lies between 79° and 88°. Thus this animal does not appear to show the cool skin found in swine when maintained at warm temperatures. Primarily, especially when the temperature is mild, the elephant's problem is not to prevent heat loss but to enhance it. According to some speculation, the elephant's ears act as radiant-devices as do the wings of the bat and the ears of a jackrabbit. There is some evidence that elephants can tolerate cold, since they are found in the wild state almost up to the snow line on the great mountains of East Africa. Furthermore, Jap, the elephant used by Benedict in his classic study of elephant physiology, was kept through a New Jersey winter in a badly heated barn. There she was ex-

---

* Furthermore, the thermal conductivity of water is over 20 times greater than that of air.

posed for several weeks in March and April to temperatures down to freezing, always without ill effects.

EXPERIMENTAL HYPOTHERMIA

Artificial hypothermia is included in this book because of the application of fundamental hypothermia experiments to understanding cold-adaptations of mammals in the free environment. The classic experiments of Andjus and Smith [161] were designed for the study of non-hibernators in cardiac and respiratory arrest; later, in the course of other experiments, they worked with hamsters (which happen to be hibernators). In both of these species they demonstrated supercooling of the internal tissues. They described supercooling (in 24% of animals with a core temperature of —1°C) and showed that it did not aid survival. These background laboratory experiments made it theoretically possible to accept the increasing instances of supercooling in animals in the free environment; examples are: (1) Kalabukhov (Cited by Smith [230]), and Henshaw and Folk [199] observed supercooled bats below —4°C in natural hibernation for several days; the bat hearts continued to beat at 8 b/m. Thus, the supercooled state is not unstable. (2) Scholander [227] found fish *living* in deep bays in Laborador where the water temperature is permanently —1.7°C and the freezing point of the fish is —0.9°C; if these fish are seeded with ice, they freeze at once. (3) Miller and Irving [218] recorded action potentials from the caudal nerves of muskrats at —6°C and demonstrated that the nerves were supercooled.

The study of deep hypothermia is of theoretical physiological significance because it has changed our view of body temperature homeokinesis. It was assumed that mammals which do not hibernate would not tolerate core temperatures below 15°C; the experiments of Andjus, who succeeded in reviving rats maintained for 40 minutes at —3.3°C, showed that non-hibernating mammals do not necessarily totter on the

knife-edge of homeothermic survival if their body temperature slides downward. Surgeons have recently accepted this point of view, especially in brain and circulatory operations; an illustration is the woman who recovered (to die later from cancer) from treatment involving cooling to a core temperature of 9°C; her heart was at a standstill for 45 minutes. [231]

Principles of Experimental Hypothermia*

There were early attempts before the classic work of Andjus and Smith to deanimate mammals. Horvath [205] in 1881 studied a hibernator at a temperature just above 0°C. He found that during the period of hypothermia he could get a a muscular response upon stimulation of a motor nerve. Walther [242] did pioneer work in 1862 by cooling rabbits to 20°C, with successful recovery. In 1940 Giaja [189] reported a case of spontaneous recovery of a rat cooled with CO_2 excess to a body temperature of 8.8°C. Other successful work was done with isolated mammalian tissues. By pretreatment and slow diffusion of a 15% glycerol solution in Ringer's solution, mammalian sperms and mammalian red blood cells were recovered from —79°C (temperature of solid CO_2) and hamster hearts resumed spontaneous beating from —20°C. [231] It has been assumed from observations in the past that insects, fish and frogs can be frozen in blocks of ice and kept for long periods of time. More recently it has been understood that where survival occurs, the organisms are either not frozen or else they are supercooled. For example, if frogs are frozen and reach —1.8°C, they will not

---

* For further details read: (A) Dripps, R. D. (Ed.) 1956. *Physiology of Induced Hypothermia* (a symposium) Nat. Acad. Sci. No. 451, 446p. (B) Taylor, A. C. 1959. Hypothermia. Ann. N.Y. Acad. Sci. 80:285–550. (C) Negovskii, V. A. 1962. *Resuscitation and Artificial Hypothermia*. Consultants Bureau, New York, 314 pp. (D) Luyet, B. J. 1965. Human encounters with cold. Cryobiology 1:4–11[214a].

survive; they will, however, survive for an extended period an internal body temperature of —1.0°C. Arctic fish do not survive total freezing, but may withstand freezing of the body surface. The technique of cooling and then recovering mammals below 0°C depends upon driving them down *slowly* below lethal temperature (that body temperature from which they cannot recover without assistance), then further cooling them *rapidly* to 0°C and below. Mammalian hibernators and non-hibernators have very different lethal temperatures; the technique of inducing reversible hypothermia in these two types of mammals must differ accordingly (Tables 11 and 12). Hamsters (hibernators), and rats and monkeys are cooled in closed containers so that their body temperature drops due to narcosis induced by hypoxia and hypercapnia. As hypothermia develops, oxygen consumption of the rat (and the dog) shows an exponential decline with decreasing body temperature. This decline in oxygen consumption is not greater than expected; it can be expressed as being physiologically adequate for the situation existing at the time. Transport of oxygen is slightly improved; for example, 32% more oxygen is physically dissolved in plasma at 20°C than at 38°C. At a core temperature of 30°C, oxygen utilization is 50% reduced and at 25°C it is 65% reduced. This appears to apply to man also.[165] Studies on delivery of oxygen from blood to tissue in hypothermic dogs under anesthesia show that the fraction of the blood oxygen that is unloaded at each circulation is about the same at 18°C as at 38°C. Cooled tissues accumulate no measurable oxygen debt. Popovic[223] has also shown this in hibernating ground squirrels.

Closed-container cooling of rats is carried out at +2°C; at the end of 2 hours, the container-concentration of oxygen decreases to between 2 and 4%, and CO_2 increases to between 15 and 16%. The body temperature falls to between 15° and 20°C. Frequently with a number of types of non-hibernators during this temperature drop the rates of metabolic process exhibit a Q_{10} of 3, the rates of contraction a Q_{10} of 2, and the rates of physical processes such as diffusion a Q_{10} of 1. The cardiac output of the rat in narcosis decreases in a linear fashion with the body temperature. The stroke volume of the heart is as large at 18°C as at 38°C, thus having a temperature coefficient of 1.

A point of special interest is that the use of an anesthetic does not enhance heat loss.

Time of Deanimation. The physical change which took place *below 0°C* in both rat and hamsters was a gradual and slow process, unless the animals were supercooled instead of frozen. According to Andjus[177] the longest period below zero for rat survival was 40 minutes; the rectal temperature was —3.3°C.* The hamsters represent a different story. In the following table, all animals were supercooled. If any individuals were supercooled before freezing or if they were frozen more than 70 minutes, the animals did not recover (Table 10).

Table 10. Effects of Supercooling on Hamsters

Time below core temperature of 0°C	Core Temperature	Length of Survival	Tissue Damage
60 min	—5°C	Indefinite	....
75 min	—5°C	Died after apparent recovery	Gastric hemorrhage
96 min	—5°C	Died soon after recovery of heart beat and breathing	....
180 min	—5°C	Recovered heart beat only	....

None of these hamsters necessarily showed signs of frostbite. When hamsters were

---

* Note that Lewis, using artificial respiration and oxygen, maintained twenty-four rats at cardiac standstill for 2½ hours at 0°C[210].

Table 11. Hypothermia Induction of the White Rat (Andjus[177])

Duration	Ambient	Change in Body Temperature	Procedure	Comments
0-2 hours	+2°C	39° to 18°C	Enclosed in 2-liter jar.	At 20°C no blood flow.
1 hour, or until attaining one hour of cardiac and respiratory arrest.	Ice water	18° to 0°C	When BT is 18°C then into crushed ice and water for 1 hour.	Rat in stupor. Head movements still possible.
....	Ice water	At 15°C	BT drops rapidly, then more slowly.	Respirations* cease, and heartbeats stop soon (14° to 8°)**. Nerves do not cease functioning until 9°C.
....	Room temp.	0°C	Out of ice water, begin heating.	If rat lowered below 0°C to −3.3°C for no more than 40 min., survival is possible.
15 minutes	Room temp.	0° to 20°C	Use microwaves, or hot water on thorax, and artificial respiration.	First breathing at BT 20°C.
30 minutes	Water bath 42°C	20° to 39°C	Warm rat in water rapidly.	No shivering.

* Smith cites different figures, stating that pulmonary respiration stops between BT 10°C and 14°C.[231] According to Adolph[158] there is no oxygen consumption at BT 15°C; others say the oxygen utilization is 90% reduced.

** The value of 8°C for cardiac arrest is from Popovic and Popovic.[222]

Table 12. Hypothermia Induction of the Hamster (Smith[231])

Duration	Ambient	Change in Body Temperature	Procedure	Comments
0-2 hours	+2°C	37° to 18°C	Enclosed in 1-liter jar.	
1 hour	Ice water	At 18°C	When BT is 18°C, then into crushed ice and water for 1 hour.	Hamster in stupor. Blood flow stops between BT 5°-10°C.
....	Ice water	5° to 3°C	Still in ice bath (same hour as above).	Respiration stops between BT 2°-6°C. Heartbeat stops between BT 0.8°-3°C. Nerves cease functioning at BT 3°-4°C.
10 minutes	−5° or colder (glycol)	3° to 0.6°C	When BT is 3°C, then into −5°C glycol bath.	Rapid BT drop.
60 minutes	Same bath	0.6° to freezing	(Same bath)	Very slow drop as hamster freezes solid progressively.
5-10 minutes	Room air	Freezing to 10°C	Diathermy and artificial respiration.	Warm up 1° to 2° per minute.
About 30 minutes	Room air	10° to 37°C	No diathermy or artificial respiration. Spontaneous recovery.	Natural breathing, animal shivers, especially between BT 15° to 20°C. Animal walks 40 minutes after being frozen.

9

actually frozen, about one-third of the animals recovered in which 45% of total body water had been frozen for 1 hour. If more than 50% of the brain water was frozen, the animal did not recover. Of the animals which recovered from supercooling, there was some spontaneous crystalization and freezing during resuscitation. If this lasted only 1 to 2 minutes, it was harmless.

The Effects of Temperature on Heart Rate. Hiebel[202] compared heart rates of four hibernators at changing temperatures, and found a decreasing Q_{10} as temperature increased in all species. These observations were essentially upheld by Kayser[208] when he compared the hibernators to the white rat and guinea pig. The "critical thermal increment" was devised[209] to facilitate comparison of temperature sensitivities of various events; this was later replaced by the Arrhenius activation energy.[208] Dawe and Morrison[174] made a complete analysis of the duration of the events of the EKG of several hibernators, and suggested that conduction times and repolarization times were most temperature sensitive.

Arousal. The awakening process of the rat (in warm air) from a core temperature of 20°C, of the hypothermic hamster from 10°C, and of the hamster from natural hibernation will probably turn out to be very similar processes. It is a massive physiological effort in which the animal generates a maximum amount of heat in a minimum of time. If the hamster is in a cold environment, his arousal may take 3 hours. Apparently when all hibernators wake up, the temperature of the tail part of the body lags behind the head part so that near the midpoint of the waking process the head may be 20°C warmer than the tail portion. The heart rate increases before there is an increase in body temperature (Lyman and Chatfield[215]). There is evidence that the heart during arousal is being driven at its maximum rate by the sympathetic system, with a complete lack of vagal action. Whether the heart rate increase should be described as a linear function or an exponential function is not yet clear.

Heart Damage in Hypothermia. Although it is rare, the hearts of both rats and hamsters may fibrillate during rewarming, but this was not observed during cooling.[213] If rats failed to revive fully, in some cases their hearts were fibrillating; some hamsters which did not revive

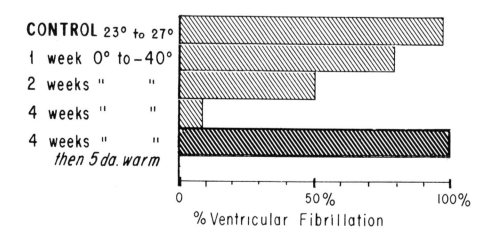

FIGURE 47. *Cold Acclimatization and Fibrillation in Hypothermia.* An index to cold acclimatization is seen in the proneness of dogs to hypothermic fibrillation of the heart. In a standardized test, after 4 weeks of cold exposure only 10% of the dogs showed fibrillation compared to 100% without cold exposure. From Covino.[171]

had hearts in fibrillation. In both hiberna-tion and hypothermia abnormally slow conduction, 2 to 1, and 3 to 1 A-V blocks have been reported. As a conducting mechanism, the A-V tissue seems to be very susceptible to the effect of cold. Par-ticularly in dogs, and to a lesser extent in human subjects, ventricular fibrillation oc-curs during cooling (Fig. 47). This is obtained at core temperatures between 26° and 19°C (usually at 26°C). Doubt is often expressed that hypothermia itself increases the tendency toward ventricular fibrillation; more commonly, changes in blood pH (in either direction) are cited as the important factors in the production of fibrillation. All authors agree that pH tends to shift toward the acid side at a core temperature of 26°C or below.

Hughes [177] points out that fibrillation at a cold body temperature is not neces-sarily serious (presumably this author meant ventricular fibrillation). Some dogs were allowed to fibrillate for 60 minutes and recovered completely. After 75 and 90 minutes of fibrillation, the survivors had only a mild hindquarters weakness. If fibrillation was 3, 4 and 5 hours, resus-citation became increasingly difficult. In Hughes' laboratory, resuscitation was ob-tained by opening the chest and irrigat-ing the pleural spaces with sterile saline solution at 45°C. With each 1°C rise in rectal temperature a defibrillation shock of 200 volts was administered to the heart for 0.13 seconds. This was continued until fibrillation ceased. The warm saline solu-tion was applied to the heart until a rectal temperature of 28°C was reached.

The slow rate of the hypothermic heart is an expression of a decrease in cardiac output roughly proportional to the re-quirement for oxygen transport. There is no evidence that the contractility is im-paired, but the contraction time is pro-longed. For this reason the filling of the hypothermic heart will be impaired if one attempts to drive it.

The different responses of typical verte-brates and mammals are now compared:

Responses to Hypothermia

Fish. In Labrador the water temperature is —1.7°C; freezing point depression of blood is —0.9°C (deep bay fish) or —1.5°C (surface fish); but all are super-cooled so that they do not freeze.

Frogs. Air temperature —25°C for 1 hour, muscles contain ice, but viscera unfrozen and heart beating. Animals re-vive unless core temperature of —1.8°C is reached.

Turtles and Snakes. Survive supercool-ing to core temperatures between —5° and —10°C.

Lizards. The consumption of measura-ble quantities of oxygen was measured in lizards supercooled to —7.8°C (Kalabuk-hov [231]).

Rabbits. Cooled with narcosis by Andjus technique [177] for 3 hours (core 18° to 23°C, HR 40 b/m, respirations 2 per minute). After ice bath for 30 minutes, respiration ceased at 15°C (range 13° to 18°C), cardiac arrest at 12°C. After 40 minutes more of ice bath, core was 8° to 10°C. This rate of cooling was too slow for survival. By speeding the cooling proc-ess core temperatures of 0.6°C were ob-tained, from which by *rapid* rewarming, rabbits were recovered.

Cats. Herring in 1905 [201] established a lethal hypothermic core temperature of 16°C. At a core temperature of 23° to 25°C, the heat regulating mechanisms are completely suppressed. Lipp *et al.* [214] cooled and recovered a series of cats (N = 16) to 25°C or below without hypercapnia or anesthesia (Fig. 48). Mean heart rate was reduced by 66% at rectal temperatures of 25°C. Cardiac arrest occurred at a rectal temperature of about 18°C. One cat was reduced nearly to cardiac arrest 4 times (by 70%, or further) and was then "re-tired" as a house pet; it later had at least two litters of normal kittens (Fig. 49).

Ground Squirrels. After 3 to 4.6 hours of restraint hypothermia at 3.5°C, ground squirrels (C. tridecemlineatus) main-tained a heartbeat of about 10 b/m for 2 hours (control 380 b/m). [213] Popo-

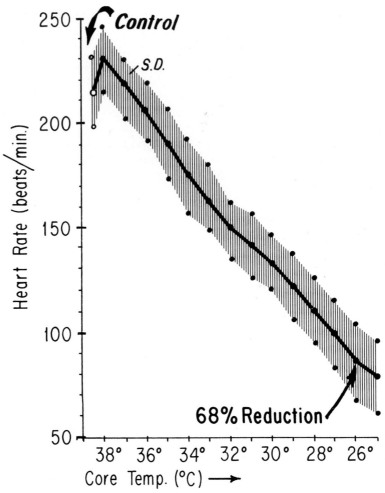

FIGURE 48. *Heart Rates of Cats in Hypothermia.* In this series (N = 16) all cats survived a body temperature of 24°C without damage; the experiment was unusual because there was no use of anesthesia or increased CO_2 during the process of hypothermia. From Lipp *et al.*[214]

vic[222] maintained adult ground squirrels at 10°C hypothermia for days, and newborn ground squirrels at —4°C (cardiac arrest) for 11 hours (supercooled).

Dogs. (*a*) *Technique.* Many dogs die in hypothermia unless acclimated at ambient 19°C. In one study, the lethal core temperature of acclimated dogs was 14.9°C, of non-acclimated was 18.6°C.[172] The animals must be prevented from shivering. Ether is preferred to barbiturates because, when desired, ether is quickly eliminated by respiration. Some workers use 2 mg morphine and 2 mg heparin injected before

the experiment. With shivering, it takes 2½ hours (using an ice bath) to reach a rectal temperature of 28°C; without shivering, it takes 1 hour. The rectal temperature may level off at 23°C for 2 hours, or it may drop to 19°C. It may rise spontaneously from 23°C by 0.5°/hour until the animal warms to 25° to 28°C. In other words, some dogs retain some temperature regulation at 23°C during prolonged hypothermia. During cooling, the rectal temperature of a dog falls slightly faster than arterial and esophageal. Hypercapnia was used with dogs in some laboratories; Lewis did not use CO_2 but gave oxygen

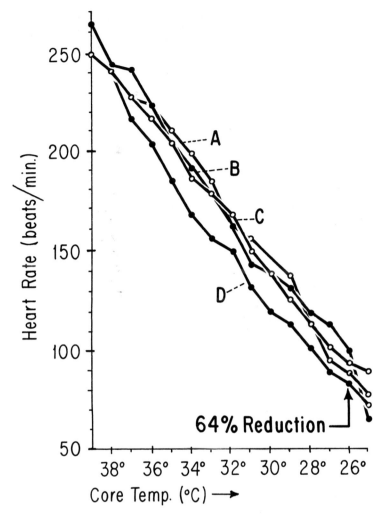

FIGURE 49. *Heart Rates of a Cat in Hypothermia.* In this experiment the cat was reduced nearly to cardiac arrest four times. There was no evidence of damage or of acclimation. She later was retired as a house pet and had at least two litters of normal kittens. From Lipp *et al.*[214]

at all temperatures below a rectal of 20°C.[210]

(*b*) *Pulmonary respirations.* Authors do not agree; some say spontaneous respiration stops between 20° to 25°C, others say adequate spontaneous respiration occurs as low as 19°C.

(*c*) *Shivering.* The dog frequently shivers when its rectal temperature reaches 32°C.

(*d*) *Heartbeat.* The cardiac rhythm frequently stops at a rectal temperature of 13°C.

(*e*) *Behavior.* Central nervous and neuromuscular functions of dogs are not seriously disturbed by body temperatures as low as 28°C; dogs respond to food and to attention by the attendant as usual.

(*f*) *Recovery.* Using extra-corporeal cooling, Gollan[192] maintained dogs in cardiac arrest for 1 hour with a body temperature of 0°C; they were revived with rewarming and oxygenation of extra-corporeal blood. A longer period of de-animation (clinical death) was maintained by Negovskii *et al.* in Moscow.[221] They maintained dogs for 2 hours at 7.5° to 13°C, and recovered 10 of them using warm donor's blood. They recovered their pulmonary respiration between 18° to 27°C core temperature. For rewarming, most other workers use a bath (40° to 45°C) instead of donor's blood.

(g) *Fibrillation in the Dog.*

Laboratory 1: below 28°C rectal.

Laboratory 2: below 23°C rectal, in 40% of normal dogs under barbiturate.

Laboratory 3: if 20° to 26°C rectal for 4 hours, 33% of dogs fibrillated.[234]

Laboratory 4: below 30° to 32°C, risk of ventricular arrhythmia. If dogs in shock first, fibrillation in only 6%, due to increased venous pressure. Spurr et al. did not find a greater incidence of fibrillation in their spontaneously breathing dogs than other investigators who employed controlled respiration.

Monkeys. Simpson in 1902[229] was able to cool a monkey to a rectal temperature of 14°C and to recover the animal. The heat regulating mechanisms are completely suppressed at a core temperature between 23° to 25°C (Herring, 1905[201]). Andjus cooled monkeys first by closed-vessel narcosis, followed by a crushed-ice bath until the rectal temperature was +5°C. There was 1 hour of respiratory arrest. The animals were revived by diathermy and artificial respiration. Lewis[177] used a different technique, artificial respiration throughout (10 to 12 cycles/min), with 5% CO_2 and oxygen, until cardiac arrest occurred. Pentothal was administered in large doses; cooling was by refrigerated blanket. Cooling took 1 hour and 40 minutes, cardiac arrest was at 14°C rectal. Final rectal was 4° to 5°C. The animals were in cardiac and respiratory arrest as long as 56 minutes. Rewarming was done by hot water on the chest; 4 of 5 monkeys survived.

Man. The cooling of human patients was used by Smith and Fay (1940[232]) for cases of advanced malignancy. Forty-two patients were carried to a minimum temperature of 25°C for as long as 150 consecutive hours; pathology due to cold or neurological defects was not observed. The detailed effects of low core temperatures have recently been reviewed by Beckman.[163]

The Procedure of Swan with Human Subjects[236]

Patients are prepared with a group of four drugs including scopolamine and curare. The anesthetic is usually ether. The patient is first placed in tepid water, then ice cubes are added. Artificial hyperventilation is carried out. The patient is removed from the tub when the rectal temperature has reached two-thirds the desired fall (Fig. 50). To cool a child requires 10 to 15 minutes in the bath, while an obese adult may require 1 hour and 15 minutes. When the rectal temperature is in the high 20's, about 50% of the patients show auricular fibrillation. Swan does not consider this serious, and most patients go back to sinus rhythm at that same temperature when rewarming. Swan believes it desirable to keep the patient in a state of respiratory alkalosis with a pH of 7.5 or greater; other workers such as Lewis strive to prevent respiratory alkalosis.[177] For a heart occlusion procedure the lungs of the patient are allowed to collapse and there is no respiration. After the operation the lungs are ventilated with oxygen. Diathermy is used to warm the patient, and he may be further warmed in water at 45°C. Apparently, heart action returns at 20°C, and patients usually revive at 34°C body temperature. An illustration from Swan (Fig. 51) shows four groups of hypothermia temperatures used in 84 operations. The two colder groups of temperatures include 28° to 26°C, and 26° to 20°C. Swan concluded that the safe parameter for an open heart procedure is: hypothermia not deeper than 26°C and occlusion of the heart not to exceed 8 minutes. The three causes of death have been ventricular fibrillation, postoperative hemorrhage, and delayed thrombus or emboli phenomena.

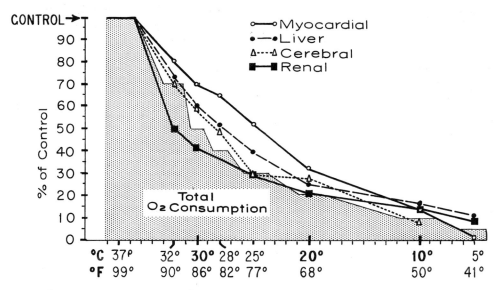

FIGURE 50. *Partitioning of Hypothermic Effects on Metabolism.* The effects of hypothermia on human oxygen consumption are presented. Note that as temperature has decreased half-way to cardiac arrest (28°C), renal metabolism is only 35% of control while cardiac metabolism is still 65% of control. From Blair.[165]

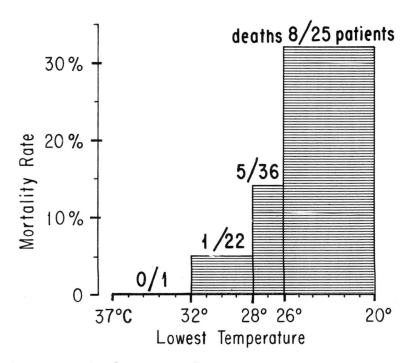

FIGURE 51. *Human Mortality in Hypothermia.* Results obtained by Swan to determine safety factor for hypothermia during surgical operations. From this series it would appear that body temperatures down to 28°C would be reasonably safe. From Swan.[235]

Cooling Index

To combine in one expression the depth of hypothermia as well as the duration of exposure, Popovic [222] has devised a Cooling Index. This is calculated as:

Cooling Index = — [Max. Survival Time (in hours) × Temperature (in °C)].

Example:

SPECIES	COOLED TO:	INDEX
New-born ground squirrels	−3°C (for 11 hrs)	+33
New-born ground squirrels*	−8°C (for 5 hrs)	+40
Rats	5°C (for 1 hr)	−5
Dogs	5°C (for 1 hr)	−5

* Supercooled.

Students of hypothermia have not yet explained why organisms will not tolerate this condition indefinitely. Dr. E. F. Adolph describes the directions of future research as follows:

"What physiologists of hypothermia need most is, first, a good theory, more comprehensive than the pioneer one of Arrhenius, as to how the concept of heat as a form of molecular energy applies in living systems, and second, a valid theory of what kills organisms that attain various low temperatures. For mammals, we have three prominent notions about cold death: (1) destruction of some limiting process or structure, (2) stoppage of energy transportations at low temperatures, and (3) disproportion among retarded processes. Each of these notions has guided a host of investigations; we now find available large bodies of detached information that have not yet crystallized our understanding of how hypothermia limits life." [159]

Chapter Six

RESPONSES TO

A HOT ENVIRONMENT

THE ENVIRONMENT OF HEAT

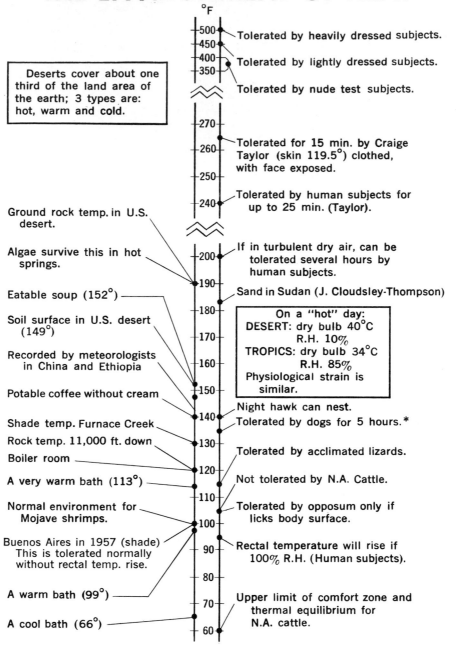

°F

Tolerated by heavily dressed subjects. — 500

Tolerated by lightly dressed subjects. — 450, 400, 350

Tolerated by nude test subjects.

Deserts cover about one third of the land area of the earth; 3 types are: hot, warm and cold.

270

Tolerated for 15 min. by Craige Taylor (skin 119.5°) clothed, with face exposed. — 260, 250

Tolerated by human subjects for up to 25 min. (Taylor). — 240

Ground rock temp. in U.S. desert.

Algae survive this in hot springs.

If in turbulent dry air, can be tolerated several hours by human subjects. — 200

190

Eatable soup (152°)

Sand in Sudan (J. Cloudsley-Thompson) — 180

Soil surface in U.S. desert (149°) — 170

On a "hot" day:
DESERT: dry bulb 40°C
R.H. 10%
TROPICS: dry bulb 34°C
R.H. 85%
Physiological strain is similar.

Recorded by meteorologists in China and Ethiopia — 160

Potable coffee without cream — 150

Night hawk can nest.

Shade temp. Furnace Creek — 140
Tolerated by dogs for 5 hours. *

Rock temp. 11,000 ft. down — 130

Boiler room

Tolerated by acclimated lizards.

120

A very warm bath (113°)

Not tolerated by N.A. Cattle. — 110

Normal environment for Mojave shrimps.

Tolerated by opposum only if licks body surface. — 100

Buenos Aires in 1957 (shade) This is tolerated normally without rectal temp. rise. — 90

Rectal temperature will rise if 100% R.H. (Human subjects).

80

A warm bath (99°) — 70

Upper limit of comfort zone and thermal equilibrium for N.A. cattle.

A cool bath (66°) — 60

* According to Yeates, the rabbit, cat, and calf have better tolerance.

138

UNUSUALLY HIGH BODY TEMPERATURES

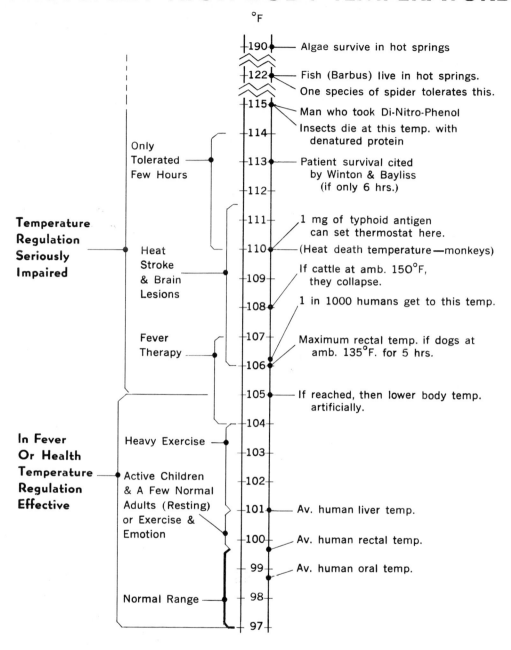

°F

- 190 — Algae survive in hot springs
- 122 — Fish (Barbus) live in hot springs.
  One species of spider tolerates this.
- 115 — Man who took Di-Nitro-Phenol
- 114 — Insects die at this temp. with denatured protein
- 113 — Patient survival cited by Winton & Bayliss (if only 6 hrs.)
- 112
- 111 — 1 mg of typhoid antigen can set thermostat here.
- 110 — (Heat death temperature—monkeys)
- 109 — If cattle at amb. 150°F, they collapse.
- 108 — 1 in 1000 humans get to this temp.
- 107 — Maximum rectal temp. if dogs at amb. 135°F. for 5 hrs.
- 106
- 105 — If reached, then lower body temp. artificially.
- 104
- 103
- 102
- 101 — Av. human liver temp.
- 100 — Av. human rectal temp.
- 99 — Av. human oral temp.
- 98
- 97

Only Tolerated Few Hours

Temperature Regulation Seriously Impaired

Heat Stroke & Brain Lesions

Fever Therapy

In Fever Or Health Temperature Regulation Effective

Heavy Exercise

Active Children & A Few Normal Adults (Resting) or Exercise & Emotion

Normal Range

Chapter Six

Responses to
a Hot Environment

More mammals suffer from heat than from cold, partly because there are more physiological mechanisms for combatting cold than for combatting heat. Furthermore some simple non-physiological mechanisms for warming up are available to all mammals including man; these include huddling together or collecting insulation. (A man has merely to place newspapers under a light topcoat to improve his insulation.) Escape from heat is not so easy. Essentially the only physiological devices available for cooling the body are sweating, panting, and vasodilation.

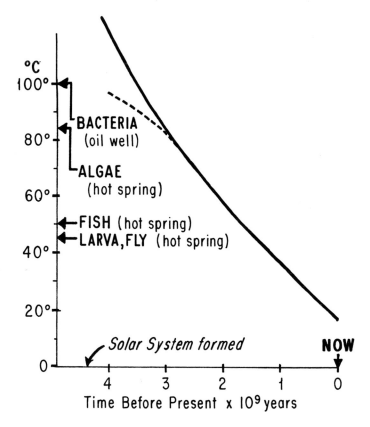

FIGURE 52. *Earth's Temperature and Origin of Life.* This compilation presents the hypothesis that at the time of the origin of life on this planet, the earth's temperature was near 70°C. The possibility that primitive ancestral protoplasm had a high temperature should be taken into consideration as we try to understand the optimal temperatures and lethal heat temperatures of mammals today. From Dicke.[262]

THE EVOLUTION OF TEMPERATURE REGULATION

Mammalian responses to heat are particularly interesting today because of the possibility that life on the planet Earth originated while this planet was hot.[262] If this hypothesis is true, then the early molecular ancestors of modern protoplasm must have had high-temperature tolerance. Dicke presents a hypothetical graph of the Earth's surface temperature starting at approximately 100°C, the calculated temperature for the time when one-fifth of the present lifetime of the now-existing solar system had been expended. (Fig. 52). The graph then extends to 17°C which is the calculated mean surface temperature of the earth at the present time. Reasoning from the oldest extensive fossil evidence of life provided by the ancient algal reefs, Dicke then states: "Apparently algae could have lived 3 x 10⁹ years ago without violation of any conditions imposed by temperature requirements." He points out that algae survive at 85°C and fish live in hot springs at 50°C (122°F).

Somewhere along the scale of decreasing temperature the mammals evolved from primitive reptiles. It is appropriate to ask: what changes are necessary to convert the temperature regulation of a reptile to that of a mammal? The changes in bony structure from reptile to mammal represent a very neat picture of proof of the rate of evolution to the higher vertebrates; these changes have been described by Broom in his lifetime study of the mammal-like reptiles of the Karoo beds of South Africa.

We now ask: what physiological changes accompanied bony changes? With large reptiles such as dinosaurs their mass alone must have contributed to their temperature regulation: in large poikilotherms of today, such as alligators and pythons, changes in body temperature may lag several hours behind air temperature. The temperature regulation of many types of reptiles is thoroughly reviewed by Prosser and Brown.[152] They point out that in the reptiles, loss of water by vaporization contributes little to temperature regulation (a large contribution in amphibia) since the horny scales of some reptiles are not permeable to water.[252a] The most important temperature adaptations of reptiles are behavioral. Snakes and lizards absorb much radiant heat; lizards in the sun at air temperatures of 13°C have cloacal temperatures of 38°C, and a lizard at —5°C in the sun attains a body temperature of 26°C. One species of desert lizard seeks protection when the air is 40°C; another species seeks shade when its body temperature approaches 43°C.[328] This second lizard can tolerate a body temperature of 48°C, but other species (*Eumeces*) can only tolerate 40°C. Thus some reptiles tolerate a broad range of body temperature; they must pay a physiological price for this, since survival at the upper limit of body temperature (about 45°C) is handicapped by the decreased affinity of hemoglobin for oxygen. For example, at 50°C the blood of one lizard (*Sauromalus*) cannot become more than 50% saturated with oxygen at atmospheric pressure.[265]

It is pertinent that some reptiles which tolerate a broad range of body temperatures have also developed a remarkable temperature sense. The pit vipers have facial temperature-sense pits and some boas have labial pits containing temperature receptors. Temperature changes are sensed by these pits, and even shadows passing over the pit are readily detected. From the modulation of the steady discharge of nerve impulses it is calculated that as small a change as 0.003°C in the pit membrane can be detected. This means that various objects can be distinguished by their radiation when their surface temperatures differ by only 0.1°C. A 0.4°C temperature rise increases the frequency of nerve impulses from 18 per second to 68 per second.[257]

In summary we find that reptiles do not make particular use of evaporative cooling (although some lizards do pant); they tolerate a broad range of body temperature, and their temperature regulation is mostly by behavior. The regulatory response to heat by mammals, on the contrary, is very frequently evaporative cooling from the skin with a considerable emphasis upon vasodilation. Above all, a constant body temperature is maintained. One may include the temperature mechanisms of the mammal under the term "dermal temperature regulation". Prosser [152] describes the transformation as follows: "A hypothesis for the origin of warm-bloodedness (endothermy) is that the skin is respiratory in amphibia, is heat absorbing in many land reptiles (ectothermy), and becomes heat-dissipating in birds and mammals. Vasomotor control may have been a preadaptation which reversed its function on the transition from ectothermy to endothermy." During this transformation process it is apparent that some of the African mammal-like reptiles must have had a very different temperature regulation from the other reptiles about them.

THE ENVIRONMENT OF HEAT

We will first consider some extreme hot environments; they are found nearer to centers of civilization than is usual for extreme cold climates. Man and his associated mammals may be exposed as follows: a temperature of 127°F was recorded in Queensland, Australia; a temperature of 136°F was recorded in Libya; a temperature of 134°F was recorded in Death Valley, California (1913). These high temperatures are most apt to be in those areas where water is not available for osmotic regulation and for evaporative cooling. For example, in the United States one locality in California had no rain for 767 days, a locality in Chile had no rain for 14 years, and a locality in the Sudan had no rain for 19 years. If we ask whether men actually experience these conditions, we realize that since they are all officially accepted U.S. Army statistics some individuals tolerated the climates to record them. Populations in large cities must sometimes endure extreme dry bulb temperatures along with a shortage of water. In 1958 and in 1965 there were record hot spells in New Delhi,

India. In one part of the city the temperature was 121°F and in Delhi itself, even at night, the temperature was frequently 100°F; the Associated Press reported that 144 deaths were attributed to this hot spell. In a neighboring state there was an exceptionally bad drought added to the heat; 90% of the wells dried up.

Some individuals choose to earn their living in a very hot environment. The chamber of mines of the Transvaal Free State in Africa reports that the mines owned by the state employ nearly 400,000 tribesmen who work for periods averaging about 1 year. Some of the mines in which these men work are more than 2 miles below the surface. A new mine on the Witwatersrand has gone 13,000 feet down. Of course the natural rock temperature increases steadily with depth. In one mine before ventilation was introduced the natural rock temperature was 105°F at 10,000 feet and was usually 120°F at 11,000 feet. Over the years improved cooling and ventilation systems have alleviated this severe environment to a large extent; nevertheless heat stroke is a daily, human problem in these mines.[302]

A final reason for exposure to heat, and one of choice, is in the realm of sports. Although racing cyclists and runners frequently experience heat stroke, it appears to be most common in American football players. Out of 29 football players who died on the playing field during 1959, four were victims of heat stroke.[264] Presumably these individuals undergo a handicap because of the protective clothing. One should also mention construction men working in deserts and tropical areas, and stokers or train engineers in many parts of Africa or Australia. Further information may be found in the two UNESCO volumes: *Climatology*,[326] and *Environmental Physiology in Arid Conditions*.[327]

Classification of Hot Climates

Hot climates can conveniently be referred to as hot-dry or warm-humid. The hot-dry climates are usually desert regions which are widespread over the globe and exist over large areas in Southwest United States. The warm-humid climates are typically represented by the tropical rain forest areas lying within latitudes of 10° or 20° from the equator.

The characteristics of the hot-dry climate are:

1. High air temperature during the day
2. Low humidity
3. Intense solar radiation
4. Wide day-night variation in temperature
5. Scanty precipitation
6. Vegetation scrubby or non-existant
7. Terrain reflects up to 30% of the incident sunlight
8. The ground absorbs solar energy and heat to temperatures as high as 190°F.
9. The ground radiates long-wave heat to cooler bodies in the environment such as man.
10. Ambient air is at a temperature higher than the skin and clothing.
11. The hot ambient air heats the body by convection instead of cooling it.

The characteristics of the warm-humid climate are:

1. Air temperatures not excessive with an upper limit of 90° to 95°F.
2. The average relative humidity is 75% or higher.
3. High moisture content of atmosphere reduces its transparency to solar radiation thereby reducing solar heat load on man. Direct solar heat is less a problem than in the desert.
4. There is little day-night or seasonal variation in temperature and dew point.
5. Precipitation is high, usually varying with season. Vegetation is abundant, providing ample shade and a favorable radiant environment.

Now comparing the two areas in more detail we find that the input of solar energy is high in both areas but in tropical regions solar energy is converted into water vapor and thus exists in the atmosphere as insensible heat. In the desert, where moisture is lacking, the solar energy directly or indirectly heats surfaces as well as ambient air and thus exists as sensible heat. Physiologically speaking, in both areas man experiences heat stress: on being exposed to the insensible heat of the tropics, his problem is how to promote more efficient evaporation of sweat, whereas, on being exposed to the sensible heat of the desert, his sweat evaporation is no problem. His difficulty there is to maintain sweat production at a sufficiently high rate to meet the requirements of body cooling.

Vocabulary of Heat Stress

In discussing extremely hot climates it is sometimes convenient to use an index which combines several factors. One approach utilizes a physical index which includes the factors which contribute to heat stress: dry bulb effects, wet bulb effects, wind velocity, and radiant thermal sources. The metabolic heat production is not included. There are two scales, one for men bare to the waist and the other for men fully clad in light clothing.* Because the body reacts differently at different temperature ranges Yaglou[331] qualified any index which he used in terms of three physical ranges or classes. The first includes temperatures less than 50°F (an important contributing factor here is wind chill). Another consists of the range from 50° to 80°F. The final classification includes environments of 80°F and higher; this temperature is near the threshold (86°F) for sweating in man and begins the zone of an extreme environment. The initial intention of the effective temperature index or scale was to assess the thermal comfort of any combination of climatic con-

---

* Yaglou also used two expressions to describe the physical factors influencing the human body: equivalent temperature and operative temperature. The equivalent temperatures which he used for the different environmental combinations do not concern us in this chapter, because they do not represent an extreme environment[296].

ditions. A simplified modification of the scale is the wet-bulb globe-temperature index. This is extremely simple to use and adequately describes the combinations of stressful environments which are considered uncomfortable. The formula is given by A. R. Lind in *Medical Climatology*.[296]

Other workers have turned to physiological indexes to indicate the extent of heat stress, rather than attempting to describe the physical environment. Belding and Hatch[251] have provided tables and nomograms which indicate the extent of heat stress. Their Belding-Hatch Index of heat stress utilizes the principle of partitional calorimetry. It comprises a series of five charts to assess the heat exchanges from four factors such as radiation in the thermal balance equation. The authors use sweat production to provide an additional assessment of the stress. A final evaluation is presented on a numerical scale. For a more detailed discussion see Henschel and McPhilimy.[279]

Robinson[296] has slightly altered the older vocabulary by estimating the degree of departure from normal physiological values; he refers to this as heat strain. Yaglou[332] describes a method for measuring solar heat load, otherwise referred to as radiation heat gain. He includes this portion of the environmental influence in his version of a heat strain index.

A graduate student who wishes to use a *stress* or *strain* index should study all five indices and then make his decision as to which is best suited to his experimental circumstances.

HUMAN PHYSIOLOGY IN THE HEAT

The conspicuous mechanisms concerned with heat loss in man are related to his ability to vasodilate the vessels in the skin, to store heat in the body, to take advantage of size, and to sweat. The latter is such an important and complicated physiological mechanism that it will be given special attention later in the chapter.

The mechanism of vasodilation is not considered an important factor in heat dissipation since it probably becomes maximum at an early stage in heat exposure. A nude man is apt to begin sweating at 30° or 31°C ambient temperature, although this threshold varies for different body regions. At ambient temperatures lower than this the skin will be vasodilated and heat brought to the skin from the core will be lost, through radiation, to cooler surfaces in the surroundings. The conspicuous evidence of vasodilation is the red face of the person who is undergoing heat strain. When blood flow of the skin increases due to dilating of cutaneous vessels, the thermal conductance of the peripheral tissues may increase 5- to 6-fold. This increases the heat loss.

Mechanisms of Heat Loss

Heat Storage. The mechanism of storing body heat is illustrated in the extreme circumstances of men being exposed to heat and dehydration at the same time; their body temperatures begin to rise. Some environmental physiologists say about such experimental subjects that they are behaving like Schmidt-Nielsen's camels. The significance of this expression will be clear when the comparative physiology of responses to heat are discussed in a later section; it is sufficient to say for the moment, that at least in the case of men and camels under some circumstances, the body temperature rises in heat exposure. In experiments with men on the desert, a group from the University of Rochester, in New York, found that the rectal temperature of man increased in a linear fashion with progressing water deficit, reaching a 2°C increase at 10% water deficit (Fig. 53). Although some investigators consider that this increase in body temperature with progressing dehydration is a failure in heat dissipation, Schmidt-Nielsen[154] takes another point of view: he suggests that a rise in body temperature reduces the heat load in a hot environment because the differ-

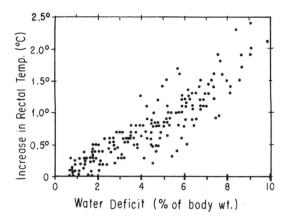

FIGURE 53. *Effect of Dehydration on the Rectal Temperature of Man.* When resting men are exposed to desert conditions, rectal temperatures increase linearly with progressing water deficit, reaching 2°C increase at 10% water deficit. This is probably associated with increased viscosity of the blood and the inefficiency of the heart during heat exposure. There is also an advantage to man of this situation since the heat flow from the environment to his skin is reduced. These high body temperatures should not necessarily be considered a failure in temperature regulation.[154] From Adolph *et al.*[245]

ence in temperature between the environment and the cooler body is diminished. The heat flow from the environment is roughly proportional to the temperature difference and goes down as the difference gets smaller. He points out that this rise in body temperature has both advantages and disadvantages but it is probably better to avoid classifying it as a failure of heat regulation.

Body Size. We must now consider the advantage of large body size under very hot conditions. If a small object and a large object made of the same material are exposed where the sun is beating down on a hot surface, after a time the small object will be burning hot while the larger object will still be partially cool. We say that the large object has a greater "thermal inertia".[154] This advantage which any large mammal (or man) has over a small mammal in the heat is expressed in the rule that any object has a surface area

which, relative to its weight, increases if its linear dimension decreases.[154] An illustration of the surface area relationship is as follows: inanimate objects gain heat from the environment in proportion to their surface, but the heat load on an animal in the desert has two components, heat gain from the environment plus metabolic heat. The first component includes conduction from the over-warmed air as well as radiation from the sun and the sub-stratum; since both types of heat exchange are surface processes, the environmental heat load will be directly proportional to the surface. It also happens that the second component, the metabolic heat production in the mammal, is also nearly proportional to the surface.[154] Therefore, the total heat load on the animal, metabolic and environmental, will also be approximately proportional to the surface. A small mammal and a small man with their larger relative surface are in a much less favorable position for maintaining a tolerable low body temperature.

Heat Balance. It is well now to consider the overall heat balance under conditions of excessive dry-heat. In temperate climates about 50% of heat produced by the body is lost through radiation to cooler surfaces, about 25% is lost by convection to the cool air, and about 25% by evaporation from the skin by insensible perspiration (see Chapter 4). When subjects work in the heat, the heat output rises from the resting level in an exponential manner, and levels off as the rate of heat loss finally balances the rate of heat production (Fig. 54). Essentially all of the extra heat is "evaporative". In fact, heat loss by radiation and convection is often less during work than during rest because the evaporation of sweat produced in the work tends to cool the skin, reducing the temperature gradient between skin and wall temperatures. Thus evaporation of sweat must dissipate all the heat produced by work and a little more in addition. This same heat loss by radiation and convection becomes progressively less as ambient temperatures rise; it reaches zero at 95°F when air, wall, and skin are at the same temperature. Under these conditions, of

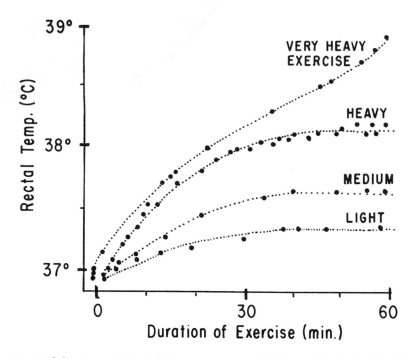

FIGURE 54. *Stabilization of Rectal Temperature at Different Work Loads.* The data illustrate an accurately regulated increase in body temperature at different work loads. The increase is always the same for a given work intensity irrespective of the conditions for heat dissipation. If work is done under very cold conditions the body temperature is still regulated to the particular level of work. Note that in this experiment no plateau was reached at the highest work level. From Nielsen.[306]

course, all heat produced in the body is lost by evaporation. At still higher temperatures, the body gains heat by radiation and convection. The environmental component is thus added to the metabolic component to give the total heat load. Evaporation is the only channel remaining for heat dissipation.

Thus far, we have considered only the circumstances of dry-heat. If we introduce high humidity into the challenge of the environment, one can predict that when an air temperature of 88°F or above is reached, an increase in humidity will result in a greater extent of sweating over the body surface to provide enough evaporation to maintain heat balance. In other words, to maintain the same rate of evaporation in tropical heat, it is necessary that a greater proportion of the body surface be covered with sweat than it is in drier climates.

Sweating. It is fortunate that mammals have a relatively high body temperature. As pointed out by Lyman, if a mammal's body temperature were set at 85°F, it would be physically impossible for it to produce enough water to cool itself by evaporative water loss at an air temperature of 100°F.[297] We must now consider what evaporative cooling *can* be accomplished by man, assisted by his high body temperature.

The subject of perspiration was introduced in an earlier chapter with a description of insensible water-loss, nonthermal sweat, and thermal sweat. The contribution of the first two types are rather subtle when extreme heat is concerned; no attention will be given to them here. The production of thermal sweat, however, is a conspicuous and costly physiological event which might be predicted to be a factor to upset homeostasis (homeokinesis) completely. Consider for a moment the quantities of water concerned. On a hot day in the desert most men can produce 12 liters of sweat at a rate of 1 liter per hour. It is true that Ladell[291] observed some men who apparently could produce only 0.5 liters per hour, while maximum capacities are given by several authors as 2.6 liters per hour[304] and 4.2 liters per hour.[266] These rates were not sustained of course, but Eichna did observe men in good condition after sweating at rates of 3 liters per hour for 4 hours. This mechanism is obviously a different type of process than those which are involved with warming the mammalian body in the cold. Shivering is primarily a muscular process not too much different from waving the arms or legs, or running slowly in place. The effect upon homeokinetic mechanisms will be those involved with exercise. On the other hand maximum sweating removes from the body a high percent of body water. Schmidt-Nielsen points out that the hourly rate of 4 liters is of the same magnitude as the total amount of water present in the blood. Although this water is taken from the blood as it passes through the capillaries of the sweat glands, indirectly the loss is replaced from other body compartments. Such a high loss of water cannot be sustained without replacement in the form of drinking water. Nevertheless the rate of sweating is not altered by moderate dehydration. The rate is still adjusted according to the need for heat dissipation. Furthermore, drinking in excess does not increase the rate of sweating.

What environmental stresses cause the sweat glands to be activated? In a comfortable climate an unclothed sitting man loses metabolic heat partly by evaporation and partly by convection and radiation from the skin. In air temperatures from 82° to 86°F (28° to 30°C) temperature regulation results from changes in the amounts of heat lost by convection and radiation from the skin controlled by changes in the vascularity of the skin. As the ambient temperature gets hotter, sweating is evoked in quantities nicely adjusted to the requirements of thermal regulation. The output of sweat increases 20 grams per hour for each 1°C rise in air temperature. Once sweating begins, the skin blood flow must continue to increase as the heat load rises, to transfer more heat from the core to the periphery; here it is dissipated to the environment by the evaporation of sweat. Undoubtedly, the skin blood flow becomes maximal soon after it begins to increase.

(a) *Sweat glands.* These remarkable glands, that can accumulate such a copious quantity of body water in human subjects, are called eccrine glands. They lie deep in the skin and are open to the surface through twisted secretory coils. It is supposed that during secretion, cells in the walls of the glands lose glycogen, alter in content, and decrease in size. The precise route for the transfer of water and other solutes through the walls of the glands is unknown. There is a possibility that water and presumably sodium and chloride may be reabsorbed in the sweat gland duct. For the eccrine glands to have any excretory function is doubtful. That the various salts are excreted in sweat may be of some value because in their absence dehydration from loss of water (in sweat) would result in an undesirable concentration of these solutes in the body fluids.

The nerve supply to the sweat glands is sympathetic; eccrine sweat glands respond to both acetylcholine and adrenalin when injected, but it is believed that there is no adrenergic component when sweating is induced naturally by heat. The reflex control of sweating seems to be partly related to the stimulation of peripheral receptors and partly to the temperature of the hypothalamus. One accepted theory is that the reflex act of sweating is initiated by the thermal receptors in the skin, while the degree of activity so induced may be potentiated by a rise in hypothalamic temperature. Another hypothesis is that the sweating is solely affected by receptors lying deep in the skin. Benzinger states, however, that an elevation of the hypothalamic temperature is essential for increased sweating during all physical work in a warm environment.

(*b*) *Sweating into water.* A special aspect of thermal sweating concerns the environment around the skin which has its surface weakened by thousands of sweat-gland pores. The skin-environment relationship includes high humidity, even 100% RH, and the situation which exists when swimming in fresh water or in salt water (3% salt solution). When exercising in fresh water, sweating could occur but simultaneously lake water might pass into the skin and circulation; conversely when exercising in the ocean, sweating may occur but other body water might pass into the ocean water through the skin. There are many aspects to this problem which has been considered extensively by Calvery *et al.*,[258] Szczesniak *et al.*,[324] Folk and Peary,[269] Peiss and Randall,[307] and Buettner.[256] All of their reports are concerned with diffusion of liquid water through human skin. A paper by Hertig, Riedesel, and Belding entitled "Sweating in Hot Baths"[281] has clarified the many issues concerned. They found that the sweat rate of subjects in hot fresh water declined markedly after reaching a peak in the first hour of exposure. A graded response of this decline occurred as various amounts of salt were added to the water until no decline occurred in 15% sodium chloride. Their experiments suggest that the fatigue of the sweat glands reported by other workers may in reality be attributed to the soaking of the skin with sweat. The authors suggest that the mechanism of suppression is more complex than blockage of the sweat ducts by the swelling of the corneum. Rather, there is an association between the amount of decline and conditions favoring diffusion of water to deeper strata of the skin.

(*c*) *Sweat composition.* The salt concentration in sweat is of considerable importance when exposure to extreme heat is concerned. Large quantities of salt are

lost to the skin during the sweating process. The urinary output of salt may go down virtually to zero (less than 1 mEq per liter). Apparently the skin of man cannot conserve salt during the process of heavy sweating.* Thus the salt output must be replaced in the diet. This means that water alone is not sufficient to make a successful desert dweller out of man; the price of salt is high in hot countries. As Schmidt-Nielsen points out "Salt is a main article of trade and taxation, it has caused wars, and at times it has been weighed against gold".

Sodium and chloride always seem to be present in lower concentrations in sweat than in the blood plasma. Most subjects have a chloride content which corresponds to 0.2% varying to 0.3% solution (Fig. 55).

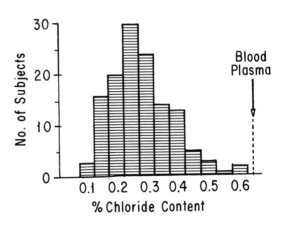

FIGURE 55. *Sweat Concentrations Under Desert Conditions.* A frequently quoted figure for sweat concentration is 0.2%. These data for concentrations of sweat collected from British subjects in southern Iraq show that considerable variation is to be expected. Some of this variation is due to the degree of acclimatization to the heat. From Ladell *et al.*[293]

---

* Some mammals conserve chloride more efficiently than does man; the sweat of the desert-donkey contains much less chloride than man's.

A few individuals will have a percent of 0.1 or 0.6; in other terms sodium and chloride in sweat range from about 5 to over 100 mEq per liter. There is a tendency for the salt concentration in sweat to decrease with man's acclimatization to heat and, according to some authors, the salt concentration tends to increase with increasing sweat rates. Robinson et al.[310, 311] provides evidence that it is a change in skin temperature rather than an increased sweat rate which brings about the increase in salt concentration. Another variable has been found in controlled experiments where the diet was analyzed as well as the salt balance; it was shown that when sweating rates and states of acclimatization are constant the skin output of salt depends on the dietary intake. In absolute figures, we find that at high sweat rates the total loss may be as extensive as 10 to 30 grams of salt per day. Ladell[292] even reports that when men worked in a room at 38°C and 80% RH, the loss was 25 grams of chloride in 162 minutes. This is a high percent of the estimated total of salt in the body; only 165 grams. During sweating the effects of salt loss are not apparent, but when water is consumed the body fluids become diluted and this may lead to heat cramps.

As a matter of historical interest, until approximately 1929 it was assumed that these cramps were due to the heating of tissue. In that year J. S. Haldane wrote a paper establishing that these cramps depend on the salt loss associated with heavy sweating.[276]

Thirst

The restoration of the water lost in sweating is under a physiological control which we refer to as thirst. The major stimulus for drinking is in the hypothalamus. Andersson[246] demonstrated that there are specific osmoreceptors in the hypothalamus which respond to a reduced osmotic concentration of the blood; when these cells were stimulated in goats, they drank large quantities and over hydrated themselves up to 40% of their body weight.

Under natural conditions drinking stops before the water has been absorbed from the stomach and could dilute the blood. Apparently the amount of water passing through the esophagus influences the animal to stop drinking. This mechanism in man is not sufficient or perfect enough to regulate the amount of water which should be consumed to replace evaporated water. By not drinking enough after heavy sweating man undergoes a voluntary dehydration which often reaches 2 to 4% of his body weight. Thirst is satisfied before water intake equals loss. This strange drinking behavior has not been explained. One handicap that man must face is his small capacity for drinking water. Schmidt-Nielsen found that while a donkey could easily drink 8 liters in 1 minute, he himself had considerable difficulty drinking 1 liter even over several minutes.

Effects of Extreme Heat

Abrupt physiological changes in man upon initial exposure to extreme heat (the first 1 or 2 days) will now be considered. Acclimatization, which takes from 4 to 10 days, will be described later. Several physiological reactions will be listed or considered in detail:

1. At first man in extreme heat shows a transitory increase in plasma volume as fluid shifts from interstitial space to the vascular bed. Several days later, more red blood cells enter the circulation and blood volume may increase from 20 to 30%. This increase does not occur at all when the daily exposure to heat is brief. When water lost by sweat is not replaced, eventually the blood volume decreases. When this happens, the plasma water contributes more than its proportional share to the water loss through the skin. In dehydrated men, a reduction in plasma volume may amount to 2½ times that expected from the total water loss. Since under conditions of dehydration there is no significant change in volume of circulating cells or plasma proteins, a consequence of the loss of plasma water is an increase in red cell concentration and in protein concentration.

This means an increase in viscosity of the blood which places an additional load on the heart.

2. The oxygen consumption increases if body temperature rises, because of the direct cellular effect of heat and also the increased ventilation.

3. There is an initial hypoglycemia.[288]

4. There is an increase in food consumption. In one study, food intake per man per day was 400 calories higher when they were exposed to heat. There was a body water gain which exceeded the total weight gain, so that the men actually lost body tissue during the heat exposure.[261]

5. There is some degree of dehydration, because man's thirst does not suffice to replenish his body water. If an inadequate supply of water is provided, then dehydration continues more rapidly. As mentioned earlier, sweating continues at the appropriate rate regardless of dehydration. If this dehydration continues, it can extend to 8 to 11% weight loss. At 2% weight loss, thirst is violent; at 4%, the mouth and throat feel dry; at 6%, the above symptoms are very severe; at 8%, salivary function has stopped and speech is difficult; at 10% weight loss, man is physically and mentally unable to take care of himself; at 11%, there is no new change in symptoms; at 12% water deficit, he is unable to swallow and can no longer recover without assistance. According to Adolph,[245] a man dehydrated to this point must be given water either intravenously, intraperitoneally, by stomach tube, or through the rectum. It is significant that formation of sweat did not stop in the subjects in Adolph's group in Rochester who voluntarily tolerated experimental dehydration to 12% weight loss. No information is available about the degree of dehydration at which sweat production fails. Schmidt-Nielsen suggests that the lethal limit in man is about 18 or 20% weight loss.[154]

6. As dehydration in man progresses the body temperature rises. The Rochester group found that the rectal temperature increases in a linear fashion with progressing water deficit, reaching 2°C increase at 10% deficit.

7. It was shown almost 200 years ago that when men are exposed to great heat there is an increased pulse rate.

8. Urine volumes are reduced in a hot climate below the amount found in a moderate climate when water intake is restricted. The urine formed contains excretory products in as high concentrations as is physiologically possible. The minimum urine volume can be further modified by changes in diet.

Attention will now be given in more detail to circulatory function during the initial few days of extreme heat exposure. The circulation of blood to the skin is responsible for the transfer of heat produced in the deeper parts of the body. This transfer depends mostly upon the high specific heat of the water of the blood; the conduction of heat from deeper parts to the surface is slow and accounts for a minor part of the total heat transfer. This transfer of heat is assisted by dilation of skin vessels when man is exposed to heat. Extreme vasodilation may create such a flow of blood to the skin in hot climates that a strain is placed on the circulatory system of man. It is important at this point in our discussion to consider the pathways and mechanisms of this vasodilation. As reviewed by Lind, dilation of the skin vessels seems to take place in succession upon the hands and the feet, the limbs, and the trunk. The mechanism bringing about vasodilation differs; the vasomotion of the skin of the hands and the feet appears to be under different control from the rest of the skin. In these locations, exposure to heat results in an increase in blood flow due entirely to the release of vasomotor tone.[296] There is no evidence to suggest that vasodilation fibers play any part in this function. The vascularity of the limbs is more complicated. We must first take into account the *venae comites;* these are networks which lie in close opposition to the arteries which serve the limbs. In cold skin, vessels constrict and venous return is directed through these networks. Much of the heat leaving the core is immediately returned to the venous system by this partial short circuit. Supposedly, in hot climates, the skin vessels dilate and the venous return is directed through the superficial veins instead of the *venae comites.* Certainly in man arterial blood is thus allowed free passage to the skin where the heat carried from the core is lost to the environment.

As a point of interest, the rabbits have very different temperature dissipation techniques and these venous networks create a difficulty for this species in the heat. Their main region of heat loss is from the ears. A report on rabbits by Yokoi describes how a rise in core temperature, artificially induced by injection of pyrogen, is partially due to increased amounts of heat recovered by the core through counter-current heat exchange in the ears.[333] The implication is that a mechanism useful in the cold proved to be disadvantageous to the rabbit in the heat.

Now continuing our discussion of vasomotor activity of man, we find that under ordinary circumstances vasodilation takes place in the arms and the legs under two separate reflex mechanisms. First there is a small increase due to release of vasoconstricted tone; this is followed by a much larger increase in the quantity of blood flowing through the limb due to active vasodilation. Probably this dual reflex mechanism with dilator fibers playing the most important part of the function is also involved in vasomotion of the skin vessels on the trunk.[296] The more a man is exposed to the heat, the more these reflex pathways call for massive vasodilation. There must be a compensatory splanchnic vasoconstriction, although there has been little study of this.

Man's heart rate increases in the heat especially as the degree of water deficit continues. The increment in pulse rate may reach 40 beats per minute above normal when 8% of the body weight has been lost. Physical work of course would add more strain to the overworked heart. The stroke volume in a dehydrated person decreases as the pulse rate goes up. The increment is balanced so that when pulse rate in-

creases about 40% then stroke volume has fallen about 40%; the cardiac output remains approximately the same. During this heat stress blood viscosity increases. A perceptive assessment of this over-worked circulatory system is made by Schmidt-Nielsen: "The blood used for transportation of heat to the skin is arterial, and is diverted from its normal function of carrying oxygen to the tissues. The tissues in general must now be supplied by a smaller part of the total blood, which already has been reduced in volume by the dehydration." [154] If a man is to tolerate extreme heat, he must have a healthy circulatory system.

Tolerance to Heat

Still giving attention to the reactions of man during the first few days of extreme heat exposure, we will now consider unusual cases of tolerance to heat. The most dramatic account known is by McGee, who described the recovery of a man lost in the Mexican Desert for 8 days with 1 day's supply of water. The man survived by drinking his own urine, breaking off spines of cactus and chewing the moisture from the ends, and drinking the blood of scorpions.[300]

The detailed study of heat tolerance is 200 years old. Dr. Sid Robinson found a study described before the Royal Society by Dr. Charles Blagden: he prepared a room at 260°F (120°C) which he entered with some friends and a dog. The dog was in a basket to keep its feet from being burned. They all tolerated the temperature without ill effects for ¾ hour. With humor rare in scientific reporting, Blagden described how a steak he took in with him was thoroughly cooked by the heat.[253]

Recently there have been experimental studies on men exposed in very hot chambers because of the current interest in learning the tolerance of men in friction-heated cockpits. Early experiments were done by Craig Taylor on himself in a room at 260°F for about 15 minutes.[325] More recently 7 men have tolerated 400°F in a hot room for periods extending up to 20 minutes.[305] The mean skin temperature rose to 43°C and rectal temperature increased 0.9°C. In Blockley's environmental-chamber experiment[255] 8 subjects tolerated 160°F for 60 minutes, 200°F for 40 minutes and 235°F for approximately 20 minutes. Their clothing consisted of a standard one-piece underwear garment and the equivalent on the hands and feet. The capability for a complex psychomotor task was tested; the duration of unimpaired performance was found to be approximately 75% of the total tolerance time. Totally different experiments were done by Strydom et al.[323] on groups of gold miners under natural conditions shoveling rock in high heat and humidity. Some groups of men (acclimatized and hyper-acclimatized) worked at a wet-bulb temperature of 96°F with a dry-bulb approximately 4°F above this. Ventilation was provided with a velocity of 100 feet/minute. At the end of 1 hour both groups of men had oral temperatures of about 102°F. These temperatures did not continue to rise in most cases. Since the risk of heat stroke was high, many subjects were withdrawn from the test after 1 hour.

Considerable attention has been given to the criteria for determination of reasonable tolerance time for exposure to heat.[252, 299] Ellis et al.[268] lists the following criteria of incapacitation which were used to make the decision to terminate the exposure of their subjects in the heat:

1. A pulse rate of over 160 beats per minute after work.

2. A pulse rate of 140 beats per minute before work.

3. A rectal temperature of 39.2°C or higher.

4. A rise in pulse rate during rest period.

5. Definite signs of physical inability to cope with the task.

6. Evident cyanosis or circumoral pallor.

7. Complaints of unpleasant symptoms such as faintness or cramp.

As their program of heat-exposure studies developed, these workers carried some experiments very close to the criteria of incapacitation as listed. In one experiment the subjects, seated and in shorts, were exposed to dry-bulb temperatures of 37.4°C, and wet-bulb 37.2°C; in a second experiment a dry-bulb of 54.5°C, wet-bulb 40.6°C. For 9 subjects the average tolerance time for the mild exposure was 144 minutes and for the extreme exposure, 37 minutes. In both cases none of the men actually lost consciousness. Most of them remained in the chamber until they were on the verge of collapse and had to be helped to leave. None were fit to do any responsible work for the rest of the day. The symptoms were sudden in onset, and the men usually felt quite well until 5 to 10 minutes before they reached the limit of their endurance. Two men on the verge of losing consciousness were unwilling to leave the chamber and protested that they were all right in a manner suggesting the reactions which may be encountered when men are suffering from the lack of oxygen. Many of the subjects had difficulty in thinking clearly and quickly and answering questions. Only one man experienced severe muscle cramps.

Acclimation and Acclimatization of Men to Heat

It is now important to consider the changes which take place when men are exposed each day for a week or more to extreme heat. Acclimation (in environmental chambers) or acclimatization (in the outdoor environment) will actually take place even if the daily exposure to extreme heat is rather short. The attributes of heat acclimation and acclimatization will now be described. There are specific changes in skin physiology which include:

1. increased peripheral conductance

2. increased sweating capacity

3. a fall in threshold of skin temperature for the onset of sweating

4. a better distribution of sweat over the skin

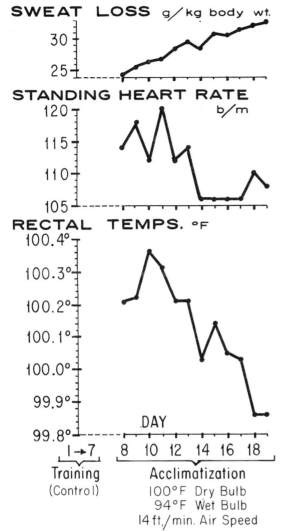

SWEAT LOSS g/kg body wt.

STANDING HEART RATE b/m

RECTAL TEMPS. °F

DAY

1→7   8 10 12 14 16 18

Training
(Control)

Acclimatization
100°F Dry Bulb
94°F Wet Bulb
14 ft./min. Air Speed

FIGURE 56. *Development of Heat Acclimatization in Man.* In this experiment 12 men ages 19 to 33 years were trained to good physical condition in the outdoor environment. They then alternated rest and work in a 100°F chamber for 3 hours per day for 19 days. During acclimatization heart rate changed most rapidly, then sweat rate and finally rectal temperature. Data graphed from Ellis *et al.*[268]

The increase in sweating is a more conspicuous feature in wet-heat than in dry. This increase typically amounts to 15% in a hot dry climate. In cooler but more humid climates the increase may be from 60 to 100% over the original values. Associated with this increase in sweating is a fall in concentration of salt in the sweat. In most circumstances, without this drop in salt concentration the body would suffer a salt deficit in the first few days of heat acclimatization. It has recently been shown that the salt content of drug-induced eccrine sweat is reduced by the administration of aldosterone in the absence of heat exposure. Therefore, the increased quantity of the circulating hormone which is known to occur during heat exposure is sufficient by itself to be responsible for the reduction in the salt content of sweat.[296]

The fall in threshold skin temperature means that an equivalent rate of sweating is achieved at a lower skin temperature after acclimation (Colin and Houdas [260]). The better distribution of sweat (more complete and even) over the skin is an important advantage in wet-heat.

In succeeding exposures to extreme heat, which results in acclimation or acclimatization, rectal temperatures and pulse rates progressively fall (Fig. 56). A final characteristic of this improvement in the physiological response to heat is subjective: as acclimatization proceeds, the disagreeable sensations associated with heat exposure are progressively reduced until men are able to work without discomfort (Fig 57). (Some authorities are apt to refer to the latter situation as habituation.)

Desert Bushmen are partially heat acclimatized. Under heat stress they have pulse rates which are lower than any other ethnic group.[330]

The rate of development of acclimatization is still debated in several environmental laboratories. It is clear that the bulk of changes appear in the first 4 to 6 days of exposure and then are almost complete in 10 to 14 days.

It is a matter of considerable interest as to how many minutes of daily exposure are needed to bring about acclimatization. According to A. R. Lind,[296] the most economical daily exposure is 100 minutes in a single continuous exposure; two such exposures daily did not improve the rate of development of acclimatization. Heat acclimatization is related directly to the conditions of exposure. If acclimatization has been accomplished for a particular energy expenditure in a given environment, a man will not be physiologically adapted for a higher energy expenditure even in the same environment, nor will he be prepared for a more severe environment. Further acclimatization takes place if a man is exposed daily to a higher heat stress. For additional relevant basic information see Yoshimura et al.[334]

Acclimation of Women to Heat

The point has been frequently expounded that human physiology is more accurately described as the physiology of men. It is unusual to find that a careful and definitive study has been done on the acclimatization of female subjects during work in hot environments.[282] Nine subjects were studied; and typically the heat stress consisted of 10 hot-room exposures at 45°C dry-bulb, 25.5°C wet-bulb, and one hot-room exposure at 50°C dry-bulb, and 26.5°C wet-bulb. Air speed was about 100 meters per minute and exercise consisted of level treadmill walking at 4.8 kilometers per hour for 2 hours. The study demonstrated that women like men can be artificially acclimated to heat and they manifested the same physiological adjustments: reduced pulse rate, reduction in core temperature, rise in skin temperature, onset of sweating at a lower skin temperature, lessened discomfort, and increased sweat rate. The females studied reached limits of endurance in the hot environment selected. This environment was easily tolerated by males. The authors suggest that two factors appear to be operating to put the female at a disadvantage in the heat: (A) lower thermal gradient for removal of metabolic heat; (B) less reserve capacity to move blood to the skin.

In another study, Wyndham et al.[329] compared heat acclimatization of human males and females under identical conditions at 33.8°C wet-bulb: the heart rates of both groups dropped from 180 b/m to 140

b/m, rectal temperatures from 40°C to 38.8°C. The women did less sweating.

Heat Exhaustion

This topic is of the utmost importance to people associated with the healing arts. The introduction to this chapter describes some of the climatic circumstances which are imposed upon large populations either each year, or in some areas during unusually severe and abnormal circumstances. The following statistics are in the records of the U. S. Government. Minard[301] has pointed out that severe heat stress is imposed on trainees by a combination of hot weather and strenuous military exercise; this is a problem in peace time as well as during rapid mobilization for war. Nearly 200 deaths from heat stroke occurred in recruits at training centers within the United States during World War II. At a military establishment at Parris Island, South Carolina, 5 recruits died of heat stroke in the 4-year period from 1950 to 1954. During the summer of 1952, heat casualties at Parris Island occurred at an average of over 50 per 10,000 per week. The actual number of cases admitted to the sick list does not adequately reveal the extent of heat distress, because for every admission there are approximately 10 cases of mild heat exhaustion treated in field dispensaries. The casualties, of course, are due to lack of acclimatization. Physical fitness alone does not provide protection from heat. There are many instances of highly-trained combat units which suffered many heat casualties although they were in top physical condition.

Heat exhaustion varies with the rapidity of heating and the mode of heating. For example, the body temperature tolerated by man is less with external heating than with internal heating. A man will lose consciousness when heated externally to a rectal temperature of 38.6°C, yet in fever the temperature may go to 42°C. It is of interest that during exercise the body temperature may reach 40°C without harm.[152] The first stage of heat exhaustion is referred to as *heat shock* or *hyper-*

pyrexia. This happens if thermal regulation fails and the body temperature rises critically. Another form of heat exhaustion can occur in man without a rise in body temperature and it is due to dehydration and changes in salt balance. This exhaustion may take place even with an abundant supply of water if amounts of salt have been lost. A somewhat milder form of heat exhaustion is called *heat-induced tetany.* For example Iampietro[286] demonstrated tetany in 89% of his subjects when they were exposed to 46.1°C dry-bulb, 43.9°C wet-bulb, wind speed 3 miles per hour. This damage is probably not due to changes in body temperature or calcium concentration since the symptoms disap-

peared rapidly on removal from the hot room, while body temperature and calcium concentration remained for a time at levels attained in the hot room. It is probable that changes in CO_2 tension and pH are implicated. The most severe form of damage due to the heat is *heat stroke* which results from brain damage. Actual heat death itself is due largely to cardiovascular failure. The progress of heat death is described by Adolph[245] as an "explosive heat rise". This has not been studied in man but observations on dogs show what probably happens when man is exposed to fatal conditions of heat. When dogs reached a dehydration in severe heat of 14% of the body weight, their rectal tem-

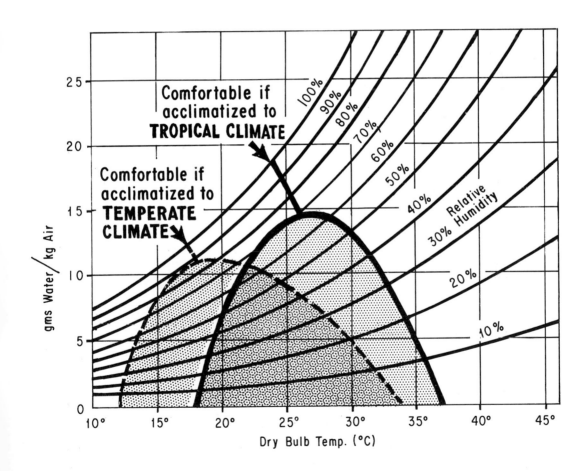

Figure 57. *Comfort at Different Humidities.* These data represent estimates for comfort of lightly clothed individuals at rest at various dry-bulb and wet-bulb temperatures. This nomogram takes acclimatization into account. From Lemaire.[295]

peratures began to rise explosively. At this stage the animal survived only if immediately removed from the hot atmosphere or if given water to drink. With water, dogs were able to survive indefinitely in air at 55°C (131°F). The explosive rectal temperature rise is caused by insufficient transport of heat to the exterior of the body. There are three contributing factors: the strain on the heart, the increased viscosity of the blood, and the reduced blood volume. The animal seems to go into circulatory shock since extreme vasodilation is present along with the decreased blood volume.

COMPARATIVE PHYSIOLOGY OF MAMMALIAN HEAT ADAPTATIONS

Mammals which live on the desert, or those which may suddenly be exposed to heat, have developed a remarkable number of adaptations for survival or for remaining comfortable. The variety and often apparent inconsistency of these adaptations is evident in the fact that some non-desert species living in temperate climates are fairly well adapted for exposure to heat and for dehydration. In the desert habitat, some of the mammals have very few adaptations and often none which are different from temperate zone mammals; living beside them are species which have very elaborate desert adaptations. For example, man has little concentrating power in his kidneys, while his ecological companion, the laboratory rat, has essentially twice the concentrating power. Two rodents living side by side on the desert illustrate the other point: the wood rat of the genus *Neotoma* must be maintained with wet food or free water, while the kangaroo rat can live entirely upon dry seeds.

The adaptations which permit tolerance to heat and the desert environment have been characterized by Kirmiz[290] as morphological, physiological, ecological and ethological (behavioral). All of these types

of adaptations must be genetic. Our interest must not be restricted to the desert since acute heat exposure may occur anywhere in the summer, even in the arctic. For example, according to Bartholomew,[249] fur seal bulls may die due to overheating when driven at an air temperature of 10°C. Much of the following discussion, however, will be devoted to the more natural circumstances of chronic heat exposure such as is experienced by desert animals.

Morphological Adaptations

Heat tolerance probably requires a trend toward a small body mass, attenuated extremities, little fat, and extensive superficial vein routing. Although we see the attenuated extremities in the camel, Eisenberg[267] reports a behavioral interpretation of the long appendages in small mammals. He points out that strong evolutionary pressure in four families of rodents have produced independent forms which have bipedal locomotion such as is found in the jerboa and the kangaroo rat. He interprets this as an adaptation to living where there is little vegetation; the bipedal method of jumping is an advantage for escaping predators such as snakes and owls. Eisenberg also notes that the desert mammals under discussion have developed a behavioral means of avoiding the accumulation of sebaceous material in their fur: this is organized sand bathing.

Physiological Adaptations

Conspicuous Features. Some superficial physiological mechanisms to combat acute heat exposure will be considered next:

1. Evaporative cooling is accomplished in man and especially in the horse group (Perissodactyla) by numerous and efficient *sweat glands*. To a greater or lesser extent most of the mammals except the rodents also have sweat glands but they are small and not very numerous and are called upon only under extreme circumstances. Seals have sweat glands on the flippers only. Apparently many of the smaller primates do not have con-

spicuous sweat glands. In our experiments which involved exposing rhesus macaque monkeys to extreme humid heat, there was no evidence of liquid moisture or droplets of moisture anywhere on the skin.[272] Hooten,[284] however, does refer to droplets of sweat appearing on the forehead and chest of the large apes. There are other exceptions; the water buffalo is presumed to be without sweat glands. For those animals which do not have sweat glands, excess saliva running out of the mouth and down the chest is an assistance, and many such mammals lick the fur. I have already described how the elephant uses its own saliva to cool its back.

2. Some mammals in particular can capitalize on their *shape* to assist in combatting heat: bats and flying rodents can extend their wings or skin-folds and greatly increase their surface area; this advantage is carried further by fanning the wings. All mammals stretch out their limbs in the heat in an attempt to increase surface area for evaporative cooling.

3. Large *size* has a certain advantage in the heat because quite a bit of heat can be stored with a relatively small rise in body temperature. The camel (and possibly even man) has made use of this characteristic. It probably explains the large range of body temperature reported for the rhinoceros (34.5° to 37.5°C).

4. A heavy *coat* of fur, wool, or hair is an anatomical and physiological factor protecting mammals exposed to radiant heat. Blair[254] demonstrated that long-haired dogs could withstand a sudden heat stress much better than dogs with short hair, and clipped dogs showed decreased resistance to heat instead of increased resistance. Schmidt-Nielsen[154] made the same observations on the camel: he found that the temperature of the fur surface on the back of a camel in the sun may be as high as 70° to 80°C, when the skin temperature underneath was close to 40°C.

The heavy coat of the camel and the dog, as well as other animals such as the sheep, protects the animal in the heat by the following physical relationships.[154] We must first consider the radiation heat gain from the sun. If we consider merely the visible solar radiation, some of this will be reflected from the coats of the animals depending upon their color. This color will decide whether the reflection is higher or lower than from the skin of man. The heat gain from the visible spectrum is independent of skin surface temperature. When the infrared energy is concerned, we find all is absorbed irrespective of coat and color. The next question concerns the radiation exchange between skin and ground; this exchange is in the far infrared and therefore independent of visible color of the hides and fur of the animals. If the fur of the animal absorbs radiation from the sun independent of surface temperature, then the surface of the fur may be nearly as hot as the ground. This means that the net radiation flux toward the skin will be greatly reduced, and therefore there will be a loss of heat by conduction from the surface of the animal to the air. In other words, whenever the temperature of the insulative surface of the animal exceeds the air temperature then part of the absorbed radiant heat will be dissipated by conduction to the air.

Conservation of Water. Some mammals tolerate long-term exposures to heat and desiccation, in many cases during the entire lifetime of the species; in these cases a parsimonious saving of water becomes of the utmost importance. Water is conserved by a reduction in the following phenomena:

1. *pulmonary water loss.* This reduction is achieved by maintaining a relatively low breathing rate in large mammals and in small mammals by entering protective areas where the vapor pressure is high. As another means of conserving water, Schmidt-Nielsen has pointed out a remarkable reduction in temperature of expired air from small desert rodents.[154] This must represent a counter-

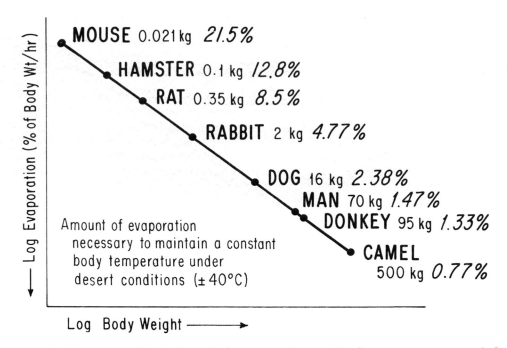

FIGURE 58. *Evaporation Needed for Tolerance to Desert Conditions.* An estimate of the theoretical relationship between body weight and the amount of water which must evaporate per hour to maintain a constant body temperature under desert conditions (40°C). From Frankel,[270] data in part from Schmidt-Nielsen.[317]

current heat exchange in the respiratory passages. For example, at a room temperature of 25°C the temperature of expired air and nasal passage walls of the rodent could be even lower than 25°C, although the body temperature was 38°C. Most heat exchangers in the various biological systems have two streams of fluid moving continuously in opposite directions; in this case the counter-current heat exchange depends upon the cooling of the nasal walls by incoming air and by evaporation. During the following expiration, heat flows from the warm air to the cool surface.

2. *cutaneous water loss.* In small mammals on the desert there is little water loss through the skin because insensible perspiration is reduced by the animal remaining in burrows with a high vapor pressure. At night they emerge on to the

desert when vapor pressure is high. Also, their skin is not interrupted by the water-permeable orifices of sweat glands. Large mammals such as the camel have water-conserving sweat glands; their threshold to sweating is an ambient of 35°C or above, while in man it is 30° to 31°C (Fig. 58).

3. *renal water loss.* There are many descriptions of the concentrating power of the kidneys of desert mammals. This water retention is probably not as important as a reduction in cutaneous water loss which is a very large factor in man. It is, however, a characteristic of the most successful of desert mammals that they can produce a very concentrated urine; in fact they can benefit from drinking true sea water (not a mere artificial 3.5% salt solution). This is in spite of the fact that the magnesi-

um salts in sea water bring about an additional loss of body water by producing diarrhea. The classic example of the ability to concentrate urine is the desert kangaroo rat studied by the Schmidt-Nielsens;[314] its maximum concentration of salt and urea in urine is compared with that of man and the white rat:

	SALT	UREA
Man	0.37 N (2.2%)	1.0 M (6%)
White Rat	0.60 N (3.5%)	2.5 M (15%)
Kangaroo Rat	1.20 N (7.0%)	3.8 M (23%)

A species of mammal that can concentrate urine to an unusual extent has a size of kidney and of glomeruli and a number of glomeruli which are typical for the *size* of the animal and not for concentration ability. The ability to concentrate urine is associated with the possession of a kidney containing only long nephrons. These nephrons are characterized by an extension of the portion of the kidney tubule, known as Henle's loop. Associated with the long loop of the tubule is a long renal papilla which extends beyond the pelvis of the kidney

and into the ureter. Superficially, the length of the loop structure of the nephron is recognizable by the relative thickness of the renal medulla. There is a correlation between the thickness of the renal medulla and the aridity of the habitat in which the mammals live.[154] Rodents, camels, and antelopes of the desert have the greatest relative development of the renal medulla, while animals with an abundant supply of water such as beavers, muskrats, and platypuses have a thin medulla and very short loops.[322] The explanation of the concentrating power of the long Henle's loop depends upon the counter-current hypothesis for the concentration of urine.[313]

The concentrating power of the kidney is often expressed as a ratio between the concentration of the urine and the plasma of the blood. For example, if the urine is twice as concentrated as the plasma of a particular animal, then the U/P ratio is 2. This figure applies to most birds in which the kidney loops are fewer and not as well developed as in mammals. Hudson [285] has collected data on the concentrating power of a number

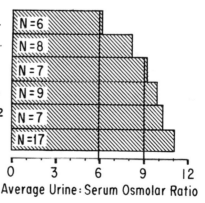

WOOD RAT ---------------------- N=6

ALBINO RAT ------------------ N=8

ROUND-TAILED GROUND SQUIRREL¹ N=7

ANTELOPE GROUND SQUIRREL --- N=9

ROUND-TAILED GROUND SQUIRREL² N=7

DESERT KANGAROO RAT -------- N=17

0   3   6   9   12
Average Urine : Serum Osmolar Ratio

¹Assuming a serum osmotic pressure of 384 milliosmols
2 "   "   "   "   ı "   " 350   "

FIGURE 59. *Maximal Urine Concentration in Rodents.* This comparison places one of the desert rodents, the woodrat, on a low position in the rank order of ability to concentrate urine. This animal must eat wet food or drink water. At the other end of the scale, the kangaroo rat shows a high concentration which probably reaches a ratio of 14. Some kidneys are more powerful than those of the kangaroo rat, especially that of the jerboa which can produce a 25% urea solution. From Hudson.[285]

of rodents which tolerate heat; the first of this series (comparing urine and serum) is represented by the wood-rat which has a ratio of 6. At the other end of this series is the kangaroo rat with a ratio of 10.3. The data for his series are presented in Figure 59.

4. *fecal water loss.* Desert mammals have reduced the water loss from the digestive tract both directly and indirectly. The percent of water in white rat feces is 68% (calculated on wet-weight), in camel feces 43%, in kangaroo rat feces 45%. In addition to the low water content of kangaroo rat feces, its food is more efficiently utilized and a smaller amount of dry matter is eliminated. The net result is that white rats use 5 times as much water for formation of feces as kangaroo rats, even when they both eat the same kind and amount of food. The explanation of the higher utilization of the feed in the kangaroo rat may be connected with its habit of eating its own feces (coprophagy). This procedure is not unusual in rodents and it is essential to normal digestion in some rats and rabbits.

5. *metabolic water.* Further conservation of water is attained by increasing metabolic or oxidation water. For an active animal there is no particular advantage in the formation of oxidation water; usually the evaporation from the lungs exceeds the water formed and the animal must drink.[154] It is true that for each gram of food metabolized 1.07 grams of water per gram of fat are formed. This metabolic water becomes more useful in dormant mammals. The intriguing idea must be considered that the bear in winter lethargy may benefit from the retention of metabolic water from metabolized fat. This may explain why these large animals do not drink during the winter. This matter will be discussed in more detail later.

Dehydration Tolerance. Conservation of water is related to tolerance of the animal to dehydration. Only recently have adequate accounts appeared in the literature on dehydration of large animals like the camel and donkey; formerly most of the attention was given to small mammals. At first one assumes that the better a mammal is adapted for survival during chronic exposure to dry heat, the more tolerant it will be to dehydration. This is indeed true for most desert species; however, a conspicuous exception is the pack-rat or woodrat (*Neotoma*) which has little tolerance to water deprivation. It survives only for about 7 days without water, while white rats under these conditions live for 2 to 3 weeks. Ordinarily tolerance to dehydration is a requirement for successful desert existance. For example, horses and camels have been compared during two expeditions of Giles[275] while crossing the desert of South Australia. On the first expedition in 1874, he found that horses required up to 50 liters of water per day beyond what was contained in their food during the summer. He started out with three horses and two camels, the camels being used to carry the water for the men on the expedition and the horses. In spite of the contribution of the water carried by the camels, all three horses died before the journey was two-thirds completed. The camels were given no water until the end of the 8-days march of 350 kilometers. Again in 1876 Giles[275] crossed the desert with 22 camels this time traveling over 480 kilometers. The camels tolerated this march without water for 17 days.

In more specific terms, we can compare the temperate zone type of mammal with the desert mammal: the cat, dog, and man tolerate a loss of water corresponding to 14 to 20% of the body weight; the desert rabbit tolerates a water loss approaching 50% of its body weight; the camel, a loss of 27% of its body weight. Details of the physiological rearrangements of the body which permit this dehydration will be described later in this chapter.

Even desert animals differ in their ability to tolerate or prevent dehydration. Some data from Shkolnik[154] are presented by Schmidt-Nielsen: this investigator kept a series of rodents from Israel on dry grain for a month at 30°C and 30% relative humidity. Some species tolerated dehydration but were endangered, others prevented dehydration. This was demonstrated by the amount of water consumed after the test:

	WATER CONSUMED (% body weight)
LEAST ADAPTED TO DESERT	
Acomys cahirinus	11.4
A. russatus	9.3
Jaculus jaculus	4.3
MOST ADAPTED TO DESERT	
Meriones crassus	none
Gerbillus pyramidum	none
G. dasyurus	none
G. gerbillus	none

One should expect that survival in extreme environments depends upon very different evolutionary solutions; a sequence of tolerance to dehydration was found by German [274] in murine rodents of the Steppe Zone. The rodents were fed only air-dried oats:

	WATER DEFICIENCY TOLERATED (days)	WEIGHT LOST (% body weight)
Microtus oeconomus	2–3	25
Microtus arvalis	3–4	35–40
Evotomys glareolus	3–4	35–40
Lagurus lagurus	10–15	50
Laboratory mouse	over 25	19

If judged by this experiment, only the laboratory mouse would be called desert-adapted.

Estivation. A reduced body temperature is a mechanism which may be useful to the animal exposed to extreme heat. This phenomenon may be described as the torpor or dormancy which occurs at relatively high ambient temperatures. Many estivators also hibernate, although there are some estivators which will not tolerate body temperatures below about 15°C. Mammals which estivate seem to have a critical air temperature which is rather high; they also have unusually low basal metabolic rates. These characteristics not only allow dormancy at moderate ambient temperatures, but are also adaptive to hot environments. Hudson and Bartholomew [2] give an account of a series of estivators; the most typical example is the roundtail ground squirrel. Another example is the jerboa, which is reported as undergoing a state of torpidity which is unlike any other rodent described.[290] Kirmiz states, "The jerboa can easily tolerate high environmental temperatures up to 45°C by entering into a state of lethargy (deep sleep)." This unusual example of estivation requires considerably more study.

Why is a reduced body temperature and its associated low basal metabolic rate an adaptation for exposure to extreme heat? The advantage to the heat-exposed mammal is that where there is a small difference between the body and air temperatures, there is a minimal amount of metabolic heat to be dissipated. For example, the roundtail ground squirrel has a relatively low level of metabolism, approximately 60% of that predicted for a species of its size (125 grams). Associated with the low metabolism, is a relatively inactive thyroid gland. The body temperatures of inactive animals which are not torpid may be as low as 32°C. This species becomes dormant during the summer so that the body temperature drops to within a degree of ambient air (22° to 25°C). This temperature drop is also an advantage in temperature regulation. As is usual with a mammal with a labile body temperature, there is a marked day-night (circadian) rhythm of metabolism and body temperature with the higher phase of the cycle prevailing during the day. The result is a lower nocturnal level of pulmonary water loss and a lower level of metabolites to be excreted so that a more dilute urine can be produced at this time. The reduction in metabolism is of the order of 30 to 40% with a 3° to 5°C drop in body temperature. Hudson [285] estimates that this slight drop in body temperature will save as much as 1.56 ml of water per day, a significant amount for a 125 gram animal. The animal does indeed occupy a territory of high temperature and limited water.

A second example is the case of the jerboa. This animal's central temperature (36.8°C) is lower than the white rat's (37.55°C). The jerboa's basal metabolic rate at the ambient of 30°C is 3.649 kcal/kg/hr, compared to a figure for the white rat of 6.156. This desert animal enjoys the same advantages possessed by the round-tail ground squirrel.

Ethological Adaptations

One of the characteristic types of adaptations is ethological (behavioral). Many of the small desert animals live in burrows during the daytime and become active when vapor pressure is higher at night and the heat sink of the cool night sky is apt to be available. We say that the digging of burrows and the nocturnal habits represent behavioral adaptations.

A second example is the behavior of the dehydrated camel exposed to radiation from the sun. This animal exposes as small an area of its body surface as possible to the incident radiation. It sits on the ground with its legs under its body, usually facing the sun with the body oriented lengthwise in the direction of the sun's rays. It remains sitting on the same spot except for changing its direction as the sun moves during the day; remaining in the same spot shields the ground from the hot sun thus reducing heat flow from the ground to the underside of the camel. Schmidt-Nielsen has called attention to an observation by Pilters-Gauthier[308] that camels often rest during the hottest part of the day huddled on the ground in small groups, each animal pressed tightly against the next. Schmidt-Nielsen concludes that the clump of camels constitutes "a giant social organism which minimizes its exposed surface to reduce heat gain."

Acclimatization To Heat

Associated with adaptations to combat extreme exposure to heat is the phenomenon of acclimatization (or acclimation in environmental chambers). The sequence of changes referred to as acclimatization to heat have been carefully studied in man. The net effect of this phenomenon is a higher capacity for activity and less discomfort from heat exposure. It is characterized by specific and measurable physiological changes day by day as exposure progresses. There seems to be every reason to assume that when desert-adapted and temperate-zone-adapted mammals (other than man) are exposed to heat that conspicuous physiological changes in temperature regulation and water balance will take place from the first day to perhaps the tenth day of exposure. There is practically no information on this topic in the literature. It is not apparent whether this is due to an absence of acclimatization among mammals or lack of study by environmental physiologists. The recent book by Schmidt-Nielsen[154] seems to lack any reference to acclimatization to heat in any mammals other than man.

There are a few scattered observations which may be evidence of acclimatization: for example, some domestic animals have a different rectal temperature in different seasons. Dowling[263] has shown that the heat tolerance of cattle at different seasons can be attributed to changes in the hair coat. Hart[2] takes the view that changes in insulation do represent acclimatization. He points out that photoperiodically induced physiological changes would tend to pre-acclimatize animals to cold in advance of seasonal changes in temperature. He gives many illustrations of what he refers to as good insulative acclimatizations through seasonal modification of the fur. What happens when the animal is gradually or suddenly exposed to heat while the thick fur developed for cold exposure is still present? The ideal time sequence apparently would be for the animal gradually to drop this insulation during the mild periods of spring and be prepared with a thin coat for the heat of summer. It should be remembered, however, that a thick coat has some advantages during heat exposure. Arctic huskies do not appear to be uncomfortable when exposed to unaccustomed heat in a warm climate (if not exercising). Also, they continue to

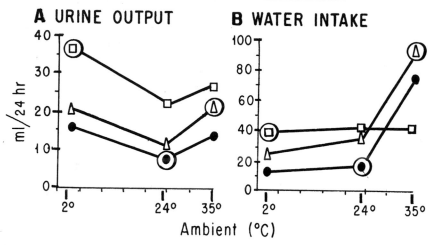

FIGURE 60. *Effects of Ambient Temperature Change.* Rats were either cold- or heat-acclimatized over periods of weeks. They were then abruptly moved to different ambient temperatures and studied for one day. Water balance was modified from control level with every change. Of particular interest is the evidence of diuresis which occurred with a change to both heat and cold. From Hale and Mefferd.[277]

grow a very heavy coat even in the summer (both in the cold and in the heat).

One possible case of acclimatization to heat which is irrespective of the change in insulation is recorded by Hart: "Sheep also undergo a seasonal variation in rectal temperature response when placed at 40.6°C and 34 mm Hg water vapor. The heat tolerance indicated by the rectal temperature was highest during the summer and followed the seasonal rhythm of temperature and wool growth. However, statistical analysis of the data showed that there was a seasonal acclimatization in heat tolerance in addition to the changes caused by differences in wool growth."[2]

An interesting description of the responses of heat acclimated and cold acclimated rats has been presented by Hale and Mefferd.[277] These authors worked with groups of animals that had lived for

months in three air temperatures, 2°, 24°, and 35°C. When a rat in one temperature was moved to another temperature, a physiological response ensued. The authors used the expression "heat acclimated rats"; these rats were very different from rats which had been maintained in the other two environments (Fig. 60). The heat acclimated rats displayed their new physiological characteristics the first day that they were exposed to heat. The time sequence of the changes in rodent heat acclimatization seem to be lacking in physiological literature. If heat acclimation is acquired in a day, it is hardly comparable to the heat acclimation observed in man over a 6- to 10-day period. The illustration of the work of Hale and Mefferd is presented here partly because of an unusual phenomenon not directly related to acclimatization; they give an account of cold and heat diuresis. A cold diuresis is an unusual situation in comparative physiology; it is common in man but uncommon in the other mammals. Of comparable interest is the heat diuresis of the room-temperature rats. This is paradoxical because of heat-exposure and the necessity for water conservation; it may be associated with the higher water consumption when the animals were heat exposed. The cold exposed rats, when placed in the heat, demonstrated heat diuresis but did not show an increased water intake. These data were obtained by abruptly changing the group of rats from one ambient temperature to another; recordings were made over a 24-hour fasting period.

More specific information is provided by Findlay[51] who states that during acclimatization to heat cattle and mice reduce their food intake (by half) and their metabolic heat production. Cattle grow more slowly in the heat at first, and then increase this rate; they also show depressed thyroid activity. Heat-reared mice have highly vascularized ears and longer tails.[278]

Much more information is needed on acclimatization to heat of mammals other than man.

Special Adaptations: Conservation of Water in Birds and Aquatic Animals

Concentrated Milk. The challenge of existence in severe heat is usually solved by judicious spending of water derived from a delicate and precarious conservation system. Part of this system is the control over the quantity of water required for the formation of milk; one possible conservation device would be to produce a very concentrated milk. Perhaps the very high fat content in the milk of aquatic mammals, such as seals and whales, is an adaptation associated with their environment of low availability of fresh water. The fat content of the milk of these aquatic mammals is 30 to 40% compared to 2 to 5% in most terrestrial mammals. When these high figures were first obtained, the same analysis was done on

camel's milk on the supposition that this might also be concentrated. The fat content of camel's milk turned out to be 4%. Schmidt-Nielsen points out that this is predictable since the young camel would be at least as much in need of water as a nursing mother. Some small desert mammals, however, keep their young in a cool burrow and the mother's water supply is almost exclusively oxidation water. It is conceivable that in such a case the nursing young not only depend to a large extent on oxidation water, but in addition is provided with concentrated milk;[154] no analyses have been done.

Salt Glands. As a matter of interest, this list of heat adaptations should include a solution to water economy found in some of the birds and reptiles. As sea water is known to be toxic to man and most mammals, there was a question for many years as to how oceanic birds obtain their supply of body water. Some workers presumed that sea birds could subsist like seals on water obtained from the food. In order to profit from the ingestion of sea water an animal must excrete salt in a concentration at least as high as that of the water ingested. The bird kidney, however, is able to excrete salts in a concentration only about one-half of that found in sea water. It was recently reported that marine birds excrete a major part of their ingested salt through salt glands (nasal glands); these are able to produce a highly concentrated salt solution. They make it possible for sea birds to tolerate the drinking of sea water. Schmidt-Nielsen has demonstrated this excretion in cormorants, pelicans, and Humboldt penguins.[318] The experiments are simple: a 10% sodium chloride solution is injected in the bird and within 1 to 5 minutes drops of a clear water-like liquid appear at the external nares. This secretion continues for 1 to 2 hours. The salt concentration in the nasal secretion is a 4% salt solution, while the salt concentration in the urine is 1.5%. More liquid is excreted by the salt gland than by the kidney; thus the amount of salt eliminated by the kidney is about 1/5th of the total amount from the two glands. A similar salt excretion has been demonstrated by the Laysan and Black-footed Albatrosses [273] and in some lizards. The salt concentration in the liquid from the nasal gland of the albatross was almost twice that in sea water.

Case Histories

In the above discussion of adaptations to combat heat and desiccation, the mechanisms and physiological devices are rather involved. At times the behavior of the whole animal in its environment becomes neglected. It thus seems reasonable to consider several "case histories" of mammalian species exposed to heat. The mammals to be discussed separately are the bat, the kangaroo rat, the rabbit, the dog, and the camel.

Bat. There are few descriptions in the literature of response to heat of those bats which hibernate; this is undoubtedly because their physiology is totally different from the usual laboratory animal; as a result they have not been studied extensively

by environmental physiologists. It has been said that the body temperature and metabolism of the resting hibernator bat varies directly with the environmental temperature.[283] If this is so, one cannot describe the body temperature of this animal in the terms used for ordinary laboratory mammals. Recently, Dr. Robert Henshaw at the University of Iowa had the courage to make an exhaustive study of some specimens of these "bundles of thermal contradictions". He compared two species, *Myotis sodalis* and *Myotis lucifugus.*[280, 199] He devised a temperature probe 1 mm in diameter for the colon of these 5 gram animals; they tolerated the probe during exposure to many combinations of dry-bulb temperatures and humidities. The animals were exposed in metabolism chambers. Although we are interested here in their responses to heat, it might be mentioned that the reputation of these thermal-labile mammals was justified; for example, he found that one of the species (*sodalis*) would tolerate a body temperature of —5°C and still have a heartbeat.

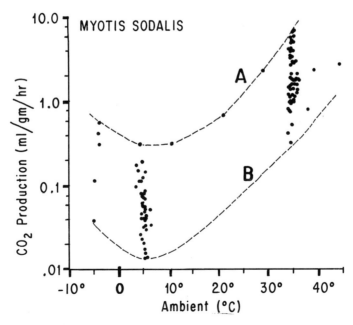

FIGURE 61. *Bat Metabolism in Changing Ambient Temperatures.* The rate of carbon dioxide production was used as an index to metabolism. Line *A* represents active animals at various temperatures. It may be that the critical temperature for this species is somewhere near 15°F. Line *B* represents hibernating specimens in cold ambient temperatures. From Henshaw.[280]

The euthermic body temperature, or thermal neutral temperature for *Myotis lucifugus* is estimated to be very close to 39°C. It was not possible to determine a similar figure for *Myotis sodalis* as it did not appear to maintain a "homeothermic" type of temperature for long enough periods of time to allow a selection of a temperature range. It is possible that this species has a critical air temperature near 15°C (Fig. 61). When exposed to air temperatures approaching 45°C it was obvious that the two species had totally different capacities to resist heat. *Myotis lucifugus* developed large negative temperature differentials between air and body (as much as —6°C); *Myotis sodalis* maintained little or no differential at air temperatures of 38° to 45°C. The poor temperature regulation in heat of *sodalis* was found in samples collected throughout most of the year including July; usually body temperatures of 41° to 42°C appeared to be stressful to the animal and frequently caused death within the respirometer. During part of the year (the months of March, April, May, and June) *sodalis* became even more sensitive to heat; body temperatures of 34° to 35°C were usually fatal. During these months when exposed to 35°C, *sodalis* became excessively active. The heart rate was above 700 beats per minute, and this was reached without comparable increases in metabolic rate. When exposed at this season to air of 25°C, the heart rates were those which were expected at 35°C at other times of the year. At this season *sodalis* had usually died by the time a body temperature of 38° to 39°C was reached.[280]

The picture of heat tolerance by *Myotis lucifugus* is totally different; this species tolerated body temperatures of 42°C at all times of the year with little apparent distress. A sample from a summer colony in an attic with an average air temperature during 1 week in July of 54°C* showed the greatest capability of withstanding high temperature. One juvenile, 1 to 2 months old, exposed to a chamber temperature of 51°C, was recorded with a body temperature of 48°C for more than 15 minutes. There was no evidence of unusual excitement in its behavior or EKG record.[280]

The tolerant species (*lucifugus*) attained its large negative temperature differential of —6°C (while *sodalis* attained none) by a series of physiological mechanisms. In these experiments or in others completed by Reeder and Cowles,[309] cooling was accomplished by panting, by a sudden massive engorgement of the blood vessels of the wings, by a gentle wing fanning at a body temperature of 40° to 42°C, and above 42°C by licking the entire body. In the Iowa experiments, panting and vasodilation were the most conspicuous mechanisms since there was little room in the respirometer to accomplish wing movements or licking.

* The saturation deficit was 50 mm Hg. This measurement is defined as the maximum vapor pressure at existing temperature minus the actual vapor pressure.

Table 13. Responses to Heat of Three Species of Flying Foxes[127]
(in °C)

SPECIES	COMMON RESTING BODY TEMPERATURES	HEAT EXPOSURE Air Temp.	Body Temp.	COOLING MECHANISMS
1. *Peteropus poliocephalus*	35.9° ± 0.7 SD	40°	39°	Panting Wing engorging Fanning Licking
2. *Pteropus scapulus*	36.6° to 39.2°	40°	41°	Very slight panting Wing fanning
3. *Syconycteris australis*	35.3° to 37.6°	35°	39.3°	Stressful panting

Responses to heat of tropical non-hibernating bats will now be compared with the North American hibernating types. Bartholomew *et al.*[127] studied three species of flying foxes in Australia (Table 13). These three species represent a delightful series for the environmental physiologist to consider, each responds so differently. The first maintains a negative gradient by physiological work; the second tolerates hyperthermia which it could prevent (because if air is 41°C, it calls on the entire "battery" of cooling mechanisms); the third is in distress-hyperthermia (positive gradient of 4°C) even at 35°C. Bartholomew discusses the ecological significance of these measurements in his usual charming and idea-provoking manner.

Kangaroo Rat. The survival of the kangaroo rat in the desert will now be considered. These rodents can live indefinitely on dry seeds and other dry plant material, without access to drinking water. They do not depend on body storage of water for their survival. When existing in this fashion, they maintain their body weight and a normal water content in the tissues, and are not gradually consuming water reserves. However, they must be losing some water through the feces, formation of urine, and through evaporation.

The feces of the kangaroo rat have a low water content (see earlier section of this chapter), and the utilization of food is very high so that water is conserved. For example, white rats use 5 times as much water for the formation of feces as kangaroo rats do when they eat the same amount of food. Furthermore the kangaroo rat makes extensive use of reingesting its feces (coprophagy). This procedure is common among rodents because during the second passage through the tract a number of vitamins can be utilized which had been synthesized by bacterial action in the cecum. The kangaroo rat, however, has a further advantage because there is a reduction in water loss by the second ingestion of the feces.

The kangaroo rat eliminates excretory products in a very small volume of very concentrated urine. The concentration of urea and salt in man represent a 6% urea solution and a 2.2% solution of salt; that of the kangaroo rat is a 23% solution of urea and a 7% solution of salt. To test the high concentrating power of the kidney, Schmidt-Nielsen did a very enlightening experiment. These rats do not ordinarily drink. He forced them to do so by feeding soy beans which have a high protein content and therefore yielded large amounts of urea to be excreted. On this feed kangaroo rats would die without water, so they began to drink. The concentrating power of their kidney was such that they should have been able to utilize sea water for drinking, even if the magnesium salts in sea water resulted in diarrhea and an increased loss of water by this avenue. In his experiment the kangaroo rats did thrive when given sea water to drink, along with soy beans.[154]

The loss of water through evaporation from the skin and the lungs must now be considered. Kangaroo rats appear to lose virtually no water by evaporation from the skin. As in all rodents there are no sweat glands in the skin. White rats, however lose water from the skin by diffusion (insensible perspiration); the amount lost is similar to that which evaporates from the lungs of the rats. In the kangaroo rats, evaporation from the lungs was very low. The mechanism of conservation depends upon the low temperature of the expired air. These animals not only have a low loss of diffusion water, but "consolidate their gains" by being nocturnal; they remain in their burrows during the day and avoid the excessive drain of water to the environment at that time. Their burrows do have a relatively high vapor pressure; this was measured very ingeniously by the Schmidt-Nielsens[315] by having the rodents pull a small dry-bulb wet-bulb recorder into their burrows. These instruments consisted of watches which turned a small smoked plate upon which the micro-meteorological record was made.

The water resources of the animal must now be considered; these consist of metabolic water and of water present in the food. The amount of metabolic water formed varies with the composition of the food but when dried barley was fed, 54 grams of metabolic water were formed for 100 grams of food. Included in this is a small amount of absorbed moisture in the food which varied with the atmospheric humidity. Having considered the balance sheet of water gain and water loss Schmidt-Nielsen calculated that they are equal at any atmospheric humidity above approximately 20% RH at 25°C. It has been assumed that these rodents are able to withstand a greater degree of dessication than other mammals. As we have said, they can become dehydrated by being forced to eat soy beans which contain about 40% protein. Kangaroo rats tolerate this diet without water for only 2 to 3 weeks. When analyzed at time of death their weight loss amounted to 34% of their body weight but the average water content of the body was the same as that while living on their normal diet: 67%. Although a considerable amount of water had been lost, the body was not really dessicated. These figures also apply to other small rodents when dying from water restriction; thus, the kangaroo rat is not different from other rodents which lacked the special ability to survive without water.[154]

Jackrabbit. There are two common species in the arid Southwest United States and they should properly be called hares rather than rabbits because they remain above ground and have no tunnels for underground escape. It has been difficult to maintain these species in captivity because they throw themselves against the wire until they are injured. Some investigators have performed cesarean sections and then raised the young by hand-feeding. When these were studied, it was discovered that jackrabbits lose weight and become unhealthy if they are maintained with just dry plant material from their usual habitat. This means that in the free environment they undoubtedly live upon green food to a large extent since their range is so small that they cannot possibly move to open water for drinking. They consume approximately 80% green and fresh food when it is available. There have also been a number of studies on the rabbit *Oryctolagus cuniculus;* this species was introduced in Australia where it thrives in arid areas. They require green vegetation but can subsist without water. When the vegetation is dry, they will survive for about 2 months but lose weight consistantly.

The temperature regulation of these three species must depend in part upon their relatively enormous ears. A related form living on the Sahara Desert (*Lepus capensis*) has ears even larger than the Western Jackrabbit of the United States. Brody's group[287] studied the temperature tolerance of New Zealand domestic rabbits and found that if the animals were acclimatized, they could tolerate a rectal temperature of 42°C and an ear temperature of 40°C. The lethal rectal temperature for a rabbit is probably between 42° and 43°C; this seems to be a common lethal temperature for mammals, although it was apparent in an earlier paragraph that bats tolerate much higher body temperatures than this. What mechanisms do rabbits have under these circumstances for preventing a further gain in body temperature? This rodent begins rapid respiration in a fashion quite different from that observed in dogs exposed to heat. The Angora rabbit attains a high respiration rate of perhaps 700 per minute, but in the New Zealand type the figures are nearer 200 to 300. This increase is gradual, not sudden and well-defined as in the dog. As the rabbit increases its rate of breathing the respiratory volume is also increased; it should probably not be called panting because it is not shallow enough. Schmidt-Nielsen calls this type of breathing hypothermic polypnea.[154] Some saliva drips from the mouth of the rabbit, but it is not spread over the fur as in cats and bats. Water is, however, evaporated from the skin; this was carefully studied by Douglas Lee,[294] in 1941, who concluded

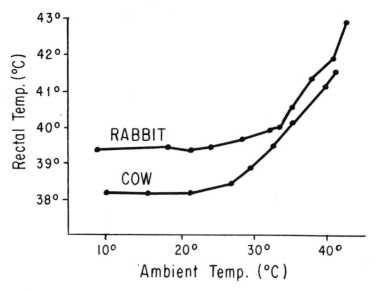

FIGURE 62. *Tolerance of Rabbits to Heat.* When ambient temperatures are increased gradually, rabbits appear to be more tolerant of high temperatures than are cattle. In this experiment New Zealand rabbits were exposed to increasing temperatures. Above an ambient temperature of 33°C the rectal temperature rose precipitously. The rectal temperature of cattle began to increase at an ambient temperature of 25°C. From Johnson *et al.*[287]

that there is an increase in cutaneous water loss at high temperatures due to increased circulation in the skin. Even with maximum evaporation through the skin and from the lungs, evaporative cooling accounted for only a small fraction of the heat dissipation.[289] Brody's group partitioned this evaporative cooling as follows: at moderate ambient temperatures, skin evaporation accounts for 60% and respiratory for 40% of the water loss; however, at high temperatures the proportion changes to about 80% from the skin and 20% from the lungs. At the high ambient temperature of 40°C this total evaporation accounted for only 30% of the heat dissipation. The rabbits could tolerate this temperature for extended periods of time; the remaining heat must have been dissipated by conduction and radiation (Fig. 62). It should be noted that at this temperature both man and cattle dissipate the entire heat production by evaporative cooling (Fig. 63). The rabbit maintained a heat flow over a gradient between its rectal temperature of 42°C and the ambient temperature of 40°C. Apparently this small gradient was enough to dissipate two-

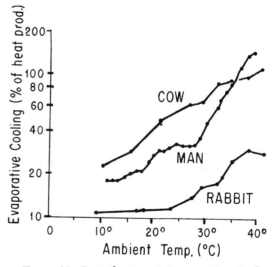

FIGURE 63. *Contribution of Evaporative Cooling in Three Species of Mammals.* At high temperatures (40°C), the heat which is dissipated from a rabbit includes a fraction for evaporation which is only 30% of the total heat production. Apparently the remainder of the metabolic heat is dissipated by convection and radiation especially from the ears. At this same temperature (40°C) both the cow and man dissipate the entire heat production by evaporative cooling. From Johnson *et al.*[287]

thirds of the body heat; this must take place mostly through the thin skin of their relatively large ears.

The contributions of the various avenues for heat exchange in the rabbit are rather unusual; Schmidt-Nielsen has assembled an elaborate and convincing hypothesis of how the jackrabbit makes use of these avenues when it exists on the hot desert.[154] An important part of the proposed scheme depends upon the micro-climate around the rabbit. Another important factor is the

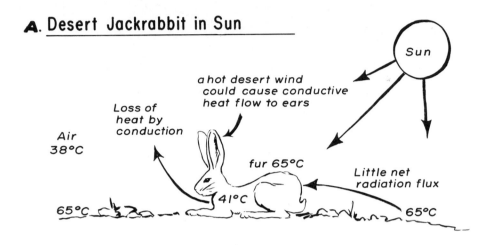

A. Desert Jackrabbit in Sun

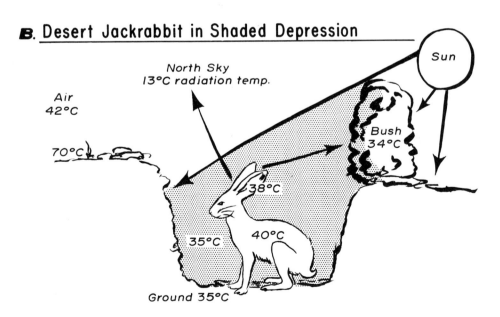

B. Desert Jackrabbit in Shaded Depression

FIGURE 64. *Desert Jackrabbit in Two Thermal Situations.* These diagrams illustrate a hypothesis of Schmidt-Nielsen. The rabbit exposed to the sun on the desert would gain heat far more rapidly than it could lose it. By remaining in a shaded depression the animal might achieve thermal balance by radiation to the sky and to cooler objects around it.

radiation temperature of the sky. When large animals are being considered, radiation temperature is not important because the integrated substratum radiation temperature provides a flow toward the organism. With a small animal like the rabbit, however, the radiation temperature of the sky could become important because a small animal can escape the substratum radiation by finding a shaded depression. The essential fact about sky radiation temperature on the desert is that it is much below air temperature during a day with a clear blue sky; under these circumstances the entire visible and infrared range is integrated. A thermal radiometer under such conditions records 20°C in the daytime and almost freezing at night. On cloudy days, however, the sky radiation temperature increases. Douglas Lee [154] recorded sky temperatures near 13°C in the desert on clear summer days. The lowest night-sky temperature measured by Lee was 7.5°C; with haziness and cloud cover these radiation temperatures approached air temperature. Now an animal on the ground, especially on the desert, is in radiation exchange with the visible sky particularly at night. The radiation exchange explains why the ground surface at night is colder than the air. Grass and leaves may reach freezing temperatures when the air is 10° to 15°C above freezing. Knut Schmidt-Nielsen [154] gives a delightful and detailed record from the proceedings of The Royal Society in 1775, of the process of making ice in the East Indies when air thermometers always recorded a temperature above freezing. By exposing thin dishes of porous clay so that the water is pre-cooled by evaporation, the water at night freezes due to the night sky acting as a heat sink, even when the air feels warm to the human skin.

The contribution of the radiation temperature of the sky is important in Schmidt-Nielsen's explanation of how the jackrabbit can tolerate the desert environment (Fig. 64). On hot days these animals are less active and tend to rest in the shade. If the animal sits in a depression in the shade on the north side of a bush, the wind of the hot desert will blow above him and have no effect. This wind ordinarily constitutes an increased heat load because of conductive heat flow from air to animal. The shaded ground where the animal is resting is cooler than the sunny surface; radiation from the sun does not reach the shade and re-radiation from the hot ground does not reach the animal in the depression.* The large ears of the jackrabbit will be in radiation exchange with the bush and with the sky where the temperature may be assumed to be about 25°C lower than the ears. Many micro-climatic studies, including radiation measurements, are necessary to test this hypothesis.

In this section the physiological contribution of the ears of the rabbit in a hot environment has been emphasized. Other desert mammals have extremely prominent and even tremendously large ears which are completely out of proportion for the rest of the body. A conspicuous example is the desert Fennec which is the most common mammal of the Empty Quarter of the Northwestern Sahara Desert. This small fox-like animal seems to live entirely independently of drinking water.

Dog. The water balance of the dog as an example of the carnivore group will now be considered. The ecology of the carnivores which live in a hot arid climate has been discussed in detail in the book *Desert Animals.*[154] This group of animals lives upon prey which have a composition of two-thirds water; this proportion changes little with the seasons. The suggestion has been made that carnivores should be able to live independently of drinking water, at least if no water is needed for heat regulation.

The physiology of the dog depends of course upon its breed. Very different generalizations would be made about the Chihuahua dog compared to the heavy-coated sled dog. The present discussion

---

* The analysis of "hot ground" is not often available for physiologists. A recent publication reports a temperature of 123°F inside a pebble when the desert air temperature was 100°F.[248]

will be confined to large dogs with thick coats. These animals were discussed in an earlier chapter because of their remarkable tolerance to cold; it was necessary there to consider their responses to heat because when they exercise, even in extreme cold, they are a "tropical animal" in very thick insulation. The present consideration of thick coats in a hot environment will enhance our knowledge of the exercising sled dog in a cold environment. One of the earliest examples of heat tolerance of the dog was the experiment (brought to light by Sid Robinson) of Blagden of The Royal Society in 1775.[253] When he took a dog with him into a room heated to 115°C, the animal was able to tolerate this heat in a perfectly satisfactory fashion as long as its feet were kept off the hot floor. Of course any blistering of the feet would have also occurred with hot sand of the desert; many desert animals have feet covered with stiff hair to prevent this damage. As the body and surface temperatures of the dog increase, the first and most important mechanism is panting, which causes water to be evaporated from the moist surfaces of the tongue, the mouth, and the upper respiratory tract. A second mechanism which comes with higher body and surface temperatures is sweating from the skin glands. Panting is associated with heat dissipation and is not concerned with exercise (a dog swimming in cold water does not pant). The panting response shows itself in a sudden change in frequency from ordinary respirations of 10 to 40 per minute to a rate of 300 to 400 respirations per minute. Panting is so efficient that dogs could tolerate a hot room of 43°C with low humidity for 7 hours without any elevation in rectal temperature. At 44°C and 65% RH they can tolerate only 3 to 4 hours and will reach a rectal temperature of almost 42°C. There are some obvious advantages of this process of panting which is so well developed in the canine species. Man evaporates from his skin more efficiently if there is a slight breeze; the dog provides his own slight breeze over the cooling surface of the pharynx region. There seems

to be no physiological economy concerned with the distribution of blood in the panting process. Under extreme circumstances of heat exposure the burden of blood transport to the tongue region seems to be as great as it is to the skin in man. Because of the increased need for blood flow during panting, the flow to the dog tongue is increased 6-fold when the rectal temperature rises to 42°C.[154] A final advantage of panting is that the dog avoids the salt loss which may cause incapacity in man.

The disadvantage of the panting process is that the increased respiration gives a greater exchange of air in the lungs causing the removal of carbon dioxide from the blood and severe alkalosis. Although there have been statements that panting is so shallow that the gas exchange in the lungs is not increased, recent studies indicate that this is not the case. In the panting dog the carbon dioxide content of the blood is decreased to one-fourth of the normal value, showing a tremendous over-ventilation of the lungs (Fig. 65). This degree of alkalosis would be intolerable to man.

A final question to be asked concerns the actual metabolic cost of panting. Does this add to the overall heat load? The design of the panting mechanism as a machine even includes a mechanism to reduce the work of the respiratory muscles. The dog minimizes its heat production by utilizing the natural resonant frequency of its respiratory system. In other words, the dog pants at the same frequency with which the respiratory system oscillates naturally; the energy requirement for panting is greatly reduced by this system.[154]

If the body temperature of the dog is extremely high, the skin glands begin secreting fluid. This usually happens in response to a local heating and especially in those areas which are closest to the source of radiant heat. Two workers Aoki and Wada[247] have shown that the threshold skin temperature for this sweating is between 38.4° to 38.7°C. If the outside of a heavy coat of hair is particularly hot, the sweating at the skin level introduces

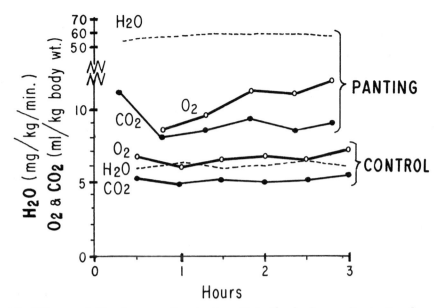

FIGURE 65. *Effects of Panting on Respiration*. Note the broken ordinate for the panting experiment; during this experiment the evaporation increased ten-fold. The first 30 minutes represent the most interesting portion due to effects on respiratory function; at first the release of carbon dioxide at the time of panting was more than twice the control rate. This very high release was not accompanied by a corresponding increase in oxygen consumption. This meant that alkalosis would develop, which would persist during the entire experiment. In other experiments the carbon dioxide content of the blood was decreased to one-fourth of the normal value. This is proof of an overventilation of the lungs. The resulting alkalosis would be intolerable to man. From Shelley and Hemingway.[320]

a very efficient system. The insulating dry fur reduces the heat flow from the hot outside air and ground to the cool skin surface. Although the fur may heat up to 70°C from solar radiation, there will be a conduction gradient from the fur to the air which might be about 40°C. Dogs were compared with men on the desert: the efficiency of a heavy coat of a dog was apparent; the man evaporated 12% of his body weight during test periods and the dog evaporated 15%. Recalculated in terms of surface area, the figure for the dog was lower than that of the man. Thus, both species evaporate at nearly the same rate when exposed to the same conditions on the desert.

The water balance of the dog is under rather delicate control. When the dog is on the desert, it drinks an appropriate quantity of water to very nearly correct the amount of water evaporated. This brings up the question of the control of thirst. It is logical to discuss this here since most of the experiments on thirst have been done on dogs. The urge to drink is controlled from a thirst center in the hypothalamic region of the brain. This cannot be the entire mechanism since partitional experiments indicate that the relief of thirst partially depends upon the distention of the stomach, partly upon the amount of water passing the esophagus, and partly upon the absorption of water from the intestine and dilution of the body fluids. All of these stimuli can send signals to the hypothalamic region of the brain.

With plenty of water, dogs will survive indefinitely in air at 55°C. If water is removed they lose weight by evaporation at the rate of about 1.5% of the body weight per hour. When dehydration reaches 10 to 14% of the body weight, the animal's rectal temperature will begin to rise explosively. A few dogs will tolerate a body temperature rise to 41.7°C and occasionally a temperature of 42.0°C. It should be noted that this appears to be a critical rectal temperature for a number of types of mammals. The bats, which were discussed in an earlier section, are an exception to this observation, and apparently cats also can tolerate rectal temperatures as high as 43° and 44°C.

Camel. There are numerous examples of the remarkable ability of the camel as a beast of burden while traversing waterless desert. Many of these accounts have been collected by Professor Monod [303] of Dakar, West Africa, who traveled across the waterless Empty Quarter of the Sahara on a march which extended a distance of 944 kilometers, or nearly 600 miles. The

beast which is capable of a feat such as this is reputed to be able to store water in its stomach. For several years Knut Schmidt-Nielsen gave attention to the degree of truth of this statement.[154] The camel does have several compartments which precede the true stomach. The controversy about the water question concerns only the first compartment which is called the rumen. The entire contents of this compartment average from 11 to 15% of the body weight; the contents consist of coarsely masticated feed formed into a semi-liquid mass. This mass is 83% water, and the fluid which can be drained from it contains 98% water. This fluid is slightly more dilute than the other body fluids; its function is to moisten the solid food for further digestion. Apparently it comes from the glands in part of the rumen; they may be considered as accessory salivary glands. Although there is a large amount of fluid in the masticated feed in the rumen, it is

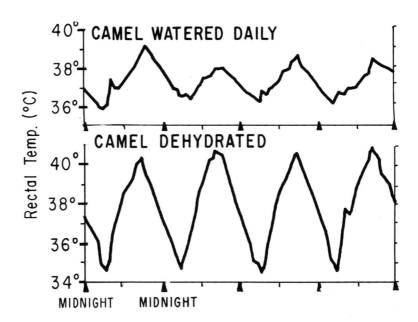

FIGURE 66. *Daily Body Temperature Fluctuation of Camels.* The day-night rhythm of body temperature in camels shows an increased amplitude when the animal is dehydrated. This fluctuation of as much as 6°C is useful in temperature regulation; when staying during the day in the hot sun, the body temperature is permitted to rise. The heat that goes into warming the body is stored. Instead of dissipating this heat by evaporation, it is dissipated during the cool night by conduction and radiation. From Schmidt-Nielsen et al.[319]

a mistake to assume that it is stored water for the camel's use on the desert; rather, it is water associated with the process of digestion. Another misconception is that the hump is used for water storage; the hump consists mostly of fat. It is true that the oxidation of fat results in a corresponding amount of metabolic water being released. The problem is that an increased oxidation of fat for the function of obtaining water would involve increased ventilation of the lungs; thus more expired air would be saturated with water vapor and considerable loss instead of gain of water would result. There would be more benefit to the camel if the hump contained starch since more metabolic water is obtained by the oxidation of starch than of fat. Then if the starch were metabolized the use of extra oxygen would again result in evaporation from the lungs which would exceed the amount of water formed. To summarize the water storage question, it can be said that there are no unusual water storage compartments in the camel. It is true that physiological subcutaneous edema can be produced by giving camels an extra ration of salt. It is a mute question as to whether this would do the camel any good on a desert march.

We now turn our attention to a totally different aspect of the temperature regulation of the camel; this is the variable body temperature and the benefit of this situation to the camel exposed to heat. In summer the range in rectal temperatures of camels is large; the temperature is usually quite low in the morning (sometimes 34°C) and high in the evening (usually about 40°C). In one case the evening rectal temperature was 40.7°C, the result of a rise of 6.2°C in 11 hours. The pattern of the daily temperature cycle shows an abrupt drop about 6:00 AM, undoubtedly due to a sudden vasodilation bringing cold blood from the periphery to the deeper parts (Fig. 66). The daily temperature variations were much greater in the animals when they were deprived of drinking water. The advantage of temperature lability is that if the body temperature is permitted to rise, all heat that goes into warming the body can be considered as stored, and this stored heat is dissipated in the cool night by conduction and radiation without expenditure of evaporated water. Furthermore the rise in the camel's temperature to a level well above 40°C would reduce the heat flow from the environment. We can conclude that the rise in body temperature is not a sign of failure in heat dissipation but is an actively regulated pattern in water conservation. Probably man, and the dog to a lesser extent, makes use of stored-heat for the same purpose.

The next contribution to the cooling of the camel exposed to heat stress is that of the heavy wool coat. If the animal is shorn, its water expenditure increases by 50%. Apparently this is because the sweat from the camel is evaporated at the skin surface without wetting the wool. The skin surface will be the coolest area and heat will flow to it from the core. The heat flowing to the skin from the sun and ground will be blocked by the thick wool. The temperature of the wool surface on the back of a camel in the sun may be as high as 70 to 80°C, while the skin temperature underneath due to sweating may be close to 40°C. The wool surface will loose heat to the air which is far cooler than the fur. The camel has more control over his initiation of sweating and his sweat rate than has man. Apparently evaporative cooling begins in the camel abruptly when air temperature is about 35°C.

The threshold for sweating, or at least for a marked increase in evaporation, was measured by a somewhat unusual technique.[154] The objective of the experiment was to compare sweating thresholds in the donkey and the camel. When this experiment was done at different air temperatures, there was not a consistant relationship between the increase in evaporation and high air temperatures. Therefore measurements were made with the black-bulb thermometer, consisting of a thermometer placed in the center of a black copper sphere. Since the experiment was

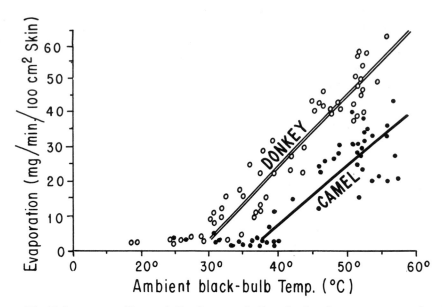

FIGURE 67. *Tolerance to Heat of Donkeys and Camels.* In this experiment the threshold to sweating was studied as a function of black-bulb temperature. The latter measurement was used to integrate the heat load from the sun, ground, and air. At a breaking-point, evaporation increased in linear fashion with the heat load. This threshold was about 30°C in the donkey but nearer 40°C in the camel. From Schmidt-Nielsen *et al.*[319]

done in still air the readings from the black-bulb gave a good measure of total heat load including the heavy radiation from both the sun and the ground. If there had been a wind, the temperature of the black-bulb would have decreased while the actual heat load on the camel and donkey would have been higher because heat from the hot air would have been conducted to the cool surface of the animal (Fig. 67). This contradiction would probably have applied more strikingly to the donkey than to the camel because of a heavier coat of wool on the camel. The threshold seemed to be about 30°C in the donkey and between 35° and 40°C in the camel. The evaporation data measured in both animals in terms of milligrams per square centimeter per minute are included in the monograph by Schmidt-Nielsen.[154] It should be pointed out that the donkey has sweat glands all over the body surface, it is a nose breather, and it does not pant.

The conservation of water by the camel

exposed to heat depends upon urine concentration and a reduced urine volume and fecal water loss. The daily urine volume of camels is relatively low. One camel studied by Schmidt-Nielsen was provided with an abundant supply of water, but produced on the average only 0.9 liters of urine per day. Other animals observed during grazing produced from 1 to 4 liters of urine daily. One camel in the laboratory that weighed 300 kilograms produced an average of 0.75 liters of urine daily; when it was deprived of water, the urine flow decreased to less than 0.5 liters. This is about the same as the minimum urine volume in man although the camel weighed 4 times as much. It is apparent that little water is used for urine formation.

The next question concerns urine concentration. The camel's kidney can produce a urine considerably more concentrated than sea water (perhaps twice as concentrated). The camel urine analyzed in the laboratory by the Schmidt-Nielsens had a total concentration 8 times that in plasma (U/P ratio = 8).[316] This is twice as concentrated as in man (U/P ratio = 4). Several investigators have studied the ionic composition of concentrated urine in dehydrated camels and found that chloride concentration remained constant, potassium about doubled, sodium increased 9-fold, and the sulfate concentration increased more than 16-fold. The camel kidney has an exceptional ability to eliminate sulfate. Because of this concentrated urine one might reason that this animal produces more than usual amounts of anti-diuretic hormone. To test this Macfarlane[298] infused ADH into camels that were dehydrated. Instead of a further reduction in urine volume he found a several-fold increase in urine output. The cause of this is apparently an increased output of electrolytes caused by the ADH.

Studies on the concentration of urea in camel urine make a particularly interesting story. An early worker reported that there was practically no urea in camel urine; Homer Smith and Silvette[321] analyzed the urine from a circus camel and found a normal amount of urea which was 60% of the total urinary nitrogen. One young and growing camel was studied by Schmidt-Nielsen. The animal was completely deprived of water and the urea concentration decreased steadily day after day. Toward the end of the experiment the total amount of urea in the urine in 1 day went down to less than 1 gram. Schmidt-Nielsen explained the observations of the occasional lack of urea as evidence of a special nitrogen cycle possessed by the camel permitting the re-use of its nitrogen in rebuilding broken-down protein. Instead of being excreted by the kidney, apparently urea enters the rumen fluid where bacteria immediately use it in the synthesis of protein. Lower down in the tract this protein is digested. To check upon this special nitrogen cycle, Schmidt-Nielsen gave intravenous injections of urea in amounts up to nearly 30 grams; less than 2 grams of this was recovered in the urine. The urea had apparently been synthesized into protein.

Urea conservation is most apt to be found in pregnant female camels that need to conserve protein for the embryo, and in young growing animals. Since urea may be either excreted in the usual way or reduced to a very small fraction of the urine when there is need for protein, it is possible that the camel can actively regulate the renal excretion of urea. The concept that urea is filtered and merely diffuses passively back to the blood does not fit this picture.

The final factor in the conservation of water is concerned with the amount of water in the feces. When camels in the laboratory were fed on dry dates and hay, they produced about 100 grams of dry fecal matter per day. Even when the animal had free access to drinking water the amount of water eliminated with the feces was only 109 grams per 100 grams of dry matter. In comparable terms the white rat excretes 200 grams of water and the grazing cow over 500 grams of water. However, when camels have been grazing in the desert the amount of water lost per 100 grams of dried feces was 2 to 3 times higher than in the laboratory on dry feed. It is remarkable that this mammal or any mammal can extract so much water from the intestinal contents.

The means of conserving water of the camel have all been considered. It is now of interest to consider the maximum utilization of these water conservation devices; what is the extreme tolerance to dehydration of the camel? Schmidt-Nielsen maintained camels in the laboratory without water in January for 17 days; apparently the camels could have continued. The experiment was repeated in an outdoor temperature exceeding 40°C. Two camels were without water 7 days and lost 26.5 and 27.2% of their original body weight. Other species would have had explosive temperature rise and died at 12 to 14% weight loss.

Attempts were made to study water loss in the separate water compartments of the body. The smallest relative loss of water was in plasma with less than a 10% reduction. This was verified in other experiments in Australia.[298] This situation would be an advantage in maintaining adequate circulation. When the animals lost one-fifth of their body weight, corresponding to 30% of the total body water, 20% of this loss was of plasma volume. Sheep would probably have lost one-half of their plasma volume. Of the total water lost by the camel, about 50% might have come from the gut, 30% from intracellular space and 20% from the extracellular space. The blood volume was determined by Evans Blue technique. Ordinarily when this material is used for blood volume studies, it is gradually lost with a half-life varying from 6 to 12 hours; in the camel the half-life of the dye was 2 to 4 weeks. In some way the plasma proteins which bind the Evans Blue behaved differently in this species.

In this section, the procedures and mechanism of dehydration in the camel have been listed; it is of obvious interest to hydrate the animal once again. In the experimental work which is being described,[154] the drinking capacity of man and the camel were compared. In 5 or 10 minutes, a man can drink only 2 liters of water, even if this intake does not make up for a water deficit. A thirsty camel can drink enough to make up the entire dehydration deficit in about 10 minutes. On several occasions the camels being studied drank amounts equal to 25, 30, and 33% of their body weight. During these bouts of drinking one of the camels consumed 104 liters of water. Follow-up studies on the distribution of this ingested water through the body compartments indicated that even the largest amounts of fluid taken in by a camel were evenly distributed through all compartments in 1 to 2 days.

An obvious question might now be asked: what are the physiological characteristics of other camel species, mostly living in South America? Apparently only one species has been studied; Rosenmann and Morrison [312] found that the Guanaco (*Llama guanicoe,* not a desert form) has the ability of the desert camel to replace a water loss quickly and to withstand severe dehydration without apparent discomfort. However, the Guanaco lacks the ability to become hypothermic and to maintain plasma volume when exposed to high temperatures during the dehydrated state. Here we see partial physiological uniformity irrespective of habitat within a particular family.

Heat Tolerance of Mammals

In this chapter we have been considering adaptations which are useful in cooling the animal exposed to extreme heat. It is now important to ask just how successful these adaptations must be and can be. Many cases of extreme tolerances to heat have been described as part of the details in earlier sections. Other mammals, especially of the small laboratory type, will now be considered from the standpoint of their tolerance to heat shock or hyperexia. Of course there are many possible causes of death at high temperature. One or several combinations of physiological events may be responsible for an animal's death, and these may be totally different from one animal to another. More importantly, heat damage differs from one part of the body to another. At increasing temperatures the frog dies as a whole animal before its muscles and peripheral nerves, and heart can be considered dead. In mammals also, different tissues have different sensitivities to heat; we often note a lack of coordination before circulatory tissue has reached lethal temperature.

In attempting to understand the cause of damage by heat to mammals let us first examine the heat tolerance of invertebrates. In spite of a somewhat similar architecture among the arthropods there is large variability in their ability to tolerate heat. These small animals all have a physiological problem in common: each animal has a surface area which is large in proportion to its mass. This means that evaporation from the surface must be cut to a minimum. Some arthropods solve the problem by burrowing during the day to avoid the heat of the sun; yet some of these which do this are perfectly able to tolerate very high ambient temperatures. Starting with the crustaceans we find that some of them cannot even survive the warm water temperature which is the equivalent of the body temperature of man (37°C). These sensitive invertebrates are tropical marine types. If we then consider crustaceans from the colder regions, we find that some may even be killed by ambient temperatures of 30°C. Marine organisms seem to live in their natural environment very close to the lethal limit of heat, but not at all close to the lethal limit of cold. Turning to the insects we find that the cockroach cannot tolerate an ambient temperature as warm as the blood temperature of man. Even the domestic cricket has a mean lethal temperature of 40°C. This is not characteristic of insects as a whole; one of the desert beetles tolerates an ambient temperature of 43°C and another one 45°C. Considering terrestrial invertebrates other than insects we find that some scorpions can survive 47°C for 24 hours at a relative humidity below 10% while some of the "camel-spiders" have a mean lethal temperature of 50°C.[259]

It will be useful to consider the fish species briefly because it is only with this experimental animal that acclimatization to heat has been studied in detail. Acclimatization occurs rapidly in the first 12 hours and in many species it is practically complete within 24 hours. The rate of acclimatization makes quite a difference and fish that have been acclimatized slowly survive heat tests more readily. Goldfish in particular are remarkable as they will survive a rapid transfer from 15° to 40°C ambient temperature.

The cause of heat death of fish and invertebrates is not understood although there has been elaborate consideration of factors such as coagulation of proteins, destruction of enzymes, accumulation of waste products, and the liberation of lipoids. When heat damage to mammals is considered, there is so little information we can only suggest which particular system of the animal is responsible for the breakdown. Perhaps the factors which are listed above for the cause of damage to invertebrates can eventually be examined to help explain the breakdown of organ systems in the mammals.

Let us next consider the survival times of mammals; there is great variation among mammals of the same species. Some of the factors which contribute to this variation are as follows: (1) the previous thermal history of the animal (acclimatization or acclimation); (2) metabolic rate; (3) age, sex, size; (4) state of nutrition, and above all, hydration; (5) the relative efficiency with which the component systems of the body appear to be performing at the particular time of test;[270] (6) the degree of physical restraint.[272]

This last factor is particularly important because rodents and cats when restrained and exposed to cold will die, while at

Table. 14. Common Survival Times and Body Temperatures in Heat[270]

(Ambient = 50°C)

Species	Body Temperature which 50% of species could not survive (°C)	Average Tolerance Time (min)
Rat	42.5°	44
Mouse	—	29
Guinea Pig	42.8°	54
Rabbit	43.4°	74
Dog	41.7°	—
Cat	43.5°	—

Table 15. Final Temperatures and Tolerance Times[270]

	Ambient Temperatures (°C)	Final Rectal Temp. (°C)	Average Tolerance Time (min.)
Rat (males)	50°	44.8°	39
Hamsters (males)	50°	45.1°	27
Mice (males)	44°	44.6°	26

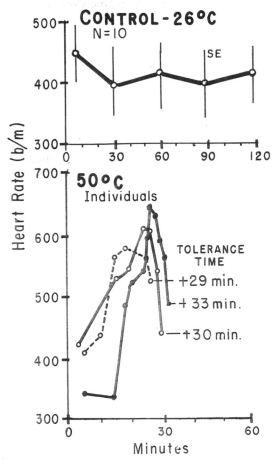

FIGURE 68. *Heart Rates of Rats in Extreme Heat.* The heart rate responses of restrained rats at control temperature 26°C and at 50°C are presented. The experiment was terminated when heart rates in extreme heat began to drop. These values represent maximum heart rates; no rates higher than 600 per minute were obtained upon exposure to 40°C. From Frankel.[270]

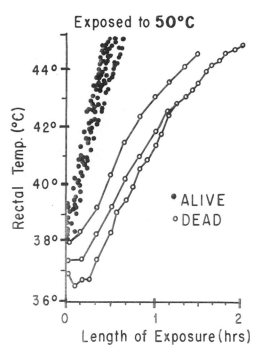

FIGURE 69. *Body Temperatures of Rats in Extreme Heat.* The rate of rectal temperature rise of live rats was compared with dead rats. An explosive rise in body temperature was characteristic of the live animals. There was very little difference in this response at this temperature compared with the response at 60°C. From Frankel.[270]

that same temperature in a reasonably large cage they will show no ill effects;[250] exactly the same reaction occurs upon exposure to heat.[271]

A survey of the results from three laboratories give some helpful comparisons of heat tolerances (Table 14).

More recent work with a large series by Frankel at the same ambient temperature provides more data (Table 15) (Fig. 68 and 69).

We can generalize from these two tables that although a frequently repeated figure, 42°C, is a fatal body temperature for the dog, smaller animals seem to tolerate higher temperatures. Of the small animals considered the guinea pig stands out as a particularly heat tolerant animal, possibly because of its tropical origin. In trying to assess the failure in heat tolerance many fine points have been neglected, especially the degree to which the exposure is acute or chronic. A careful experiment on heat exposure must include a thoughtful plan concerning the time factor; for example, some investigators studying heat convulsions have found that the rate of body temperature rise is more closely related to the onset of these convulsions than the actual final temperature achieved.

Consideration must now be given to whether the cause of heat damage is more concerned with ionic equillibrium or some other factor which might be considered physical. The data from the literature and from an extensive study by Frankel lend consistent support to the view that serum potassium, specific gravity, and blood hematocrit are higher in heat-exposed animals than in controls. Serum sodium is essentially unchanged and serum calcium varies with the temperature of exposure. An enlightening observation to accompany the electrolyte determinations has been consistent: on necropsy a vascular engorgement is found in all heat-exposed animals, and pulmonary edema is found in animals exposed to temperatures greater than 45°C. Combining these two observations we find support for a theory emphasized by Schmidt-Nielsen that animals exposed to high environmental temperatures die as a result of circulatory failure. The blood changes that have been mentioned above are concomitant and not causitive factors.

This death by heat shock comes earlier if an animal becomes dehydrated during heat exposure. The animal becomes more and more intolerant to the heat because there is a little less water to evaporate from the respiratory tract. This factor, however, is small because water is sacrificed for the demands of the cooling mechanism. Of much greater importance is circulatory failure which slows the transfer of blood to the cooling surface. The heart is overworked by its high pulse rate and by the demands of the increased blood traveling to the cooling surfaces; while these demands become greater and greater, blood volume is being reduced by dehydration from plasma, causing an increase in viscosity of blood since the protein remains in the plasma. One could informally state that the animal is circulating a "sludgy" sort of blood. The mammal dies of a failure in the transport of heat, causing a high core temperature and irreversible circulatory failure.

Chapter Seven

HIBERNATION

Hibernation

The understanding of hibernation has challenged biologists since the time of Aristotle.[335] Field biologists in most parts of the world have become perplexed by this adaptive mechanism, perhaps upon finding tightly-curled hamsters under cold winter rocks in the mountains of Rumania; or observing dormant pocket mice on a cool midsummer morning in the Sierra Nevada; or watching a mountain ground squirrel digging himself out of snow that he had been under for 8 months; or perhaps observing that captive birch mice of Norway each morning become as stiff and quiet as in death; or digging out a dormant winter colony of vipers or lizards from beneath a mass of grass roots above the Arctic Circle in Scandinavia. Many times observers have judged these dormant animals to be winter-killed, only to see the animal slowly moving a leg as it awakens.

The types of questions asked about this phenomenon in this chapter are: with what environmental extremes is this physiological behavior associated? What is the physiological difference between mammals which do and do not hibernate? Does a so called "cold-blooded" reptile respond to cooling and to rewarming like a mammalian hibernator?

VOCABULARY OF HIBERNATION

Homeotherms and Poikilotherms

The animal kingdom is divided into two groups: A) the homeotherms, which maintain a relatively constant body temperature (birds and mammals) and B) the poikilotherms, which take on the temperature of the air, of other conducting media,

or the radiant environment around them (invertebrates, fish, amphibians, reptiles). We may say that hibernation in some form occurs in all vertebrates except fish, if we accept for the moment that this phenomenon is *the act of resting in a dormant state in a protected burrow.*

The Definition of Mammalian Hibernation

One of the most useful definitions has been reported by Menaker: hibernation is the assumption of a state of greatly reduced core temperature by a mammal (or bird) which has its active body temperature near 37°C, meanwhile retaining the capability of spontaneously rewarming back to the normal homeothermic level without absorbing heat from its environment.[384] This state differs from hypothermia of non-hibernator mammals in which the body temperature is reduced (usually artificially) but cannot be raised by autogenic (metabolic) means. Thus there are two distinct groups of mammals: hibernators and non-hibernators.

Now that the broad view of hibernation has been discussed, we are prepared to go into some physiological details. Mammalian and avian hibernation is a state of dormancy associated with a reduction in heart rate, respiration, body temperature, and total metabolism. Dormancy usually means cessation of coordinated locomotor movements. The body temperature remains about 1°C above environmental temperature and the animal usually awakens if cooled to a critical level which is often about 1°C. Two consistant and characteristic changes are found in the blood: an increased production of heparin [351] and a rise in serum magnesium.[393]

An experiment will emphasize the differences in the two types of mammals (hibernator and non-hibernator) and a reptile. Using the technique of Andjus and Smith [161] one can place a 13-lined ground squirrel, a white rat, and a snake in a condition of hypothermia; we can carry the body temperature of the ground squirrel down to 5°C, that of the white rat and the snake to 19°C. Now let us expose these three animals in a container in which the air and the wall temperature is maintained at 18°C. The ground squirrel will spontaneously raise its body temperature, and will pass through the air temperature of 18°C, until it reaches its usual body temperature of 38°C; the white rat and the snake will retain a body temperature near 19°C until eventually they will die. They do not have any ability to regulate body temperature or to counteract the induced cooling. Most varieties of snakes will not eat at this temperature. They will remain in a suspended state with a low metabolic rate unless they can slowly crawl to a source of higher air temperature or radiant heat that will raise their body temperature. According to Benedict,[340] the snake is producing less heat per gram of tissue than the two mammals. He illustrated this point by metabolic measurements on a snake (a poikilotherm) and a rabbit (a mammal) each weighing 2.5 kg and having a body temperature of 37°C:

	kcal/kg/24-hr	kcal/m²/24-hr
Rattlesnake	7.7	91
Rabbit	44.8	619

Benedict also stated that mammalian hibernators have a lower metabolism than non-hibernators, but this is incorrect. The comparison between the two groups of mammals was made in detail by Kayser;[367] he compared the metabolism of rats, hamsters, and ground squirrels and of their tissues in and out of hibernation. He concluded that differences between homeotherms and mammalian-hibernators is not at the cellular level. On the other hand, several recent authors take the view that there are inherent metabolic differences between hibernator and non-hibernator, notably Zimny,[407] South,[396] Cassuto,[344] and Hyduke. For example, the last author demonstrated an unusually high rate of glutamic acid metabolism by tissues of ground squirrels. Luyet[377] found a difference in the tissues of hamsters and white rats. When hamsters' paws were frozen for 20 minutes at −10°C, they recovered in 2 or 3 days; rats' paws treated in the same way required 5 to 7 days for recovery. He attributes the difference to the ability of the hamsters to reestablish quickly the interrupted circulation.

Heterothermic Mammals

For many years biologists have been aware of occasional mammalian species or groups which have a fluctuating body temperature. The term "heterotherm" has been devised, apparently by Prosser,[152] to cover such mammals; he implies that primitive mammals and the higher mammals which hibernate should be called heterotherms; many of these only show body temperature fluctuations in certain seasons. Although the temperature-labile mammalian hibernator and the primitive mammal ordinarily maintain body temperature well above that of the environment, still it may fluctuate with air temperature especially in periods of inactivity. During normal activity, heterotherms have lower body temperatures than do other mammals. Heterothermy is shown in varying degrees among Monotremes, Marsupials, and Edentates. Unfortunately the term heterotherm in our present context is not useful simply because there are two types of heterotherms, those that hibernate and those that do not. It is necessary to continue using the term *mammalian-hibernator*.

Hibernation of Poikilotherms

In an earlier section an experiment was described comparing the thermal activity of a snake, rat, and ground squirrel. We should consider in more detail the thermal behavior and the hibernation of amphibians and reptiles. A second term to describe these lower invertebrates in addition to poikilotherm is "ectotherm". This means that these vertebrates must seek out heat and receive it from the external environment; when a season turns cold they must always hibernate. Survival depends upon their ingenuity in selecting an area of earth or vegetation that will stay above a critical temperature in the winter; most importantly, this area must warm up at the appropriate time and release them from their cold micro-climate. Because these animals are not able to be active in the cold, we may refer to this type of hibernation as required-hibernation.* The ingenuity of these animals in finding appropriate terrain for hibernation is shown by the distribution of reptiles in Europe as far north as the Arctic Circle.[342] Required-hibernation means that the animals in this condition remain inactive all winter until they are warmed directly or indirectly by the sun in the spring. It should be emphasized that mammalian hibernation is completely different in that during the long winter hibernating period, the mammals awaken, usually for approximately 12 hours, and then go back spontaneously into another bout of dormancy; these bouts may last from 2 to 30 days, depending upon the species.

TYPES OF MAMMALIAN HIBERNATORS†

There are several conspicuous types of mammalian hibernators; as listed by Hoff-

* In an earlier publication I used the term "obligatory" instead of "required"[349]. The use of this earlier term in reference to poikilotherms should be discontinued until formal terms can be selected at an international meeting of students of hibernation.

†There are three symposium volumes on the expanding field of hibernation; they are edited by Lyman and Dawe[382], Suomalainen[400] and Fisher and South[347].

man they are "permissive", "seasonal", and "obligate".[357] This means that all temperature regulation exists in 5 forms: 1) homeothermy, as in most mammals and birds; 2) permissive-hibernation, as in the hamster; 3) seasonal-hibernation as in the arctic ground squirrel, the 13-lined ground squirrel, and the marmot; 4) obligate-hibernation, as in the pocket mouse, and 5) poikilothermy, as in lower vertebrates.

Permissive Hibernators

Mammals like the hamster store and use food prior to hibernation and during periods of arousal; hibernation is optional even in the winter.

Seasonal Hibernators

The seasonal hibernators each year experience a rhythm of preparation for the coming of an extreme environment; the capacity or inclination to hibernate is followed by a season of breeding and active feeding. One of the best examples of seasonal-hibernation is provided by the arctic ground squirrel. We have kept these under constant conditions of light and temperature for several years in an animal colony; in spite of the lack of environmental clues, these animals have a totally different temperature regulation in the fall. At this season their body temperature drops for part of each day, nearly to the ambient temperature of the animal room; they can usually be picked up and handled in this season. Large quantities of subcutaneous and mesenteric fat accumulates. A second example of a seasonal hibernator is the European ground squirrel. The important point about this type is that their behavior and physiological status can be predicted on a yearly schedule.

Obligate Hibernators

The hibernation of obligate-hibernators must be triggered; this was first demonstrated by Bartholomew and Cade[336] working with the little pocket mouse (Perognathus longimembris). This is one of the smallest of the North American rodents, weighing 5.5 to 10 grams; it is in the same family as kangaroo rats (Heteromyidae). When these animals are kept for 2 to 3 weeks at temperatures of approximately 6°C with food, they maintain their body temperature; if food is removed, they enter hibernation. The same type of manipulation of body temperature was done by Hudson with the pygmy mouse (*Baiomys taylori*), weighing 4 to 8 grams.[360] Torpor in the pygmy mouse, induced by removing food and water, occurs only down to an ambient temperature of 20°C. Apparently these two species usually go throughout the year without calling upon their ability to hibernate. They do not show a seasonal preparation for hibernation. The differences between the two types of hibernators can be listed as follows:

Seasonal-Hibernation	Obligate-Hibernation
spontaneous	induced
genetically controlled	no preparation
Endogenous	exogenous
starts prior to stress	result of stress
imperative	opportunistic
starts slowly	starts quickly
occurs regularly	need not be regular

A different situation is found in the California pocket mouse; if its body temperature is below 15°C, it cannot arouse from torpor.[402]

How do we classify animals which show day-night torpor but which do not go into seasonal hibernation? The best example is the hummingbird: nocturnal torpidity has been described by Pearson[388] and Lasiewski.[375] During the day also, hummingbirds will relax allowing their body temperature to decline slightly, although it is elevated when they are disturbed.[387] Although this torpor may seem to result in physiological economy to avoid stress, under some circumstances it may be costly. *Perognathus* will assume torpidity even at high environmental temperatures; this is a costly procedure to the energy balance of the animal, and they lose weight rapidly. They could not subsist for extended periods in this state. We must consider obligatory hibernation at warm temperatures as a type useful to the species for only short periods.

The Special Case of the Bats

The temperature regulation of bats has been particularly difficult to study because of the continuously changing physiological state of many species of these animals. The North American cave bats can be described as a "bundle of thermal contradictions". For many years they have been considered as a special group in that they, besides their seasonal hibernation, show a remarkable lability of body temperature throughout the year. The day-night rhythm in the body temperature of bats was described as early as 1832 by Hall.[352] He proposed the term diurnation as opposed to hibernation. Hock[283] stated that he on the contrary found no evidence for a difference in the daytime sleep of bats (*Myotis*) and common hibernation. A statement by Hock has been frequently quoted: "The body temperature and the metabolism of the resting bat varies directly with the environmental temperature." There are a few reservations about this statement because there are some groups of bat species for which it does not apply. Furthermore, Stones and Wiebers[397] state that *Myotis* bats, when provided with sufficient food in a cold environment, will remain active and do not drop their body temperature. Much more work needs to be done in this area using North American cave bats as material. It is of related interest that the statement by Hock at least partially applies to the birch mouse studied by Johansen and Krog.[363] Although they do not specifically state this in their paper, it would seem that when the birch mouse is inactive its temperature falls. On the whole, these animals are relatively inactive from 7:00 AM until 3:00 PM; it is during this period that if they are quiet their body temperature sinks down to nearly that of the environment. After 3:00 PM they are quite active and maintain the homeothermic state. The only question is how much of the day is spent with a low body temperature?

Among bats (order Chiroptera) are examples of homeothermy, seasonal hibernation, and obligate hibernation. The homeothermic types are found in the tropics. Wimsatt [405] working with the common vampire of Mexico (*Desmodus*), demonstrated that an active body temperature above 30°C is maintained continually in an ambient temperature of 5°C by increased food intake and activity. The animals die if they are exposed for an extended period to this cold environment. Other examples of the homeothermic state have been given earlier in the chapter on Heat (*e.g.,* fruit bats).

Some bats are seasonal hibernators. Prior to experiencing environmental stress, they prepare for a prolonged state of torpor, even though the clue from the environment has not yet been experienced and although the animals have not hibernated for many months. One of the best examples is the California mastiff bat which remains homeothermic in the summer but goes into daily hibernation during the winter when there is a shortage of food.[376] Another example is the most common of the cave bats and the most extensively studied: *Myotis lucifugus*. This animal has a seasonal pattern of hibernation which it cannot modify by itself. During the summer it lays down fat in preparation for winter hibernation. The winter hibernation period is what would be expected with frequent arousals during which the individual bats lick water from the cave walls; of course, there is no food to be obtained. When the seasonal sequence of physiological events returns to the summer, we find the animal in a totally different condition. If placed in hibernation in the summer, he cannot spontaneously awake from dormancy in the cold, nor can he be stimulated out of the state of torpor in the cold.

When looking for examples of obligatory hibernators within the bat group, we must look for cases of environmental stresses which are quickly and irregularly imposed and there must be no preparation for hibernation by the bat. An example given by Herreid [354] is that of the Mexican freetailed bat (*Tadarida*) which maintains an active body temperature day and night in its home cave but enters torpidity when placed in the confinement of the laboratory respirometer.

AMBIENT TEMPERATURES FOR HIBERNATION

An interesting detail of hibernation concerns the suitability for dormancy of variable ambient temperatures. These temperatures will affect the amount of activity which the animal displays while dormant. Considering first the ambient temperature, we find that some hibernators are limited to a distinctly cold zone, others tolerate a variety of zones, and others require a warm zone.

Cold Zone

The hedgehog hibernates quite well at −5°C with a body temperature of 2.5°C and a heart rate of 19 beats per minute.[373] It should not be implied that this is the usual hibernating ambient temperature for these animals; the investigators of this study concluded that the optimal ambient temperature was near +4°C. To determine the upper limit of tolerance for hibernation, the ambient temperature was gradually raised. All hedgehogs awoke after 4 or 5 hours at 12°C; apparently this temperature acts as a stimulus.

Variety of Zones

In our experience the arctic marmot hibernates very well at an ambient temperature of 14°C for the entire winter. The same species also hibernated at temperatures considerably below freezing; some individuals nested and hibernated all winter in relatively small quantities of straw in extreme cold which at times was as low as −48°C. When temperature probes were placed in contact with the marmots, they often recorded −5°C. This species represents an animal which can adapt to a hibernating environment which is variable over a wide range.

A second group which will tolerate a variety of ambient temperatures for hibernation includes the arctic ground squirrel, the 13-lined ground squirrel, and the Mohave ground squirrel. Both arctic ground squirrels and 13-lined ground squirrels will tolerate hibernation at ambient temperatures near freezing; they will also hibernate well at 15° and 16°C, and can be in a torpor at 20°C which will permit them to be handled. Bartholomew and Hudson[338] gives an account of the hibernation of the Mohave ground squirrel in which the ambient temperature was raised from 10° up to 32°C. As the temperature was raised and the body temperature reached 27°C, they still appeared completely dormant; however, by the time the body temperature reached 32°C, they were active and appeared normal. When the hibernating ground squirrels were cooled back down to 10°C their reactions were:

Body Temperatures	Observations on Dormant Mohave Ground Squirrels
25°C	Squeaks when stimulated; easily aroused
21°C	No vocalization; shows coordinated movements
15°C	Unable to right themselves when on their backs
10°C	Responds to touch by withdrawal

Warm Zone

The final group of hibernators to be considered are those which restrict hibernation to a warm zone of air temperature. The pygmy mouse will become dormant without food and water even if the ambient temperature is not below 20°C, and will spontaneously go into and out of dormancy with arousal usually at night. At times it will maintain the state of hibernation for longer periods; if under these circumstances the ambient temperature is dropped below 20°C, it will arouse. It does not arouse due to an increase in ambient temperature.

Responses While Dormant

Other hibernating mammals show conspicuous variations in their responses while in deep dormancy. The behavior of the Mohave ground squirrel has been described above. At 5°C body temperature, arctic ground squirrels and 13-lined ground squirrels show slight flexing movements of the body. Many times I have placed sterile safety pins for electrodes in the skin of

such animals, and have made incisions in the skin down to the scapular region for the insertion of cannulae without initiating arousal. The golden hamster is the most inert in hibernation, the only visible movement being 3 or 4 respirations per minute which occur after periods of apnea which last 2 or more minutes. Many species of ground squirrels and the woodchuck periodically rock from side to side when in hibernation at a body temperature of 5°C; the woodchuck vocalizes and moves sluggishly when disturbed at this temperature. The California ground squirrel may lift its head, cock its ears, and even vocalize at a body temperature of 7°C.[399] With a rectal temperature of 4.5°C, the birch mouse re-

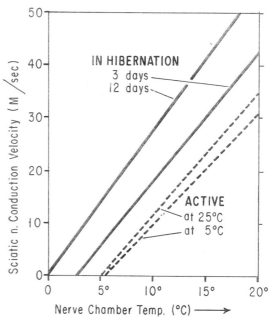

FIGURE 70. *Conduction of Nerves of Hibernators.* Conduction velocity was studied in the 13-lined ground squirrel as a function of temperature and time in hibernation. The nerves of non-hibernating specimens maintained in a warm temperature and in the cold were studied; there was little difference in their conduction. When nerves were tested from animals in hibernation, they were found to function at temperatures that would otherwise block conduction; in addition to that, the conduction velocities had increased. From Kehl and Morrison.[372]

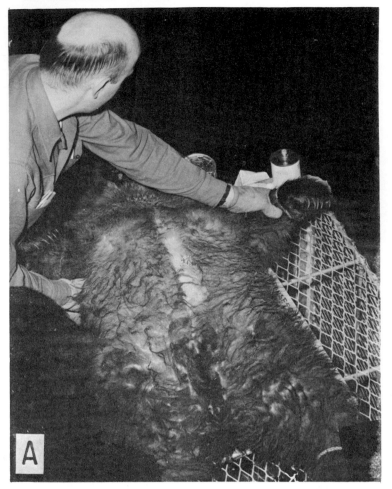

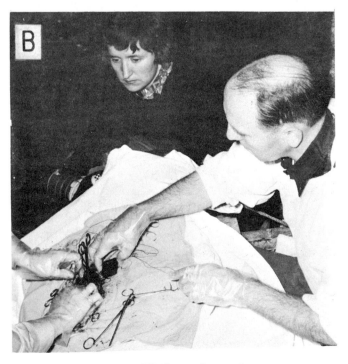

FIGURE 71. *Legend opposite.*

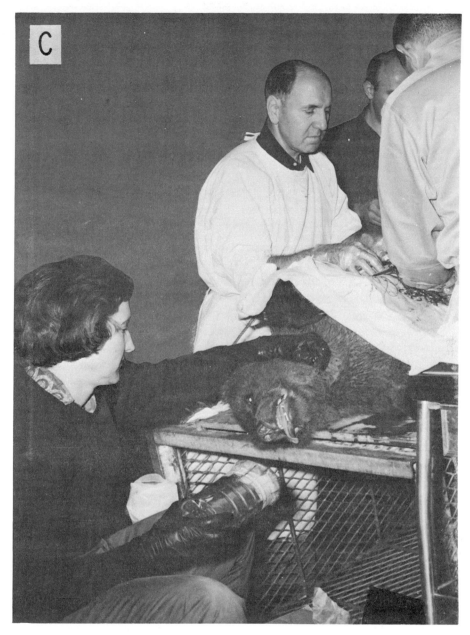

FIGURE 71. *Implanting Physiological Radio-Capsules in Bear at Point Barrow.* The procedure for implanting physiological radio-capsules in large carnivores such as bears and
wolves consists of immobilizing them with tranquilizing drugs and then applying ether
anesthesia. Bears weighing over 300 pounds have been implanted in the field. The operations
on bears were done in the bear cages. At the time of the operation above at Point Barrow,
outside the building the wind was 25 mph and the temperature, −35°F. The radio-capsules
transmit from the body cavity the heart rate, EKG pattern, and body temperature. These Iowa
radio-capsules are designed for short-range, long-life applications. The same capsules
have been used on wolverines, then taken out and used with the same procedure in birds;
they have recorded heart rates in the golden eagle varying from 174 b/m to 240 b/m
and in the longtailed jaeger a resting rate of 164 b/m varying to a flying rate of 664 b/m.

sponds to slight disturbance by a piping vocalization; with more intense stimulation it always starts to awaken.[363] The activity of any particular species during hibernation seems to be correlated with the amount of electrical activity recordable from the cerebral cortex. At brain temperatures of 5° to 18°C, no spontaneous electrical activity was recorded from the cortex of the hibernating hamster at any amplification;[345] yet a definitive and exhaustive series of experiments with the California ground squirrel showed complex electrical activity, particularly from the motor cortex, at brain temperatures of 7°C.[398] The 13-lined ground squirrel when hibernating has a sciatic nerve which will conduct near 0°C (Fig. 70).

WINTER LETHARGY OF CARNIVORES

The term hibernator for many years has been applied to some of the carnivores such as the bear, the badger, the raccoon, and the skunk. These species spend long periods in burrows or dens in the winter. There is a dearth of physiological information on these animals in the winter resting state. Hock has named this condition "winter lethargy".[355, 356] Many more measurements need to be made; data should accumulate rapidly now that radiotelemetry instrumentation is available. Only one topic can be taken up here, the condition of bears in their winter dens. Hock has obtained and plotted a series of data including rectal temperatures using wild bears and from specimens in captivity. The lowest figure which he obtained from a thermocouple which stayed in place for 3 days was a temperature of 31.3°C.[355] A similar temperature (33°C) was obtained by Rausch[392a] on a wild black bear immediately after being shot in its den on February 16, 1959. This careful measurement was by long glass thermometer which passed beside any possible fecal plug which might have closed the rectum. The usual active temperature of a bear is 38°C,[355] thus there is a striking drop in body temperature of at least 5°C. This picture of winter leth-

argy was supported by measurements on the metabolism of a black bear in its den obtained at —40°C: Hock states that the metabolic rate was about 50 to 60% of summer rate (the rectal temperature was not measured). During the winter of 1965 we were able to obtain heart rate measurements and body temperatures of bears in lethargy by radiotelemetry (Fig. 71). The summer sleeping heart rates of 4 bears (2 black and 2 grizzly) ranged from 40 to 70 beats per minute.[138] When 3 of the same bears were recorded in lethargy throughout the winter by radiotelemetry, their lowest daily heart rates dropped steadily each day until in December they reached in a few instances 8 beats per minute with numerous readings of 10 to 12 (Fig. 72). The body temperature was reduced by only 4°C. This reduction in heart rate supports the measurements of Hock of a metabolic rate depression. These data suggest that the bear is physiologically intermediate between hibernators and non-hibernators. Further experiments supported the concept. When 3 adult bears were exposed to hypothermia, their hearts stopped beating at a core temperature which varied from 17° to 21°C, but the heart rate was much lower than the rate in hypothermic dogs when their hearts stop. The hearts of true hibernators under these circumstances would have continued beating down to freezing or below. Johansson[364] became curious about the same question and exposed badgers to hypothermia. This species behaved even more like a mammal which can hibernate, for the hearts continued to beat at a core temperature of 13°C. Many more studies need to be done of the physiology of the carnivores which show winter lethargy.

ESTIVATION

Mammals sometimes show daily or prolonged torpor at relatively high ambient temperatures. The only known physiological difference between estivation and hibernation is the inability of estivators to withstand low body temperatures during dormancy.[361] Estivation may be character-

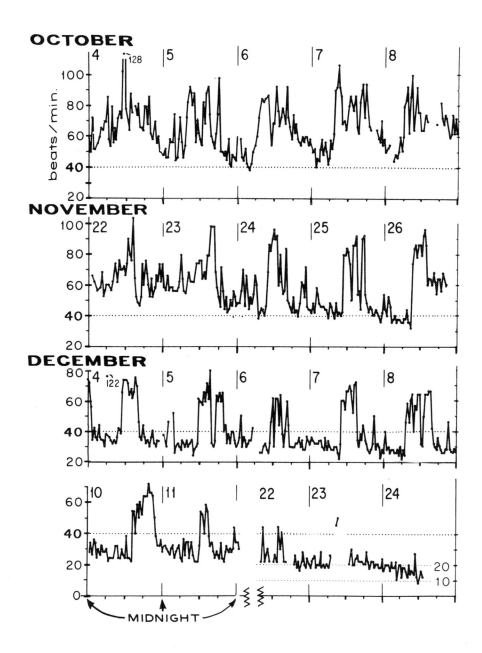

FIGURE 72. *Heart Rates of Black Bear in Winter Den.* A captive black bear went into carnivore-lethargy for 4 months at Barrow, Alaska. Its heart rate and body temperature were recorded by radio-telemetry over much of this period at half-hour intervals. Note the gradual drop in sleeping heart rates from 40 to as low as 8 beats per minute. From Folk.[138]

ized by shallow torpor. The physiological behavior of the pygmy mouse when deprived of food and water was described above; it should serve as the classic example of estivation. These animals will not tolerate a body temperature lower than 20°C. This particular temperature is interesting because many other mammals have a change in physiological behavior below this figure. Fibrillation of the heart, or cardiac arrest, occurs in many mammals near 20°C. A satisfactory definition would be: "Estivation is dormancy at a body temperature of 20°C or higher." There are some species which are dormant from about 1°C body temperature to 27°C; when above 20°C, it is estivation. Bartholomew and Hudson describe a means of distinguishing sleeping animals with a body temperature of 27°C from animals in estivation at this temperature: the estivating animals have prolonged periods with no visible respiratory movements, while animals which are sleeping have regular respiratory movements without periods of apnea.

The same question which has been asked about hibernation can be asked about estivation: Is the state an accidental one due to poor temperature regulation, or is there an advantage to the species? In the chapter on Heat evidence was presented that there is a measurable advantage when desert species estivate. Apparently estivation is a physiological tool which is used by some species to carry the animal over climatically severe times of the year.

PHYSIOLOGY OF HIBERNATION

Dissociation Of Function

The physiology of hibernation illuminates conspicuously some of the principles which are less evident when there are only small changes in body temperature. Let us first consider the statement that the hibernator shows a dissociation of physiological function. In introducing a manner of thinking on this topic, I am reminded of the teaching of George Wislocki who emphasized not a physiological but an anatomical dissociation. Instead of emphasizing the close association and integration of anatomical units of the body, he sometimes stressed the opposite and taught us to think of units such as the brain, heart, kidney, the alimentary tract, and skin as separate compartments or boxes which can carry on quite a reasonable existence when isolated from the rest of the body. In a similar fashion at times we should depart from the concept of homeostasis and its simultaneous integration and coordinating of many totally dissimilar systems and mechanisms of the body. For example, students of day-night physiological rhythms realize that a man may have a high body temperature setting but a low heart rate setting at noon, and at midnight, a low body temperature setting but a high heart rate setting (see chapter on Biological Rhythms).

Now let us look for dissociation in hibernating mammals. It can be seen as the woodchuck goes into dormancy (Fig. 73). This process lasts about 9 hours. During the first 2 hours the base line of body temperature, heart rate, and oxygen consumption drops steadily, but there are peaks and valleys superimposed upon this trend. These occasional resumptions of the active state last about 2 hours. During the steady decline of the base line, the heart rate drops first, followed by oxygen consumption, and then by body temperature. When the animal rewarms, the heart rate and oxygen consumption increase before the body temperature. Popovic [392] provides another example of this physiological dissociation: he was able to give a ground squirrel in hibernation a strong stimulus and found that oxygen consumption increased 10 to 15 times, but there was no significant increase in body temperature. In another laboratory,[398] the heart rate of a ground squirrel going into hibernation was recorded; the rate changed from 153 to 68 beats per minute within 30 minutes. During this time the brain temperature declined only 0.6°C.

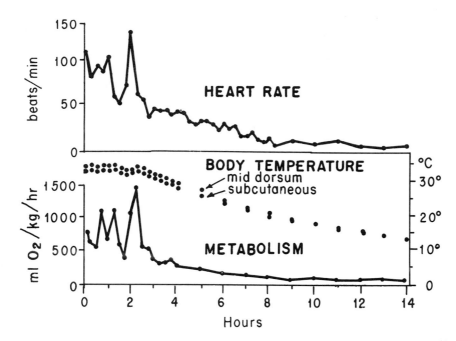

FIGURE 73. *Correlative Measurements During Entry Into Hibernation.* These records of a woodchuck going into hibernation demonstrate a sequence of physiological events. The heart rate drops first, followed by oxygen consumption, followed by body temperature. From Lyman.[378]

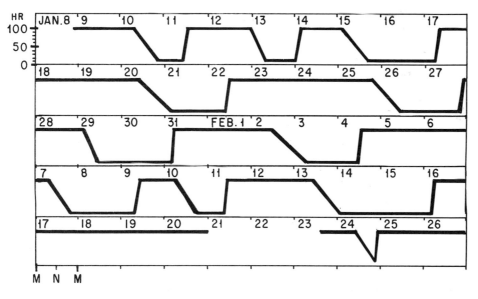

FIGURE 74. *Entering and Awaking From Hibernation.* An arctic marmot in a controlled environment (50°F) hibernated all winter in a nest of straw. Its heart rate was monitored by implanted Iowa radio-capsule. Ten bouts of dormancy over the winter period were recorded. Note the gradual decline of heart rate going into hibernation and the abrupt increase in rate upon awakening. All awakenings were spontaneous.

Circulation in Hibernation

The homeostasis (homeokinesis) of the mammal in deep hibernation is not well understood. The animal is regulating at a body temperature of 2° to 5°C; in many hibernators, if the body temperature is lowered, they take physiological action by increasing metabolic heat or by awakening. This homeostasis at the usual body temperature of 5°C shows some variabil-

ity. Although the environmental temperature and the body temperature may be steady, there are fluctuations in the heart rate and oxygen consumption. Heart rates of hibernating hamsters, woodchucks, ground squirrels, and hedgehogs may vary as much as 3-fold during one bout of hibernation. In the illustration of the hibernation of the arctic marmot (Fig. 74 & 75) note that for about 30 hours the animal had a heart rate of about 15 beats per

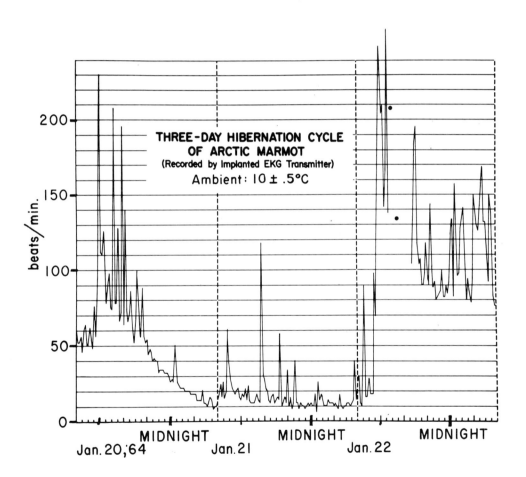

FIGURE 75. *Heart Rates When Entering and Awaking From Hibernation.* In the previous illustration a continuous three-month record of hibernation bouts of the arctic marmot was presented. In the present illustration each heart rate is shown every 15 minutes as the animal enters hibernation, remains dormant for about 24 hours and then awakens. Partly because the ambient temperature was relatively warm, this animal showed occasional high heart rates during the period of hibernation.

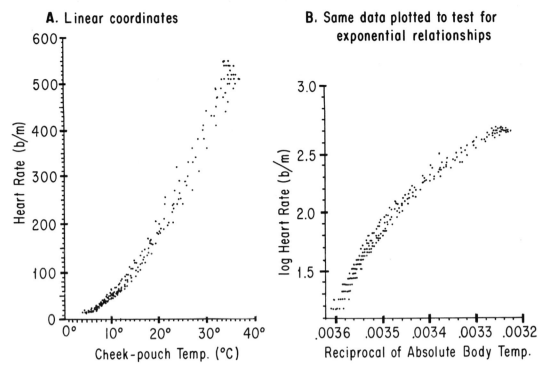

FIGURE 76. *Heart Rates of Hamsters During Awaking From Hibernation.* These records of heart rates of 6 hamsters awaking from hibernation, contribute to the question as to whether the relationship of heart rate to temperature is a linear function. The body temperature was measured in the cheek pouch. Graph *A* shows that as body temperature increases the heart rate increased slowly and then more rapidly. This is probably due to an increased effectiveness of sympathetic activity. In Graph *B* the logarithm of heart rate of waking hamsters was plotted against the reciprocal of the absolute temperature to determine whether the relationship fits the Arrhenius equation. This equation describes simple physico-chemical processes. Since a straight line was not obtained it is evidence of the exponential character of the heart rate-temperature relationship. From Lyman and Chatfield.[215]

minute; twice, however, for at least 1 minute it had a heart rate of 60 and once for at least 1 minute a heart rate of 118. Some of this departure from a steady state in hibernation is correlated with the day-night change in the physical environment. The cooled "biological clock" still measures off units which are close to 24 hours.

The somewhat unpredictable heart rate in deep hypothermia makes it difficult to assess the extent of depression of the work of the heart. The overall depression is frequently expressed in terms of metabolic rate: this (at 5°C) is usually about 2 to 5%

of the rate at normal body temperature. A similar calculation for the heart rate depends more closely upon the particular temperature of hibernation (Fig. 76). Some examples are of interest: the active heart rates of the genus *Myotis* in the bats may frequently be 500 beats per minute and sometimes 700 beats.[199] When these hearts were studied in hibernation, the rate varied from 20 ± 5 SD at 5°C down to 8 beats per minute at —7°C. The variation in the hibernating heart rate of the hedgehog is described in a thorough and detailed study by Kristoffersson and Soivio:[373]

Ambient Temperature (°C)	Body Temperature (°C)	Heart Rates (b/m)
4.5	5.1	8
0.0	4.6	15
−1.5	2.8	17
−5.0	2.8	19

For the active hedgehog a common heart rate is 210 ± 27 SD; sleeping values are 147.[350] Some hedgehogs, however, may have a rate as high as 318 when awaking from hibernation. The figures for the birch mouse also show a large reduction. The range of values for active animals was 550 to 600 beats per minute and the reduction (at body temperature 4° to 8°C) was to 30 beats per minute.[363]

The characteristics of the hibernator's heart have also been studied by analyzing cardiac behavior when the animal is entering dormancy and when awaking. The curves of heart rate and body temperature do not fit the Arrhenius constant which describes simple physical-chemical reactions. This is because the heart is under strong inhibition when the animal is going into hibernation, but is being driven during arousal from hibernation. When the hibernating heart is isolated, the rate is described by a straight line in an Arrhenius plot. Further details of the control of the autonomic nervous system over the hibernating heart have been reviewed in detail by Hoffman.[357]

There have been few measurements of cardiac output in hibernation. Popovic[223] reported a cardiac output in the 13-lined ground squirrel at a hibernating body temperature of 7°C of about 1 ml per minute, which is about 65 times smaller than in the active state.

Vasomotor function in dormancy should now be considered. A number of years ago Lyman and Chatfield[381] called attention to the pink color of the feet of hamsters during hibernation; during arousal the feet turn white. Lyman interprets this observation as vasodilation while going into and remaining in hibernation,

followed by vasoconstriction while awakening. The same observation was made on the birch mouse by Johansen and Krog.[363] While going into hibernation and during hibernation the feet were reddish; the hind feet especially became pale soon after start of arousal.

Strumwasser[399] has proposed alternate vasoconstriction and vasodilation to explain the hibernation test drops which are shown by some species of ground squirrels. Lyman suggests that various areas of the vascular bed may have similar periods of vasodilation and vasoconstriction during deep hibernation perhaps in response to an accumulation of metabolites.

During arousal the front half of the hibernator "wakes up first"[379] and blood is moved through this portion of the animal much faster than through the rear half. Johansen measured this fractional distribution of blood by use of radioactive indicators.[362] Using arctic ground squirrels he demonstrated that the blood flow to the front of the arousing animal is more than 16 times greater than in the normothermic squirrel. Furthermore the perfusion rate to the myocardium is twice as large in the arousing animal. To complete this picture, a substantial increase was shown in blood flow to lungs, diaphragm, and brown fat, but the blood flow to the alimentary tract was greatly reduced. Flow to other parts of the body was approximately the same in the awaking animal and in the active animal.

In two species of ground squirrels the blood pressure has been measured during hibernation by chronic intubation; the results from both species indicated that blood pressure varies considerably even when heart rate is constant. According to Lyman[379] these variations may be due to changes in the degree of vasoconstriction. Recently Popovic in a series of exquisite experiments has used chronic cannulation of the aorta and the right ventricle with plastic tubes in order to measure the arteriovenous difference of oxygen contents of the blood of hibernating 13-lined ground squirrels. There was some decrease in the oxygen content of the blood but the arteriovenous difference was unchanged.[223]

Many measurements on the circulation in hibernation have been contradictory; this particularly applies to analysis of blood. Some examples of reliable data are: the hematocrit readings from mammals in hibernation are very different from species to species. Usually they decrease such as in the 13-lined ground squirrel which shows a hematocrit value of 40% in hibernation, compared to the normal value of 57%. There is a trend for blood sugar to be reduced in hibernation, but this is by no means characteristic.[367] One laboratory reports an increase in plasma protein in hibernation.[401] Clotting time is doubled in hibernation and then drops to one-tenth the hibernation value during arousal.[370]

Respiration

There are many different types of respiratory patterns found in the state of hibernation. The dormant hamster frequently has 3 or 4 respirations per minute following periods of apnea lasting 2 or more minutes. On the other hand the hedgehog at a body temperature near 4.7°C does not breathe at all for as long as 56 minutes, then has a breathing period for about 4 minutes; this pattern is typical Cheyne-Stokes respiration. According to Kayser, this pattern is unusual. He states that the Cheyne-Stokes type of breathing is not a characteristic of mammals in hibernation.[370]

Studies on the birch mouse provide another point of interest.[363] The breathing in hibernation of this species shows a synchronization of heartbeat and breathing; there was one breath for each heartbeat at a body temperature of 7°C. Kayser, however, believes that there is no correlation between respiratory frequency and heart rate in the ground squirrel and the marmot.[369]

Electrolytes

The serum electrolyte which has received the most study in hibernating mammals is magnesium. Temperature regulation can be altered by the ratio of serum magnesium to calcium and by the injection of magnesium. It is also known that increased serum magnesium levels are found in both hypothermic vertebrates and in hibernating mammals. This observation represents an argument against the importance of increased levels of serum magnesium as a part of a theory of hibernation. However, the serum magnesium levels in hibernation are higher than those in hypothermia (Table 16),

Table 16. Reports On Serum Magnesium During Hibernation*

COMMON NAME	INCREASE OVER CONTROLS
13-lined Ground Squirrel	65%
Woodchuck	63%
Golden Hamster	25%
Little Brown Bat	62%
Big Brown Bat	53%
Hedgehog	{ 92% / None }

* References for these data are given in M. L. Riedesel and G. E. Folk, Jr. 1957. J. Mammal. 38:423–424.

and the elevated magnesium levels in the mammalian hibernator are not found until after the core has fallen below 13°C. Non-hibernators will not tolerate such a low body temperature under natural conditions.

It is surprising that more attention has not been given to potassium and sodium during hibernation. First we should note that in the cold the excitable tissues such as cardiac muscle have depressed ionic pumping; in non-hibernators this leads to a lowering of the membrane potential and failure of conduction. In the tissue of mammalian hibernators, excitability and regulation of water content are relatively normal at low temperatures. To carry this analysis at the cellular level further, Willis [404] studied the electrolyte gradient of the tissues of hamsters and ground squirrels. Samples of kidney, diaphragm, and heart muscle were analyzed to determine if the low body temperature of hibernation might cause a loss of potassium and a gain of sodium. In these tissues the gradients between tissue and plasma were maintained, or even increased during hibernation.

Endocrine Glands

The contribution of the endocrine glands to the hibernation process represents an extremely complicated picture partly because of the different responses of various species to changes in climate; also it must be clear by now that there are a number of different types of mammalian hibernators. A typical statement of reviewers of the topic of endocrines and hibernation is that hibernation cannot occur without morphological and physiological involution of the endocrine glands; this does not mean absolute suppression of the endocrine contribution to homeostasis. It would be unbiological for the endocrine structures to become completely unimportant to the entire physiology of the mammal. Many workers spend a great deal of experimental time and energy attempting to explain the contribution of these involuted glands to the hibernation state. It is true that in the morphological sense many endocrine glands do involute, but this is not always the case. Boulouard [343] studied the cortical hormones of European ground squirrels at 28°C and ones in hibernation at 8°C. Both groups had the same levels of corticosteroids, and the adrenal weights of the hibernating group were twice that of the warm acclimated group (49 mg compared to 20 mg). The varying points of view about the endocrine glands have been very fairly reviewed by Hoffman. [357] A few generalizations hold for a variety of hibernators. The obvious decline in activity of the pituitary gland during the summer probably means that

it becomes refractory to certain stimuli, and also is being actively inhibited. Hibernation under natural circumstances does not take place in the presence of an active reproductive system or a stimulated thyroid gland; however, later in the winter season natural hibernation can continue in the presence of increased activity of the endocrine organs. This especially applies to the pituitary gland. There must be increased endocrine activity in hibernation in those animals in which the reproductive organs quickly become active at the end of hibernation. The relationship between hibernation and the adrenal glands is even more complicated. Hibernation does not take place in the absence of adrenal glands, suggesting that a minimal activity of these supposedly involuted glands is necessary for successful hibernation.

We must next consider the challenge of fitting the General Adaptation Syndrome (GAS) into the circumstances bringing about mammalian hibernation. It is obvious that hibernation is not a response to cold stress, since the syndrome which is identical to hibernation can occur over a temperature span from warm to cold. Some investigators even suggest the opposite, which is an insensitivity of the various systems to cold as the time for hibernation approaches. This insensitivity is recognized by a decline in the basal metabolic rate, an increased fat deposition, and a decreased mean body temperature. On the other hand Suomalainen suggests that the different phases in the preparation for hibernation represent slowly developing stages of the General Adaptation Syndrome. He considers the sequence of events during the summer months to be an adequate stressor to the animal, resulting in setting off the alarm reaction; he deduces that the status of the adrenal glands during hibernation are indicative of the exhaustion phase of the GAS. Other investigators interpret the available data as a simple result of pituitary inactivity. Some investigators debate the relative functions of the two forms of the hormone from the adrenal medulla, epinephrine and

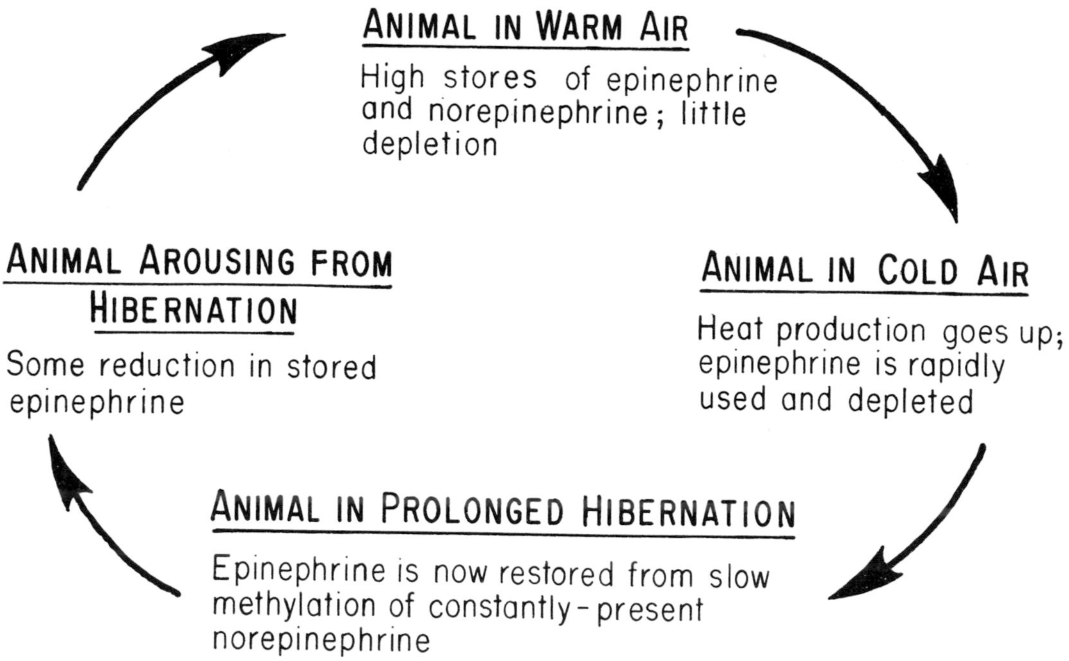

ANIMAL IN WARM AIR

High stores of epinephrine and norepinephrine; little depletion

ANIMAL IN COLD AIR

Heat production goes up; epinephrine is rapidly used and depleted

ANIMAL AROUSING FROM HIBERNATION

Some reduction in stored epinephrine

ANIMAL IN PROLONGED HIBERNATION

Epinephrine is now restored from slow methylation of constantly-present norepinephrine

FIGURE 77. *Hypothesis of Kayser for Explaining Depletion of Epinephrine.* Diagram to illustrate a theory involving the exhaustion and repletion of epinephrine and norepinephrine during bouts of hibernation.

norepinephrine. One ordinarily associates the function of epinephrine with the cardiac contribution to hibernation, and that of norepinephrine with peripheral events such as the possible oscillation between vasoconstriction and vasodilation. As long ago as 1939, Kayser and Aron[371] developed an elaborate theory involving the exhaustion and repletion of these hormones. Their views seem to fit in well with both the investigators which stress the similarity of hibernation to the GAS and those that believe it is quite different (Fig. 77).

Brown Fat

Description. There are two kinds of fat found in many species of mammals, one the yellowish or white fat occurring mostly in subcutaneous depots of all mammals, and the other, "brown fat", has been found most abundantly in mammals which hibernate. Some expressions such as "hiber-

nating gland" have been coined to describe masses of brown fat. This material may have been described as far back as 1551.[364] In spite of this, for many years brown fat was mistaken for thymus tissue. Small amounts of this same brown fat is found in the white rat, in man, and in mice. Brown fat in the rat is found surrounding the aorta as it descends from the thorax into the abdomen, in the back between the two scapulae, and in the axillae. Brown fat cells have cytoplasm which is more abundant than in white fat cells which have multiple fat droplets. The amount of brown fat shows a decrease during hibernation, accompanied by an increase in the brown color. Studies with the Warburg technique showed that oxygen consumption was higher in brown fat than in white. The brown type is most abundant in September and October. When the correct substrate is used, there is no difference in oxygen consumption of brown fat obtained from hibernating and non-hibernating mammals. The cause of the brown color has not been satisfactorily explained; the rich vascularization probably explains part of this.

Distribution Among Mammals. Some workers attempted to find an explanation for the function of brown fat by looking for it in as many mammals as possible. Brown fat is usually found in all hibernators. The group of animals which are not considered *true* hibernators lack brown fat: these are the mammals that show carnivore lethargy in winter including the badger, raccoon, bear, and presumably the skunk. Although brown fat is found in some non-hibernators such as rats and mice, less is found in the more temperature-sensitive mammals such as the guinea pig.

Function. One of the obvious approaches to studying this material has been by extirpation experiments. Because it is difficult to locate in the body, most investigators have had to be satisfied with removing about 50% of the total amount of brown fat. There have been contradictory results: Kayser[366] could not find any differences in the resistance of rats and hamsters to cold after removal of this fat; Zirm[408] found that hedgehogs die upon exposure to cold during hibernation after removal of 50% of the total brown fat. Zirm also succeeded in preparing an extract from brown fat which caused a drop in body temperature and blood pressure in mice. No one has succeeded in repeating these experiments.

An entirely new point of view about this controversial material has developed from the experiments of Robert E. Smith[395] and more recently by Smalley and Dryer.[394] By injecting latex into the circulatory system near the dorsal brown fat deposits, Smith traced distribution of vessels in this region. They were arranged in such a fashion that the utilization of a countercurrent heat exchange system appeared reasonable. The theory proposed by Smith is that brown fat tissue is strongly thermogenic in homeothermic animals exposed to

cold and especially in hibernators during cold-induced arousal from deep hibernation. He believes that this cold-induced thermogenic response protects the animal by contributing heat to the thorax region, to the cervical and thoracic regions of the spinal cord, and the sympathetic chain; he also presents evidence for control of this thermogenic activity by the sympathetic nervous system. The thermogenic activity of brown fat in bats was demonstrated by direct measurement by Smalley and Dryer. Some workers feel that this thermogenic activity is less than that of non-fat tissue such as heart and liver. This material must play a part in the arousal from hibernation of mammals. Arousal is a striking and unusual physiological event, in a sense a physiological reincarnation of the nearly-lifeless animal from its winter vacation; extensive work on brown fat is certainly justified.

Preparation For Hibernation

A conspicuous effect of weather and climate upon some species of hibernators is found in the preparation process. The physiological adjustments and changes before cold weather sets in are brought about in some species by changing hours of daylight.[358] Temperature, humidity, and change of diet must also be important. The conspicuous response is *usually* one of fat storage, or as in hamsters, the storing of enormous amounts of food. The amount of conditioning by cold exposure required before hibernation varies with the individual animal and with the species. Acclimation to cold does occur with at least some hibernators.[390, 391] As yet it is not possible to generalize about the relationship between physiological preparation and the process of going into deep hibernation. In our colony of 13-lined ground squirrels maintained in an unchanging light cycle for 3 years (12 hours of daylight), we have found that some individuals will go into hibernation in 24 hours or less after being moved from a warm constant-temperature room (24 ± 1°C) to a cold room (6° ± 1°C). Yet in the hamster conspicuous acclimation to cold takes at least 7 days.[186] The apparent lack of dependence upon climatic preparation by some species may be due to the presence of the annual internal physiological rhythm. There is a yearly chain of events consisting of hibernation, mating, raising young, and putting on fat for the winter. Associated with this internal rhythm is a variable dependence (differing with species) upon the action of the physical environment as a synchronizer (timer). For 3 years we have observed evidence of this internal rhythm in the spring season. Our 13-lined ground squirrels were in hibernation for 4 months each winter except for occasional 12-hour periods of normothermic* body temperature.[79] Toward the end of each winter some ground squirrels awakened and refused to go back into the dormant state. They then existed for weeks with a homeothermic body temperature in the cold room without going back into hibernation. There was no known clue from the external environment. Undoubtedly the internal rhythm called for cessation of the lazy period of the cold winter-dormancy. This laboratory model of ground squirrel hibernation can be matched by similar observations in the field. Probably signals from the physical environment cannot penetrate down through the snow or into burrows to the ground squirrels in March or April causing them to come out of hibernation; the internal rhythm causes them to investigate the climatic conditions outside of the burrow.

An experimental variation in photoperiod to test the time of beginning of hibernation in the 13-lined ground squirrel was studied by Morris and Morrison.[385] Two groups were studied for 18 months; one group was given a 9 hour day and the other a 19 hour day. However, the onset of hibernation was the same in both groups. This species represents a physiological type which is independent of photo-

period, and can go into hibernation very rapidly at the appropriate time of its internal rhythm. It apparently does not depend upon a build up of fat as part of its preparation because lean 13-lined ground squirrels will readily hibernate. It should also be noted that at the end of a winter of hibernation both 13-lined ground squirrels and arctic ground squirrels may still retain large stores of unused fat.

Another type of hibernator does depend upon photoperiod for preparation for and going into hibernation. An example is the dormouse (*Glis glis*). Morris and Morrison compared this species with the 13-lined ground squirrel, using the 9 and 19 hour photoperiods. The dormouse in the short day quickly adjusted its cyclic response, prepared for hibernation, and became dormant early.[385]

The third type of response to photoperiod is found in the golden-mantled ground squirrel (*Citellus lateralis*). These animals were tested with a variety of lighting conditions; the onset of hibernation could be changed only slightly by changing the day lengths. Onset of hibernation did depend upon the occurrence of a specific stage in the annual weight cycle of these animals. However, by manipulation of the length of the exposure to particular temperatures it was possible to change the weight cycle, causing animals to hibernate in the summer and become active in winter. This type of hibernator seems to depend upon the annual weight cycle more than the 13-lined ground squirrel does.

Entrance Into Hibernation

We will now concern ourselves with the details of the physiological changes in the animal as it becomes capable of being dormant. This is one of the most interesting aspects of all the phases of hibernation because an understanding of the first act of becoming dormant would constitute the explanation of what hibernation

---

* The term "normothermic" applies to having a typical basal mammalian body temperature similar to that found in dog, cat, and laboratory rat.

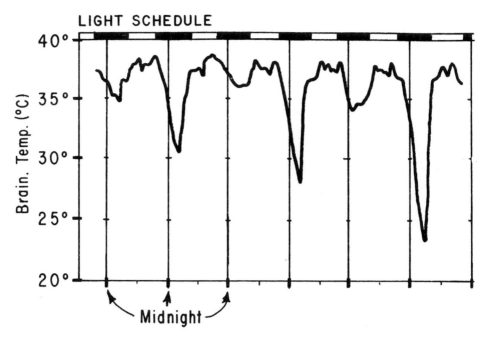

FIGURE 78. *Temperature-Drops Preparatory for Hibernation.* In this excellent experiment where brain temperature was recorded continuously during preparation of the animal for hibernation, the California ground squirrel demonstrated test drops of body temperature as it became more and more dormant. Apparently most species of hibernators do not show preparatory test drops as distinctly as this species. From Strumwasser.[498]

itself is. There appear to be four types of mammalian hibernators each of which proceeds from the homeothermic state to dormancy in its own unique fashion.

The 13-lined ground squirrel and the bat may be called Type I: these can go into hibernation very quickly. The experiments described in preceding paragraphs were conducted at two different seasons; observers recorded respiratory rates of ground squirrels at intervals. They found that some 13-lined ground squirrels went into hibernation within 12 hours. Johnson also describes a rapid and spontaneous change in body temperature of the 13-lined ground squirrel from about 37° to 4°C within less than 8 hours.[365]

In our own experiments it should be noted again that these animals were maintained at 24 ± 1°C; some individuals became semi-dormant for short periods at this temperature. Other types of hiber-

nators make progressively deeper short term body temperature drops called "test drops". It is very possible that the 13-lined ground squirrel maintained at 24°C undergoes its body temperature test drops from 40° to 25°C when the appropriate time for hibernation comes in the fall. If test drops occur in the cold room, in some cases they must be very rapid and transient.

The pocket mouse probably belongs with Type I because it never needs preparation and readily enters hibernation. However, in an earlier section we called the 13-lined ground squirrel a seasonal hibernator and the pocket mouse an obligate hibernator; there are other intrinsic differences between the two species.

The hamster is a Type II. It seems to be prevented from hibernating until biochemical and physiological preparations are sufficiently advanced for dormancy to commence. It may be pertinent that the body temperature in this species without cold-exposure is relatively constant at all seasons and in my opinion, unusually low.[187]

The mammals which show conspicuous test drops when they enter hibernation may be called Type III (Fig. 78). The classic example is that of the California ground squirrel; Strumwasser[398] pointed out that this species does not enter hibernation in one temperature decline but undergoes successive preliminary periods of torpor and arousal. It is as if the species enters hibernation while preparations are still under way; it proceeds only to the level of dormancy dictated by the particular state of preparation. We have recently studied a series of arctic ground squirrels during the first 6 days of entrance into hibernation. They appear to belong to Type III, because many of them demonstrated semi-hibernation and then re-attained the homeothermic state for a few hours. In typical animals this meant that the attainment of deep hibernation took approximately 3 to 6 days. The illustration from Strumwasser shows that the California ground squirrel requires 5 days to attain deep hibernation.

The woodchuck represents Type IV. Test drops certainly occur in these animals but only during the first few hours of the initial entrance into hibernation, compared to the 5-day sequence of the California ground squirrel. The illustration from Lyman's work on the woodchuck, shows that based on heart rate, the first test drop was in 30 minutes, the next one, 1 hour after that, and the last drop, 1 hour later (Fig. 73). These three test drops occurred over the first 3-hour period; after that any test drops were extremely inconspicuous.

We obtained similar information from four arctic marmots equipped with internal radio-transmitters. One illustration of a 3-day hibernation cycle (ambient 14° ± 1°C) shows a very similar picture to that of the woodchuck (Figs. 74 and 75). The sleeping heart rates of the normothermic animal varies from 80 to 140 beats per minute. A reading was taken every 15 minutes; as the marmot left the normothermic level, the pattern of change of heart rate resembled the action of a springboard with depressions becoming deeper and deeper. The animal had a low heart rate of 75 beats per minute for one reading, then in the next 15-minute period the heart rate was 208 beats per minute, followed in the next 15-minute period by 78. These changes are best described as oscillations. As with the woodchuck, after 8 hours of these oscillations, the marmot settled into a steady drop lasting 12 hours. The first entrance into hibernation of this marmot set a pattern which was repeated closely for each of the next nine entrances into hibernation. The average time for each period of dormancy was 29.8 hours (SD 14.4). The length of time for going into hibernation was about 13.9 hours (SD 3.7). The most consistent physiological behavior was observed in the length of time emerging from hibernation (average time 1.5 hours, SD 0.65). In the illustration the most striking change in heart rate was the increase from 70 to 250 beats per minute within 15 minutes.

Arousing From Hibernation

Hibernation is not a prolonged period of constant torpor. The ten bouts of hibernation within a 2-month period just described for the arctic marmot, are typical of most hibernators. The individual periods of hibernation are shorter and more frequent in early and late hibernation, and longer in mid-hibernation.[348] In the marmot these longer bouts in mid-winter were characterized by more regular heart beats.

There is very little information on the stimulus for periodic arousals during the winter. There are fewer awakenings at low temperatures; therefore, Hoffman[357] suggests that the arousal stimulus might be the accumulation of metabolic end products. Other investigators have suggested that a full bladder could be the primary stimulus. Evidence to the contrary was obtained from the golden-mantled ground squirrel; urine formation and urination does not take place during hibernation in this species.[389] This happens only during and after the final arousal process. Many profitable experiments are yet to be done on the mechanism of arousal.

The awakening process is often assisted by shivering, especially when the body temperature is between 15° and 20°C. Also, Lyman [378] reports shivering in wood-chucks in deep hibernation. This shivering may explain the occasional high heart rates which we obtained from the arctic marmot during some of the bouts of deep hibernation.

Arousals in warm air seem to take place at a rate of 0.2°C per gram per minute. One ground squirrel possesses an adaptation for awakening from dormancy: *Citellus lateralis* shows exceptionally high metabolic heat production from shivering.[406] Awaking is a costly process; according to Kayser it takes as much energy to wake up as it does to stay in hibernation for 10 days.[370]

A Theory of Hibernation

Although several theories of hibernation have been proposed,[368, 381] that of Morrison [386] is proving the most useful. Consider the over-simplified example of white rats being exposed to only one environmental change, that of cold. The response to cold for this non-hibernator will be an increase in basal metabolism and occasionally an increase in insulation;[353] the usual body temperature is maintained. Morrison theorizes that a hibernator may draw upon the mechanism of hibernation by "turning off" the otherwise normal cold-response just described. If the animal is the size of a marmot or smaller, if the air temperature is relatively cool, and if the animal remains resting, then its body temperature will drop steadily. If the animal is larger than the marmot (*i.e.*, the size of the raccoon or bear), even though the environmental circumstances may be the same, little drop in body temperature will occur. In the small mammals which do drop their body temperature to hibernate, other physiological events precede the decline; some active process appears to depress

heart rate and energy metabolism. This compartmentalization of function has been mentioned earlier. Note that in Lyman's illustration, (Fig. 73) the heart rate of the woodchuck drops first followed by oxygen consumption and then body temperature. This same sequence occurs in the hamster; as dormancy deepens, oxygen consumption starts to decline prior to temperature reduction, and oxygen consumption reaches minimal levels about 190 minutes before the temperature stabilizes at the dormancy level.

There have been few studies of breathing rate during the drop into dormancy; in an unusually thorough study, Landau and Dawe [374] report that respiration in the 13-lined ground squirrel is the first function to decline, followed by heart rate and then body temperature. We have mentioned that the small hibernator "turns off" the cold-response for combatting cold. When this happens, Hoffman suggests that the thermal regulatory mechanisms are not simply abandoned but are rather readjusted, probably as a result of depressed respiration, heart rate, and other factors.[357] The key functions in attaining this readjustment are breathing and heart beat. Lyman and O'Brien suggest that the changes proposed could be mediated only via the autonomic nervous system.[383]

ADVANTAGES OF HIBERNATION

It seems reasonably well established that hibernation and estivation are the same physiological phenomenon. This means that the body temperatures of some hibernators will passively follow ambient temperature from 2° to 32°C without eliciting arousal. What is the advantage of such behavior to these animals? Some small mammals and birds, because of high metabolic rates, are faced with an acute need for a continually available supply of food and water. An ability to lower their metabolism drastically conserves the food and water supply. Experimental proof has been obtained by Bartholomew and Cade who found that dormant pocket mice at cool temperatures over a few days lost less weight than the non-dormant controls.[336] They also showed in birds that a torpid poor-will could survive for at least 100 days on the energy derived from 10 grams of fat.[337] The medium-sized hibernators, such as ground squirrels, make use of this ability on a seasonal basis, not a daily basis. Some naturalists believe that dormancy may prolong the life of mammalian hibernators. The unusually long life of cave bats of 24 years is cited as evidence.[351a]

To summarize the advantages of hibernation, a thought-provoking quotation from Morrison will help: "Animals with adequate food either in stores or accessible in the environment need not fast. Fasting (and hibernation) is only found in animals with inadequate external food reserves, whatever the reason. Animals without external reserves must use internal reserves and often hibernate."[386] This illustrates the close association between Environmental Physiology and Ecology.

GEOGRAPHICAL DISTRIBUTION AND HIBERNATION

Hibernation or estivation appears to be a physiological adaptation of animal populations in hot, arid, and cold areas. Discussing cold areas first, we ask: is hibernation a necessary mechanism in the cold? We will consider only mammalian hibernators; these are all the size of marmots or smaller. There are about twenty-three non-migrant species of this size which inhabit Northern Canada; only *four* of these hibernate.[341] There are eight non-migratory mammals which have a distribution covering most of the United States and Canada; only *two* of these are hibernators.[341] Obviously most mammals combat an extreme environment by turning to a well-filled "bags of tricks". The beaver uses engineering skill to keep his environment safe during the winter. The red squirrel simply raises his metabolism.[353] Only a few of the mammals resort to hibernation.

The above examples were taken from the list of North American mammals; there are, of course, some well-known hibernators in Europe including dormice, ground squirrels, hedgehogs and birch mice.

It is of interest to consider also the distribution of hibernation within the orders of mammals of the world. At least 5 of the 18 living orders of mammals contain species which hibernate.[380] In the Marsupial group there is a small opossum-like mammal in both South America and Australia which has recently been shown to hibernate. In the Insectivora group the European hedgehog and the Tenrec of Madagascar are hibernators. Among the primates there are at least two Lemurs which are reported to hibernate. Most of the bats (Chiroptera) of temperate regions hibernate throughout the winter. The two groups that are not represented are the ungulates and the carnivores. Although some of the carnivores appear to show a moderate reduction in metabolism, their physiological state at that time should be referred to as winter lethargy. An important point, however, is that within each order there are very few species which hibernate.

The small number of hibernators compared to the total number of mammals in any given area shows that the ability to become dormant probably does not play a role in governing the distribution of mammals. The broad distribution of several species of hibernators over many climatic areas is evidence that large populations of the species do not make use of their physiological ability. One illustration is the 13-lined ground squirrel which is found from the Gulf of Mexico to the middle of Canada (Fig. 79). Four climatic areas are included within this range. Hibernation is important in the ecology of this animal of the north, the dormancy of estivation is important in the south, and in the middle of the range the species probably maintains a normothermic body temperature most of the year. This species would be referred to by Darlington as a "dominant species" showing general adaptation which makes it superior to others in several different climatic areas.[346]

The relationships between climate, ge-

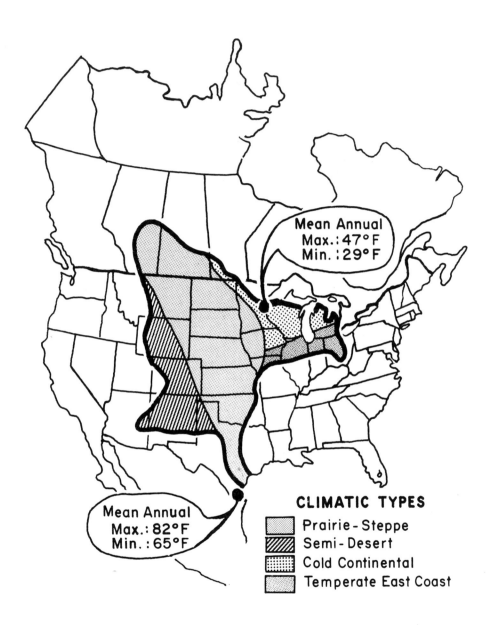

FIGURE 79. *Distribution of 13-Lined Ground Squirrel.* The distribution of this squirrel over North America includes 4 climatic areas; this species must have a very different "winter physiology" in its northern range in mid-Canada compared with the populations near the shore of the Gulf of Mexico. Range from Bert and Grossenheider.

ography, and physiological mechanisms are complicated; Bartholomew [359] presents evidence that physiology helps to explain how mammals can live where they do, but it rarely explains the exact limits of their distribution. For example, the manatee is unable to survive cold water,[403] and the fur seal in unable to survive warm water or hot air.[339] The distributional control of these species appears to be physiological. However, as Bartholomew points out, "in the case of desert animals, the heat and aridity may actually limit the occurrence of these species but the desert comprises only part of the perimeter of their ranges. On other parts of the perimeters, different factors must be limiting."[359] Presumably some of these factors would be competition, habitat-selection, diet, and behavioral mechanisms. Now carrying this idea over to the importance of hibernation, we must decide that the ability to hibernate does not appear to be a "distributional determinant".

LOW PRESSURE

FROM TERRESTRIAL ALTITUDE

PHYSIOLOGICAL EFFECTS OF ALTITUDE
(First American work done by E.C. Schnider at Pikes Peak in 1904)

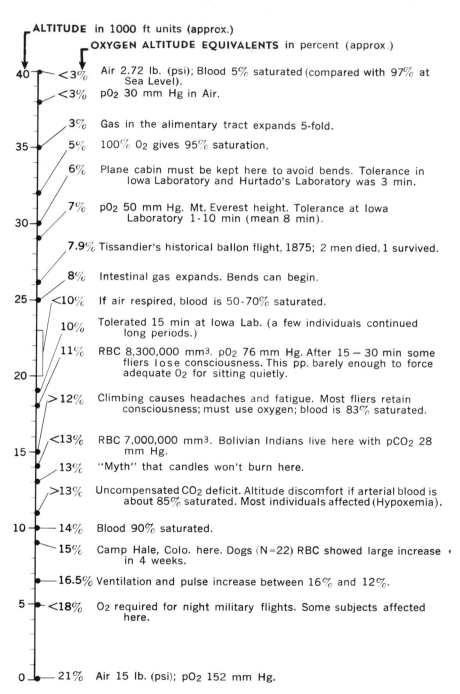

ALTITUDE in 1000 ft units (approx.)

OXYGEN ALTITUDE EQUIVALENTS in percent (approx.)

40 — <3% — Air 2.72 lb. (psi); Blood 5% saturated (compared with 97% at Sea Level).

<3% — pO_2 30 mm Hg in Air.

3% — Gas in the alimentary tract expands 5-fold.

35 — 5% — 100% O_2 gives 95% saturation.

6% — Plane cabin must be kept here to avoid bends. Tolerance in Iowa Laboratory and Hurtado's Laboratory was 3 min.

7% — pO_2 50 mm Hg. Mt. Everest height. Tolerance at Iowa Laboratory 1-10 min (mean 8 min).

30 —

7.9% — Tissandier's historical ballon flight, 1875; 2 men died, 1 survived.

8% — Intestinal gas expands. Bends can begin.

25 — <10% — If air respired, blood is 50-70% saturated.

10% — Tolerated 15 min at Iowa Lab. (a few individuals continued long periods.)

11% — RBC 8,300,000 mm3. pO_2 76 mm Hg. After 15 − 30 min some fliers lose consciousness. This pp. barely enough to force adequate O_2 for sitting quietly.

20 —

>12% — Climbing causes headaches and fatigue. Most fliers retain consciousness; must use oxygen; blood is 83% saturated.

<13% — RBC 7,000,000 mm3. Bolivian Indians live here with pCO_2 28 mm Hg.

15 —

13% — "Myth" that candles won't burn here.

>13% — Uncompensated CO_2 deficit. Altitude discomfort if arterial blood is about 85% saturated. Most individuals affected (Hypoxemia).

10 — 14% — Blood 90% saturated.

15% — Camp Hale, Colo. here. Dogs (N=22) RBC showed large increase in 4 weeks.

16.5% — Ventilation and pulse increase between 16% and 12%.

5 — <18% — O_2 required for night military flights. Some subjects affected here.

0 — 21% — Air 15 lb. (psi); pO_2 152 mm Hg.

Low Pressure
From Terrestrial Altitude

MAN'S EXPOSURE TO TERRESTRIAL ALTITUDE

We will consider the effects upon mammals of living at altitudes between 7,500 and 20,000 feet. When the stewardess in a jet airplane instructs us in the use of the oxygen mask, we realize that the average person often has a chance of experiencing altitude effects. Again in a plane, an unpleasant physiological phenomenon may remind one of the problems of altitude; this event, which illustrates Boyle's Law, occurs when a person with a gas pocket inside a cavity in a tooth, experiences a change in pressure. This physiological barometer not only tells the observer by the sharp tooth twinge when a change is being made such as from 8,000 feet to 14,000 feet in an unpressurized plane (or altitude chamber), but checks upon the degree of control of the pressurized cabin in commercial aircraft.

Is the average traveler apt to experience high altitude effects with land transportation? A convenient definition of terrestrial altitude is: any land higher than 7,500 feet. The highest mountains in *eastern* North America are not much over 6,000 feet. A different situation exists in the western United States: in the state of Colorado alone, 15 railroad passes are found between 10,285 and 12,095 feet. If we consider other parts of the globe, the list includes 54 points on railroads and high-

ways which are over 7,500 feet. There are railroads that go up to 16,000 feet. Six well-established universities flourish at high altitude: one of these is at 7,500, three are near 9,600, one is at 11,000 and one at 12,500 feet (Fig. 80). One wonders whether the professor of physiology at these locations takes the local altitude-effects for granted or teaches mostly altitude physiology.

These statistics remind us that much of the terrestrial part of the globe is mountainous. Airplanes carrying passengers are constantly passing over these mountains, and terrestrial rescue teams must be prepared to go into them at all times. An additional note of interest is that the 1968 Olympic Games were held in Mexico City which is 7,347 ft. above sea level.

We must now consider the physiological effects that are taking place if a man and his dog take a walking tour from a medium altitude to some location such as the high altitude research station on Ticlio, Peru (16,000 feet). Even under the circumstances of gradual acclimatization, both animals experience distress and severe fatigue. The man will note that the viscacha (a relative of the guinea pig) scamper over the rocks without handicap. If the man with the dog wishes to climb higher, to 20,000 feet, they must wait several days to become further acclimatized before attempting such a feat. When they do, the man will have to stop frequently because of his violent breathing, although his porters who live locally will show no altitude effects or fatigue. To analyze this sequence of events, we must consider the effects of altitude on man and domestic animals, both visitors and natives.

The basic physiological problem is the rate at which the change takes place. A number of years ago it was reasonable to consider two questions: gradual acclimatization and the problems of aircraft. Now it is quite usual for men to be transported rapidly from sea level to high altitude either as a work crew or a research expedition, and they are expected to adjust suddenly to the effects of high mountain living. A shuttle service by helicopter between Mount Wrangell Research Station (14,168 feet) and sea level locations operates every summer. There is also helicopter service from Bishop, California to the White Mountain Barcroft Laboratory

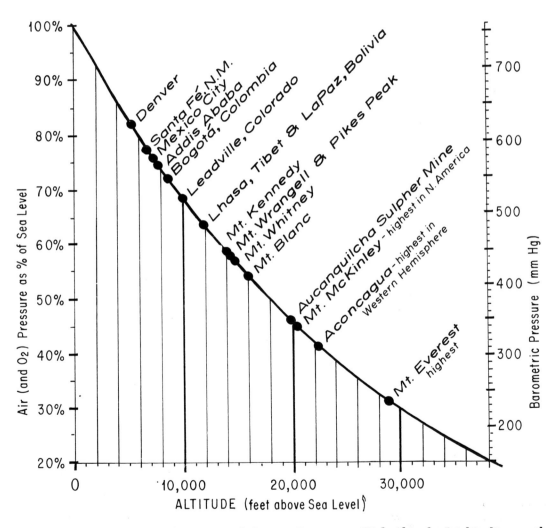

FIGURE 80. *Barometric Pressure and Oxygen Pressure at High Altitude.* In this diagram the pressure of air and oxygen are expressed as percent of sea level and compared with barometric pressure. On the graph of altitude as related to these functions the height of the highest known civilized villages or work areas are indicated.

at 12,470 feet; at times the pilot will reluctantly land at the higher Summit Laboratory at 14,250 feet. In fact the ordinary commercial traveler in South America is liable to somewhat unexpectedly experience the physiological effects of altitude. The airport at LaPaz, Bolivia, is considered the highest airport in the world at 12,200 feet. Thus, we must define any physiological question about altitude; does it concern the man who took the walking tour gradually to high altitude, or the investigators who must quickly unload their equipment from air transportation and begin to work and live in the "thin air"? With these comments on where and how a person may encounter a reduced atmospheric pressure, we will now consider some of the details of the "physiology of slowly smothering".

Circulation

We will review briefly the chronic and acute effects on man of slow and rapid transportation to high altitudes.* With

---

* More detailed accounts of the quantitative effects of altitude are given in several standard medical physiology texts such as A. C. Guyton: *Medical Physiology*, (1961).

gradual acclimatization to an altitude of 15,000 feet, the basic operation of the circulatory system, the respiratory system and of acid-base balance must all be changed. Many studies of the circulatory system have been completed because of the convenience of the measurements.[423] One of the earliest organized bits of research was done by Bert in 1878.[413] He proposed the hypothesis, supported by experiments, that when animals live at altitude the blood gradually begins to transport more oxygen. Mosso, in his book published in 1898,[436] reports his own measurements on pulse and respiration, and compiled the work of others. Table 17 is a consolidation of the cardiovascular changes discussed in his report. It is apparent that when man is at rest at altitude his resting pulse increases; the elevated pulses of older men appeared to decline faster than those of younger men.

Mosso gives the following evidence that the pulse is not only high while living at altitudes, but it is erratic. On one occasion he walked very leisurely up to the hut on Monte Rosa. The next day, after a good night's rest and before rising, his pulse was taken by a trained observer; the consecutive readings were as follows: 73, 76, 75, 76, 93, 80, 84, 80, 76, 75.

Table 17. Data From Human Subjects During First Three Days At The Regina Margherita Hut (14,957 feet)*

		YOUNG MEN 18–19 years (N = 9)			OLDER MEN 22–50 years (N = 6)		
		Rate b/m	c/m	% Increase from normal	Rate b/m	c/m	% Increase from normal
Normal (Control)	Pulse	67			71		
	Respirations		18			16	
1st day	Pulse	102		52%	98		38%
	Respirations		21	17%		22	37%
2nd day	Pulse	102		52%	100		40%
	Respirations		21	17%		24	48%
3rd day	Pulse	88		31%	85		19%
	Respirations		16	−10%		20	20%

* From Angelo Mosso. 1898. *Life of Man on the High Alps*[436].

When a non-native acclimatized man exercises at altitude, his maximum pulse will be lower than the maximum rate for the same exercise at sea level. The heart rate during exercise at sea level, whether of an athlete or a non-athlete, can reach about 180 to 200 beats per minute. The International High Altitude Expedition (1935) from the Fatigue Laboratory, Harvard University, made many pulse measurements on the investigators who were exercising at 17,000 feet up to 20,000 feet. The reduction in their heart rates from maximum sea level values, was in most investigators, as great as 40 to 50 beats per minute (maximum rates 130 to 150 b/m). Because of this diminished cardiac output in exercise at high altitude there

must be a diminished capacity for transport of oxygen.[*]

The explanation for the drop in maximum exercise heart rate must depend to varying degrees upon: (1) the increased blood volume and blood viscosity; (2) the direct effect of hypoxia on the pacemaker; and (3) primary hypertension (a reflex effect[439])

Basal Blood Pressure. Blood pressure is the value in millimeters of mercury by which the pressure in the vessels exceeds atmospheric pressure. Atmospheric pressure varies with altitude and these variations might have subtle effects on blood pressure. In spite of this, homeostatic con-

---

[*] Recent reviews on the effect of altitude on exercise have been contributed by Kellogg, Pugh and Velásquez in the book edited by Weihe[242a].

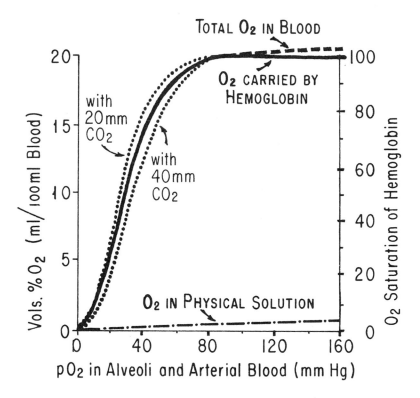

FIGURE 81. *Dissociation Curve for Oxygen and Oxygen Transport.* This curve relates partial pressure of oxygen in blood with percent saturation or with absolute amount of oxygen carried. It can also be called the Association Curve to emphasize what is carried at each partial pressure rather than what is unloaded. The Bohr effect is demonstrated; the curve moves to the right with a higher content of carbon dioxide in the blood. At the bottom of the diagram the oxygen transported in the water of the blood is graphed.

trol would "damp-out" these effects: it is not suprising that many expeditions at altitude have reported blood pressures within normal limits.[439] A few have found a rise of 10 to 15 mm Hg in diastolic pressure. At 16,000 feet, members of the N. Pace expedition to Makalu found that both systolic and diastolic pressures showed a uniform initial elevation which fell to normal with acclimatization.

Oxygen-Combining Capacity and the Heart. Another aspect of the circulatory system is oxygen transport. This is of course related to the providing of oxygen through the lungs, the physiology of breathing. Our first consideration must be the transport of hemoglobin by the blood. The most accurate measurement of circulating hemoglobin is obtained from the oxygen-combining capacity by the Van Slyke procedure. I will assume that the reader already understands the all-important dissociation-curve or "association"-curve for oxygen-combining capacity. This "S"-shaped curve expresses the relationship between oxygen-saturation and pressure; data from many other physiological relationships plot out to this same shape. Figure 81 shows the relationship when the partial pressure of oxygen varies, and readings are taken in either percent saturation of hemoglobin or volumes percent. One effect of living at altitude is usually

an increased proportion of red cells and also the total quantity of hemoglobin. An occasional individual at great heights may have the proportion of red cells that one expects at sea level. We will also find this to be true of animals in the free environment at high altitude. On the whole, however, one expects the mean red cell count to change from approximately 5 million at sea level to approximately 7 million at altitudes of 17,000 feet. These changes do not appear to relate to exercise or to being an athlete. Runners are not particularly "red-blooded" at sea level; the mean value for their hemoglobin concentration is the same as that of ordinary men.[134] The capacity to change the affinity of blood for oxygen has been experienced by all of us before and after being born. Barcroft *et al.*[410] first pointed out that the fetal blood of the goat has a notably higher affinity for oxygen than maternal blood; he emphasized this in the title of an address, "Everest in Utero". Physiologists express this affinity in terms of either "volumes percent" (the number of milliliters of gas which can be extracted by vacuum from a blood sample of 100 milliliters in volume), or alternatively, results are expressed as "percent saturation". Due to the low partial pressure of oxygen at 17,500 feet, the percent of saturation is only 73% even though the carrying capacity is high (Table 18). A convenient saturation figure for comparison is: in the arteries

Table 18. Effects of Low Atmospheric Pressures on Alveolar Gas Concentrations and Arterial Oxygen Saturation

Altitude (feet)	Barometric Pressure (mm Hg)	pO$_2$ in Air (mm Hg)	BREATHING AIR		
			pCO$_2$ in Alveoli (mm Hg)	pO$_2$ in Alveoli (mm Hg)	Arterial Oxygen Saturation (%)
0	760	159	40	104	97
10,000	523	110	36	67	90
20,000	349	73	24	40	70
30,000	226	47	24	21	20
40,000	141	29	24	8	5
50,000	87	18	24	1	1

of man at sea level, blood (not hemoglobin) is approximately 97% saturated (Fig.

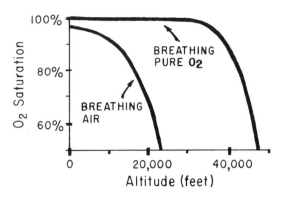

FIGURE 82. *Oxygen Saturation of Blood at Different Altitudes.* The transport of oxygen when breathing air is compared with breathing pure oxygen. For example, at 20,000 feet when breathing air the blood is 69% saturated but when breathing oxygen, it is 100% saturated. At 40,000 feet when breathing oxygen the blood is 85% saturated. From Guyton.[421]

82). At very high altitudes arterial blood saturation is apt to drop to near 56% in men who are not acclimatized or who cannot acclimatize. This figure is close to the critical value for man; death is apt to result if it drops lower than this.

What is the effect of the compensatory increase in red cells and hemoglobin on cardiac function? Experimentally in the laboratory an increase in blood hematocrit, if much above the normal level of 47, reduces the cardiac output because of increased blood viscosity; as a result, oxygen-carrying capacity of the blood is reduced. At altitude the heart must compensate for increased blood viscosity by doing more work.

Redistribution of Blood. Another acclimatization modification of the circulatory system at altitude is a redistribution of blood supply. This takes place by the opening up of new capillaries in minute vessels to suit the character of the blood passing through them.[428] In some individuals there is an increase of 1/3 in the proportion of

red cells and this increases the viscosity about 3-fold. The work of the heart would be greatly increased if it were not for a capacity for adjusting the number of open capillaries. A more important aspect of redistribution of blood is found in the thorax. This phenomenon has been described by Dr. Carlos Monge,[431, 432] the talented physiologist and sociologist who began his work on altitude with his thesis at San Marcos University (Lima) in 1911. Because of his thorough description of altitude effects, the sickness that may result may be referred to as Monge's disease (especially in already-acclimatized subjects). The redistribution of blood is described by Dr. Monge as follows: "At high altitudes, blood supply increases, and more of it is contained in the thorax to fix the relatively scarce atmospheric oxygen." In some unfortunate cases this increase fails to stop at the point of equilibrium and the patient virtually "drowns in his own blood".

In summary, it should be emphasized that the heart and the internal respiration are the principle limiting factors in muscular activity at great heights, at least before acclimatization is complete.

Respiratory Function*

The rate and depth of pulmonary ventilation starts to increase at about 8,000 feet, driven by chemoreceptors which are re-

---

* The relationship between pressure of the atmosphere and physiological events at different altitudes is presented in a table on the first page of this chapter. It should be noted that the per cents of oxygen for each altitude refer to oxygen equivalents; a figure of $X\%$ oxygen at Y altitude represents the situation of the animal breathing $X\%$ oxygen at sea level. In actual fact, although the pressure of the atmosphere is variable, the ratio of oxygen to nitrogen in the air remains constant at about 1:4. Even the samples collected in the highest stratosphere flights (from 13 to 21 miles) have revealed only a very slight difference in the value of this ratio. We say the decrease in partial pressure in oxygen is almost directly proportional to the decrease in air pressure. Other meteorological equivalents at altitude are given on p. 406 in Consolazio *et al.*[450a]

sponding to a drop in arterial oxygen saturation to about 93%. Ventilation continues to increase until about 16,000 to 20,000 feet at which a maximum of approximately 65% above normal will be reached. Further increase in altitude does not further activate the chemoreceptors.

We have established in the preceding section that it is the circulatory system which is a limiting factor for newcomers at high altitude; the ability to ventilate the lungs remains normal at high altitude. The "thinness" of the air seems to make the task of the respiratory muscles easier. On the International High Altitude Expedition it was found that the volume of air breathed per minute measured at the prevailing pressure and 37°C was greater than the volume attained at sea level. It is remarkable that the diaphragm and costal muscles utilize oxygen so effectively that they can ventilate the lungs this well under hypoxia. An abundance of myoglobin in the diaphragm must contribute to this unusual efficiency. Hurtado et al. did find that dogs born and reared in high altitude may have twice as great a concentration of myoglobin in a given tissue as that observed in sea-level dogs; the greatest increase was in the diaphragm tissue.[190] These observations have been confirmed with human muscles.[440] This companion pigment to hemoglobin is ideally suited for storing oxygen to sustain muscle from one contraction to another. It also assists oxygen transport within the tissue.

Cheyne-Stokes Breathing. Along with deeper breathing there is a change in breathing-rhythm. In his definitive work on the physiology of man on the High Alps, A. Mosso presented pneumograph records obtained at high altitude from numerous subjects including himself, his brother, the hut keeper and a dog brought from sea level. The pneumograph records were particularly striking because they showed long periods of arrested respiration during sleep. These intervals of arrest would last 12 seconds after two or three deep breaths. Of this periodic respiration at the Summit of Monte Rosa (14,957 feet), Mosso wrote:

"the periodic breathing sometimes continued for hours. A physician would say, on seeing these traces, that they were of a dying person." Two English physicians, Cheyne and Stokes, first described this intermittent respiration, and this form of breathing bears their names. Mosso was impressed with the remarkable diminution of breathing movements at rest. His many recordings and observations, especially during sleep, include periods when respiration was so superficial that it seemed to have stopped altogether. This is often experienced by non-acclimatized individuals who wake up frequently due to discomfort and distress associated with breathing. In fact, some hut keepers who remain for several months at altitude continue to show Cheyne-Stokes respiration during sleep (at altitude).

In the unacclimatized resting subject at high altitude there is a secondary large increase in volume of respiration, gradually over a day or so. The most efficient subject will increase tidal lung volume to 5 liters or more. If a physiological breakdown occurs, there is apt to be a poor respiratory response; this shows itself as rapid shallow breathing often resulting in fainting. The most successful subjects seem to increase the depth of breathing especially: *i.e.*, the tidal air more than the frequency.

The members of the International High Altitude Expedition of 1935 had the experiences with adjustments to altitude as described above. In 1962 six members of the original expedition did a follow-up study at 10,674 feet, at 12,500 feet and at 14,250 feet on Mt. Barcroft.[418] The goal was to learn how successfully they would acclimatize compared to when they were 27 years younger. As Dr. Dill[417] expressed it: "the objective evidence and subjective impressions pointed to a slower rate of acclimatization than in 1935. Headaches, dyspnea of exertion, and night-time Cheyne-Stokes breathing with associated loss of sleep were experienced by all of us in varying degrees but to a more severe and prolonged extent than before."

A concise way of expressing the effects

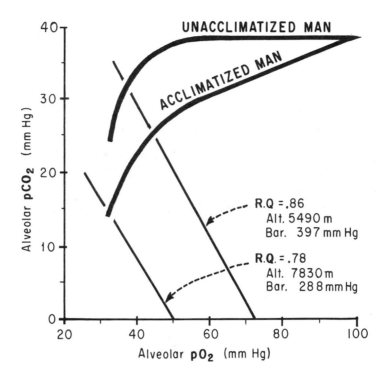

FIGURE 83. *Alveolar Gas Tensions Above 18,000 Feet.* The data above are presented on a Rahn-Otis diagram. Plotted points show mean values of end-expiratory Haldane samples taken at various altitudes on two mountains. The upper curve is the line for acutely exposed unacclimatized men. The lower curve is the line for acclimatized men. The samples provide a useful index of the degree of hypoxia tolerated by mountaineers after suitable acclimatization. In the unacclimatized subjects it is seen that elevation of alveolar pressure of oxygen due to increased ventilation is greatest in the region of 13,000 feet (4,000 meters). From Pugh.[2]

of respiratory gases at different altitudes is by the Rahn-Otis plot. An example is given in Figure 83; the upper curve represents findings in unacclimatized subjects acutely exposed to hypoxia, the lower curve acclimatized subjects. The success in elevating alveolar pO_2 due to increased ventilation is different in acclimatized subjects. At a given altitude, the alveolar pCO_2 is always lower and the pO_2 higher in the acclimatized man; also, the alveolar pCO_2 does not fall in the unacclimatized man until an alveolar pO_2 of 50 to 60 mm Hg is reached, whereas in the altitude residents, the fall begins at sea level (about 100 mm Hg). The gas samples from Everest and Makalu show the degree of hypoxia and the gain in arterial pO_2 due to acclimatization for those

particularly mountaineers (at 25,800 feet: pO_2 32 mm Hg; pCO_2, 15 mm Hg; arterial pO_2, 30 mm Hg; and arterial O_2 saturation 60%).

The return to sea level after acclimatization at 22,500 feet is typified by temporary retention of two acclimatization characteristics, persistant hyperventilation which is apt to disappear in 2 weeks, and the increased hemoglobin which may take 6 weeks to return to normal.[437]

Sense Organs and Brain

A slight decrease in oxygen saturation of the arterial blood depresses the function of the rods in the retina so that by the time 16,000 feet has been reached, the amount

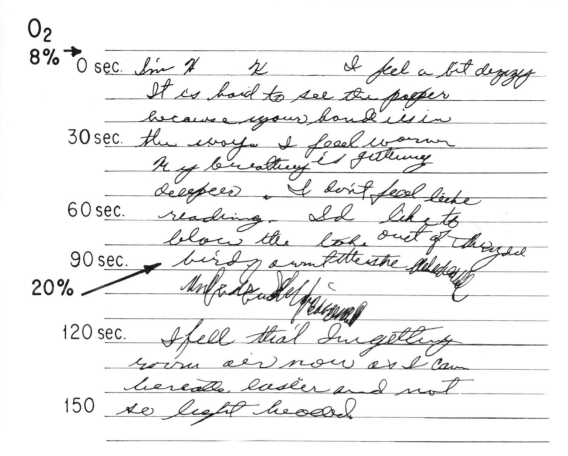

FIGURE 84. *Mental Effect of Hypoxia.* A common test under conditions of hypoxia is to have a subject write continuously. Such a test is shown with a volunteer medical student exposed to severe hypoxia. His name has been removed from the record. He was writing on a tablet held above his face during the experiment. He quickly began to make spelling mistakes with duplication of letters. Soon severe effects set-in with complete inability to carry out a mental and mechanical task. When the low oxygen supply was replaced with room air he recovered rapidly.

of light needed must be increased 140% for normal vision.[240]

Some individuals at 12,000 feet begin to show the following symptoms: sleepiness, headache, lassitude, mental fatigue, and sometimes a euphoric state (Fig. 84). At still higher altitudes the cerebral symptoms sometimes progress to the stage of twitchings and convulsions.

The possibility of after effects is of interest. Pugh[439] states that none of the climbers who ascended to 28,200 feet without oxygen equipment have suffered permanent after effects. All have been successful in careers demanding a high standard of mental ability; the list includes three university professors, a general, a colonial governor, and a prominent surgeon. One other man did have difficulty "remembering names of guests" when he returned to everyday life.

Acid-Base Balance

There is an alteration in acid-base balance due to the increased ventilation of the

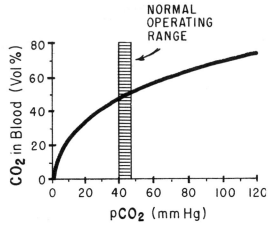

FIGURE 85. *Pressure of CO_2 at Source, and Blood Transport.* The relation between pressure of carbon dioxide in the tissues and transport in the blood is such that physiological function is served with a small variation in pressure. The range of partial pressures of carbon dioxide from tissue to alveoli usually lies between 40 and 46 mm, while that of oxygen varies from 20 to 100 mm. From Guyton.[421]

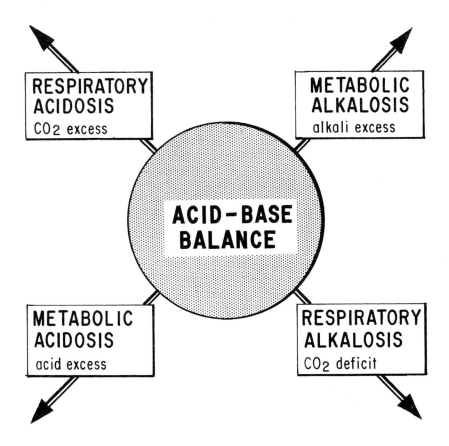

FIGURE 86. *Pathways of Acid Base Malfunction.* Four pathways of acid base disturbance are ordinarily understood; one of these takes on particular importance at high altitude. Because of increased ventilation a carbon dioxide deficit results which sets up respiratory alkalosis.

lungs at altitude. The interested reader should review the relationships between free and combined carbon dioxide and its influence upon acid-base balance (Fig. 85). This relationship is expressed in the Henderson-Hasselbach equation. Some of the principles are included in Figure 86. It is apparent that the major factors consist of: (1) holding back CO_2 by decreased breathing; (2) increased blowing off of CO_2; (3) increased bicarbonate or phosphate in the urine; or (4) a decrease in urinary excretion of these products. There are approximately nine states of equilibrium which can be attained by the variations just listed; combinations include normal range of pH, high pH, low pH, and compensated or uncompensated alkalosis or acidosis.

A specific example will be useful: the unacclimatized person at altitude may increase both the depth and rate of breathing (Fig. 87); the stimulus for this response cannot be a building of CO_2 in the body since this is automatically being eliminated so fast that the pH may rise to 7.8. This fall in CO_2 due to hyperventilation is called acapnia, and in this case the condition is called uncompensated CO_2 deficit. This begins when the ambient O_2 corresponds to 13% at an altitude of 11,000 feet. It must be due to sensitivity to O_2 of the vascular twigs or net in which nerve endings are found in the aortic and carotid bodies (in large arteries near heart). Compensation takes place by formation of acid metabolites, by kidney-rentention of acid products, and by excretion of bicarbonate. The condition would be compounded by vomiting (*i.e.* acid loss).

Gradually there is a reduction of combined CO_2 so that a person gets back to the original ratio of free to combined CO_2 as established at sea level. This means that the original homeokinetic state of the pH of the blood will be reestablished. At high altitude many people are not residents long enough to attain this reestablishment of the normal range of pH.

Mention has been made of the reduction in combined CO_2; this must entail the shift in concentration of other ions in serum. This decrease in bicarbonate in the individuals studied on the International High Altitude Expedition was about ½ balanced by an increase in chloride and about ¼ by reduction in sodium, leaving about ¼ unexplained. Further discussion is found in Hurtado.[2]

Lactic Acid in Blood. An unexplained characteristic of severe exercise at high altitude was revealed during the International High Altitude Expedition. With severe exercise at 12,000, 15,000 and 20,000 feet, blood samples showed a lactic acid content which was hardly above the usual resting level. The oxygen debt in men working to exhaustion decreases with altitude. Dill explains this unusual observation as follows: "It is as though the body, realizing the delicacy of the situation with regard to the oxygen supply, sets up an automatic control over anaerobic work which

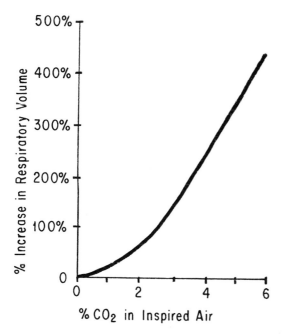

FIGURE 87. *Carbon Dioxide and Respiratory Volumes.* When carbon dioxide concentration in inspired air is raised the volume of respiration increases to many times normal level. An increase in respiratory volume does not bring about a corresponding increase in oxygen uptake. From Scott.[444]

renders impossible the severe acid-base disturbances which can be voluntarily induced
at sea level." [134] Thus it appears that after
prolonged residence at high altitude the organism responds in a labile fashion in certain directions and is resistant in others.

The Excretory System

It is possible that the sensation of thirst
is impaired at altitude; apparently the
members of early expeditions to Mount
Everest were severely dehydrated. Particular attention was given to hydration on
the 1953 Everest expedition. It was found
that for climbers, 3 to 4 liters of fluid per
day were required to maintain a urine output of 1.5 liters per day.[240] There is a high
fluid loss from the lungs due to the increased ventilation and the dry cold air.*

Acclimatization to High Altitude is Specific for Specific Altitudes

One point has not been discussed earlier
and that is whether acclimatization at a
moderate height helps to prepare the individual for much higher altitude. A careful
study by Pace on a climb up a mountain
next to Everest has helped to elucidate
this question.[437a] The goal was the summit
of Makalu (27,790 feet). The party spent
some time at 16,000 feet where it was apparent that acclimatization commenced after about 14 days. Then they moved to 21,-
500 feet and the symptoms which had been
experienced upon arrival at the lower stop-
ping place reoccurred; there were new
symptoms to overcome as well. All discomfort was greatly improved in 10 days. According to Pugh there is never complete
acclimatization over 20,000 feet, instead
there is always an underlying process of
deterioration.[2]

The Use of Oxygen Equipment

Until 1953 exploration and studies at high

---

* The Gemini Astronauts (June 1965) experienced this same dehydration because their space
suits evaporated moisture as fast as it was formed.
While on earth they required 1 liter of fluid per
day, when aloft they needed over 2 liters.

altitude were done without breathing from
oxygen equipment. Some groups made out
fairly well. The International High Altitude
Team lived at 17,500 feet for 3 weeks; all
of the party of 10 tolerated this altitude although some individuals were uncomfortable.[134] Another expedition occupied a hut
at 19,000 feet for 5½ months (Pugh[2]). Six
out of eight members felt well and ener-
getic but the remaining two had to descend periodically for a rest at lower altitude. Nine expeditions reached 28,200 feet
on Everest without oxygen equipment and
had to turn back. Pugh reports also that five
other expeditions without oxygen equipment tolerated high altitude each for a different duration: 11 days at 23,000 feet; 11
days at 24,600 feet; 5 days at 25,700 feet;
5 days at 25,900 feet; and 3 days at 27,400
feet. And still Everest (29,028 feet) was not
conquered until the 1953 expedition, when
Hillary and Tensing used open-circuit oxygen apparatus. In 1959 a peak of 26,800 feet
was climbed without oxygen equipment.
Most of the successful teams have followed
the example of Hillary; after 1953 the four
remaining mountains which are 27,900 feet
or higher have been scaled with the aid of
oxygen. It is pertinent that on the summit
of Everest, Hillary and Tensing stopped
using oxygen and spent 10 minutes breathing atmospheric air; while the Swiss party
in 1956 did this for 2 hours. A partial explanation of the apparent tolerance to
altitude by some men (such as a height of
28,200 feet without oxygen equipment) is
the discrepancy between calculated and actual barometric pressure in the warm season. The actual pressure on Everest when
it was climbed was nearer 250 mm Hg,
instead of the calculated 230 mm Hg.[2]

Human Acclimatization

An early belief in acclimatization to altitude was recorded by Glaisher in 1871.[421] He
was convinced that frequent balloon ascen-
sions result in acclimatization. In the earlier
sections of this chapter we did not distin-
guish between acquired acclimatization,
and natural acclimatization of natives who

are born at high altitude. These natives pose an interesting question about which there is little information: is their ability to tolerate altitude a genetic condition (based upon Darwinian adaptations)? In some cases they can carry over their ability to higher altitudes. Some natives of an Andean town at 14,900 feet were tested in an altitude chamber at a simulated 30,000 feet; half of them retained full consciousness and were able to write for an indefinite time.

The generalizations compiled in Table 19 for *acquired* acclimatization seem reasonable, each contingent upon the altitude.

Table 19. Acquired Acclimatization

At 14,000 Feet (from numerous publications)

The Response to Altitude	*Acclimatization*
1. Increased basal heart rate.	1. Basal heart rate in some subjects returns to normal in 3 days.
2. Subjects cannot sleep.	2. After 3 days most subjects can sleep.
3. All subjects show Cheyne-Stokes respiration during sleep.	3. Most subjects cease Cheyne-Stokes respiration in sleep. All subjects show increased sensitivity to further increase in altitude.
4. Resting tidal volume increases conspicuously. The hypoxic "drive" from chemoreceptors does not change with acclimatization.	4. There is a redistribution of blood, an increase in the chest area; the lung capillary bed is continuously dilated; the functional residual capacity increases.
5. Uncompensated alkalosis.	5. Many subjects achieve normal acid-base equilibrium (time needed varies).
6. Oxygen delivery to tissues is inadequate.	6. There is an increase in oxygen delivered to tissues. Total hemoglobin goes up as much as 90%. The hematocrit rises from a normal of 40 to 45 to as high as 60 to 70; hemoglobin goes from 15 to 22 gm %; blood volume increases 20 to 30%; plasma volume stays the same.
7. Some subjects experience headache and nausea.	7. These symptoms disappear in 3 days.

At 16,000 Feet (Pace Expedition [437a])

1. Fatigue, headache, loss of appetite, sleeplessness (all subjects). Systolic and diastolic pressure showed uniform elevation.	1. All returned to normal in 14 days.

At 21,500 Feet (Pace Expedition [437a])

1. Symptoms above returned, plus progressive exertional dyspnea, irritative coughs, impatience, depression and nocturnal muscle cramps.	1. All improved in 10 days.
2. A persistent increase in heart rate, expected even after acclimatization.	

COMPARATIVE PHYSIOLOGY OF ALTITUDE EFFECTS

Small Domestic Mammals

Dogs suffer from mountain sickness and exhibit the same symptoms as man. If they are exposed to acute altitude effects in a pressure chamber, they are troubled with sleepiness, vomiting, labored breathing, muscular weakness, and inability to stand on their legs. These symptoms are lost rapidly and they acquire excellent acclimatization. When men are exposed in a pressure chamber, after several hours one-fourth of the subjects show no change in the number of red blood cells; the greatest change which can be attained in a pressure chamber is a rise of 5 to 10%. Much larger percentages are obtained from dogs, indicating that they can mobilize red blood cells on short notice.

Dill[2] observed dogs at 16,400 feet and at various heights up to 20,130 feet. The owners had observed that as the dogs became acclimatized, they lost weight and became more irritable than at lower heights, effects which are commonly observed in man. The dogs' physical ability was not impaired; two of them were observed by Dr. Dill at 16,000 feet as they ran about 15 miles at 15 mph behind a truck without showing fatigue. Another climbed to over 20,000 feet without symptoms of fatigue.

The domestic cat is very susceptible to the action of rarefied air. According to Mosso, in South America cats are never seen in places higher than 11,000 feet; he states that cats transported to an elevation of 13,000 feet, where all other domestic animals thrive, show depressed activity and after a few days most of them die in convulsions of an epileptic character. On the other hand Dr. Dill on the High Altitude Expedition saw healthy cats at 12,000 feet, one at 15,600 feet but none at 17,500 feet.

Mosso[436] tested cats in altitude chambers and made the surprising observation that with a resting or sleeping individual, as altitude was attained, the breathing became slower and more superficial. The respiration is ordinarily approximately 30 c/m. A barometric depression to an equivalent of 9,400 feet reduced the rate of breathing by 10 cycles per minute.

The explanation of the altitude sensitivity of the cat is not clear. Many other mammals are essentially like the dog, especially in respect to oxygen capacity. If blood characteristics were the only criteria, the ability to tolerate altitude would be similar in many mammals, for the oxygen capacity of red cells in a series from man to sheep is very similar. This is strikingly demonstrated by an artificial test: the measurement is the oxygen capacity of a liter of red cells from each animal. Most types of red cells carry about 45 volumes per-

Table 20. Hemoglobin and Red Cells of Some Vertebrates

(Modified from Dill[134])

	Red cells in blood million/mm³	ml/liter	Oxygen Capacity of a Liter of Red Cells vols % (ml/liter)
Man	5.00	460	457
Dog	6.68	517	445
Horse	8.18	380	492
Ox	6.98	416	463
Rabbit	4.55	354	441
Sheep	10.53	353	455
Llama	12.11	275	584
Vicuna	14.90	305	571

* Other values for oxygen capacity of blood at high altitude and sea level are given in Prosser and Brown, page 223[152].

cent of oxygen (Table 20). The cells of the llama and vicuna are an exception, since they could carry 57 to 58 vols% (¼ more). These unusual members of the camel family should be considered next.

Large, Free-Living Highland Mammals

We have been considering domestic animals; we may now turn our attention to free-living animals at altitude. The vicuña will serve as an example of a large mammal adapted for life at great heights. This camel has highly prized wool, so that exportation of skins and fur from South American countries is prohibited. Their ability to adapt to high altitude was demonstrated on the International High Altitude Expedition when the party in an automobile chased a band of them at an altitude of 15,000 feet.[134] Dill remarks, "The automobile seemed to be more handicapped than the vicuña at this altitude."

This expedition transported a vicuña by train to 15,000 feet and by truck to 17,500 feet. Although it is known that in high altitudes the concentration of hemoglobin in the blood of man increases, this increase was not found in the vicuña or its domesticated relative, the llama. The specimens studied showed up to an 8% increase, or a slight decrease. As a basis of comparison four llamas studied at sea level all had more hemoglobin than the ones studied in high altitude. The blood of these South American camels had a greater affinity for oxygen than that of any other mammal so far studied. This physiological advantage is apparent on the dissociation curve (Fig. 88). When arterial pO_2 is 40 mm Hg, the vicuña transports 18 vols %, man transports 14, and the sheep, 8.0. The vicuña can utilize 0.7 of the oxygen-carrying capacity of his blood, man can utilize 0.6, and the sheep can use only 0.4 (under this condition of pO_2 40 mm Hg). The ability of the vicuña and the llama to deliver oxygen to tissues at high altitude does not depend upon the number of cells per unit of blood; in fact the blood of these camels is relatively dilute (hematocrit 28 and 31%). The explanation of the high oxygen capacity of the two species is the close packing of the protein hemoglobin in the red cells.

Man and domestic animals brought from sea level compensate for their disadvantage by increasing the quantity of hemo-

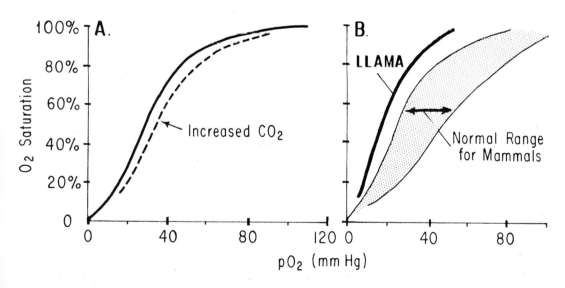

FIGURE 88. *Oxygen Binding Capacity of Different Hemoglobins.* Curve A demonstrates how the oxygen dissociation curve is moved to the right by the increased presence of carbon dioxide. For a single passage of blood, oxygen loading can be read on the solid curve and unloading on the dotted curve. In Curve B the behavior of a blood is demonstrated for the llama which lives under conditions of low oxygen pressure. This blood binds oxygen more readily than does that of other mammals. From Schmidt-Nielsen.[441]

globin in the blood. A man could deliver as much oxygen as the vicuña provided he had 1/6 more hemoglobin, while the sheep would require nearly double the amount of hemoglobin to accomplish this. The vicuña and the llama do not need an increase in hemoglobin; their sea level oxygen supply is adequate for their needs even at 17,000 feet.

A relevant point should be made about the survival of erythrocytes in high altitude camels. Experiments with mammalian species indigenous to high altitude have revealed their longer erythrocyte survival times.[415] Approximate erythrocyte survival times (in days) for control and high altitude mammals are:

Control		*High-altitude mammals*	
rat	55	Barbary sheep	170
man	120	tahr goats	165
horse	140	wild llama	235

In the high-altitude group all measurements were made at sea level. Their response to altitude still remains to be studied.

Large Domestic Mammals

The mule seems to have unusual ability to adapt to high altitude; several were used at the Quilcha mine camp, used as a base by the International High Altitude Expedition. The mules carried personnel from 17,500 feet up to the 18,800 foot level. Dill suggests that this rugged performance depends upon the ability of the mule to gauge accurately its own capacity for work and to refuse to be pushed beyond a safe limit. The mule stops and pants when he has accumulated an oxygen debt. Horses can acclimatize to 14,000 feet but are not found higher.

Domestic sheep have a low oxygen saturation of arterial blood both at sea level and at altitude. This is in spite of a large increase in hemoglobin at altitude. Sheep studied by Dill at 17,500 feet had an arterial saturation of 56%. In order to exist at this altitude these animals must

unload nearly all the oxygen carried by their blood (venous blood was 6.8% saturated); thus the sheep circulates one-half his hemoglobin without using it in oxygen transport. In spite of this handicap this animal is able to tolerate 17,500 feet and even to reproduce at 14,000 feet.

Small Free-Living Animals

Some small mammals at high altitude have the adaptations described earlier in large mammals. Morrison has devised an interesting test (with a sharp end point) for these adaptations.[433] The mammal is placed in a cold environment so that its metabolism increases; then the oxygen environment is lowered. When the transport of oxygen for this particular species reaches a critical point, hypothermia results. Well-adapted animals at altitude could still maintain their temperature regulation effectively at a pressure about 1/3 that of sea level. Of species collected by Morrison at sea level, the least effective was a rat-sized rodent related to guinea pigs (Table 21). The critical pressure for this rodent was sometimes reached at a pO_2 of 110 to 120 mm Hg, a reduction of only one-quarter from that at sea level. The other extreme was seen in a species of the high altitude type, a small rodent, which could still be effective at a partial pressure of 50 to 60 mm Hg, or about one-third that of sea level. The animals from high altitudes were on the whole much more effective than animals from sea level, but this was not always the case. The best species collected at sea level was more effective than several of the species collected at altitude. According to Morrison the different performance of different species from the same environment appeared to relate to general "fitness". Thus the best performing lowland species was markedly the most vigorous of the lowland species, and its greater metabolic potential would be expected to be effective under the handicap of hypoxia. In a similar manner, wild guinea pigs showed greater performance than their more sedentary domestic relatives at the same altitude. The superior test-performance of most rodents from high altitude in the Andes

Table 21. Hematological Comparisons of Mammals From High and Low Altitude

A. *Highland Species Studied in Native High Altitude Habitat*

ANIMAL	RESULTS	REFERENCE
1. Man resident at high altitude	Elevated erthrocyte count and hemoglobin level	[2]
2. Russian mice (mountain race)	Elevated erythrocyte count	[430]
3. Peromyscus (deer mice)	Elevated hemoglobin 45% at 12,500 ft., 90% at 14,300 ft.	[425]
4. 5 species of high altitude rodents (Chile)	Hematocrit not higher than 8 sea level species	[435]
5. More vigorous species at high altitude (and sea level) (Chile)	20% higher hematocrit than in less vigorous species	[435]

B. *Lowland Species Moved To High Altitude*

6. White rat (chamber hypoxia)	Hematocrit of 85%	[422]
7. Mus (feral)	Increase from 47% to 57%	[435]
8. White rat (field laboratory)	At 13,000 ft. a 45% increase in hematocrit	[445]

C. *Highland Species Moved To Sea Level*

9. 3 highland species of rodents in Chile	No reduction in hematocrit after 2 months, nor in offspring	[435]
10. 4 highland species of rodents in Peru	No reduction in one month, then a reduction of 5%	[435]
11. Peromyscus (deer mice)	A decrease in running performance from that at 13,000 ft.	[425]

Note: a lowland Phyllotis (in Peru) had a higher hematocrit than any of the highland Phyllotis (three species).

seems to relate to the improvement in transport capacity with which the species has adapted to their hypoxic environment.

What adaptations permit some species at altitude to be effective, and what signs of acclimatization are found there in small mammals? Usually highland species do not have a higher hematocrit (recall that the highland camels have rather dilute blood) (Table 20). On the contrary when lowland rodent species are moved to altitude, they increase all three of the following: erythrocyte number, hematocrit value,

and hemoglobin. With deer mice, heart weights increase with altitude.[425] When the highland species were moved to sea level, (Table 21, C), for the most part their hematocrit level proved to be a genetic adaptation since it did not change at sea level.

A few comments on high altitude birds will be of interest: Humboldt[427] reported condors at 23,000 feet; these were observed when he was breaking a high altitude record for man in 1802 by climbing to 19,286 feet. The chough (a crow-like bird) was observed even higher at 27,000 feet on

Everest. Dill observed pheasants at 16,000 feet. What adaptations these three species have is a problem for the present generation of Environmental Physiologists.

COMPARISON OF ALPINE AND ARCTIC ENVIRONMENTS

There are characteristics of high altitude other than low oxygen pressure; these are low air temperatures, deep snow, and barren terrain. We will find it profitable to compare two areas which have these 3 characteristics: (1) the Alpine or high altitude area, and (2) the Arctic or far north tundra area. This comparison may be justified by the concept of Merriam who pointed out the striking botanical correspondence and climatic similarity between the high altitude portion of mountains and the Arctic tundra. There are also negative votes cast on the possibility of making a reasonable comparison between these two cold-weather areas; one ecologist claims that there is no more reason to compare alpine and arctic areas than there is reason to compare a pine forest in Texas and a spruce forest in Canada. Furthermore, do tundra flora and fauna represent a special group in an ecological sense or are they more of a biological-wastebasket? The first question, as to whether the alpine and arctic areas are similar will be answered in detail in the next few pages. Perhaps the justification can be found in the case of an ecologist in Texas who has an Alpine area within a 6-hour bus ride from his laboratory. He must be prepared to discuss with his students whether or not this is a relic Arctic area. He will find that some rodents there are only comparable to tundra rodents; this naturally turns his attention to the characteristics of other tundra mammals.

What is The Alpine Area?

If we use a physiological index to define the alpine area, our first clue is that altitude effects on man may begin as low as 6,500 feet; at 10,000 feet rather conspicuous symptoms may begin. During a recent research project conducted on Mount Evans, Colorado, some of the investigators attempted to house their families at motels at 10,000 feet. Some individuals were unable to tolerate this altitude and became ill, especially while trying to sleep; thus we see a conspicuous physiological cutoff point for some people at 10,000 feet, although there is no striking clue in the geographical appearance.

Above this level, starting about 10,600 feet, there are apt to be conspicuous changes in botanical, faunistic, and climatic conditions, so that such an area is now referred to as "alpine". Opinions as to the starting-altitude vary; six starting points listed by six authors vary from 10,600 to 12,000 feet. This is understandable since these "alpine islands" must "cap" their individual peaks and ridges slightly differently in variable geographical areas.

In the discussion to follow, we will disregard those high mountain tops in Alaska which might correspond in structure to alpine areas in the "lower 49 states." The reason for this is that they are permanently snowy, icy, and barren areas, with very few mammals living there; for example, the dry snow line on Mt. Wrangell, Alaska, (14,168 feet) is at 12,000 feet.[426] The wet snow line is nearer 6,000 feet.[438]

What is Tundra?

For the sake of convenience we will select as an example of tundra the Arctic Slope found north of the Brooks Range in Northern Alaska. Ehrlich and Holm, 1962, define the tundra biome as a treeless northern plain with no floristic or faunistic "source" or "center of origin";[419] this thought-provoking statement reflects their attempt to describe the complicated origin of the tundra. Another author has described the tundra as a wet arctic grassland frozen most of the time. We can also say that beginning above latitude 65° tundra can be found at sea level, but farther south it is only on the mountain sides.

Similarities Between Arctic and Alpine Areas in the U.S.

A comparison of some of the biological and physical factors typical of arctic and alpine areas will be of value. We will first consider what they have in common:

1. A striking botanical correspondence:

   (a) The Presidential Range, N. H., has 70 alpine species of plants all of which are also found in the arctic.

   (b) In Colorado there are over 250 species of alpine plants, 40% of which are found in the arctic.[414]

2. Only a few species of animals and plants live in each area. There is a uniform set of conditions with specific requirements. There are few habitats, thus the few species of mammals. Both places have a simple biologic structure.

3. A "master physical factor rules these lands"—lack of heat. "Seasonal distortion" is found in both areas; the frost-free period is often less than 60 days but sometimes lasts 80 to 90 days. There is a short growing season thus few food types. Insects are present only 2 months. Large herbivores cannot find enough food in any one local area to support themselves. Both areas are poor nutritionally.

4. Both places have high winds, but this has more meaning in the arctic area because there is less protection there. Mount Washington, N. H., has a record wind speed of 225 mph.

Differences Between Arctic and Alpine Areas in the U.S.

1. Photoperiod: 82 days of continuous light and 82 days of continuous darkness at Barrow, Alaska. The growth of mammals is affected.

2. Arctic summers have even temperatures; alpine summers are very fluctuating.

3. Arctic has little moisture with thin snow cover. At Barrow in the month of greatest snow depth there are 15.9 inches (20-year average). In some alpine areas there can be as much as 76 inches of snow a day, or 1,000 inches per season.

4. Oxygen pressure is low in the alpine area; breathing air at 14,000 feet corresponds to breathing 13% oxygen. The arctic tundra is close to sea level.

5. The arctic tundra has permafrost. This is several hundred to more than 1,000 feet in depth. Each year the upper 6 to 8 inches of soil thaws. This has an influence on the digging of burrows and dens by arctic mammals. Apparently there is no permafrost in alpine areas which can affect mammalian populations.

6. Drainage differences: the alpine is well-drained; the arctic has a great deal of trapped surface water and thus it supports more grass. Near Point Barrow, the lakes and streams cover one-half the surface, but they are frozen most of the time.

7. There is a desert influence on alpine flora; in Colorado of more than 250 species of alpine plants, 65 are desert forms.[414]

8. The lichens dominate the arctic slope but not the alpine area.

9. There are differences in limitation: the alpine "islands" are only hundreds of feet in vertical area; the Arctic Slope encompasses 40,000 square miles. In the alpine area, migrations take place down to coniferous forests (Fig. 89). There are fewer species-migrations in the arctic.

FAUNA OF THE ARCTIC AND ALPINE AREAS

I first became interested in comparing the fauna of alpine and arctic areas after reading the statement by Schwartz[443] concerning the origin of some tundra animals: "In the Arctic the mountain mammals are still strictly confined to the mountains and nowhere do they penetrate the tundra. This contrasts to that of some of the avian and insect fauna which apparently have been preadapted for tundra life by alpine living." His statement was

FIGURE 89. *Bristlecone Pine Zone.* A view of the bristlecone zone between 8,500 and 11,500 feet in some areas of the Rocky Mountains. These are the oldest living trees, up to 4,900 years.[416] The zone is of particular interest to students of the arctic-alpine area because here tundra and forest mammals meet in their distribution. Courtesy Gordon Kent.

made about Siberian tundra: it seems useful to look for similarities and differences in lists of mammals from American mountains and American tundra. Two samples of mammals living on typical high mountains are presented for this discussion. By consideration of the vertical ranges of these mammals we may understand more clearly the factors of adaptation to altitude. We will also be in a position to select the most profitable animals for future physiological experiments on acclimatization and genetic adaptation. A diagram is presented to illustrate a very interesting area, part of Owens Valley (near Death Valley) in California (Fig. 90). By chance there are 42 species

in this area, in the valley and on both mountain slopes,* and there also happen to be 42 species on the Arctic Slope if the aquatic mammals are included. By way of comparison, Morrison cites the census for the tundra of Siberia as 33 species of land mammals.[434] The habitat-diagram of the species living in the Inuo-White section of Owens Valley shows some of the mammals with the largest vertical range and therefore the ones most likely to show genetic adaptations or an ability to acclimatize to altitude. The deer mouse at various alti-

---

* Note that in the entire Owens Valley area including Mount Whitney, there are 100 species of mammals.

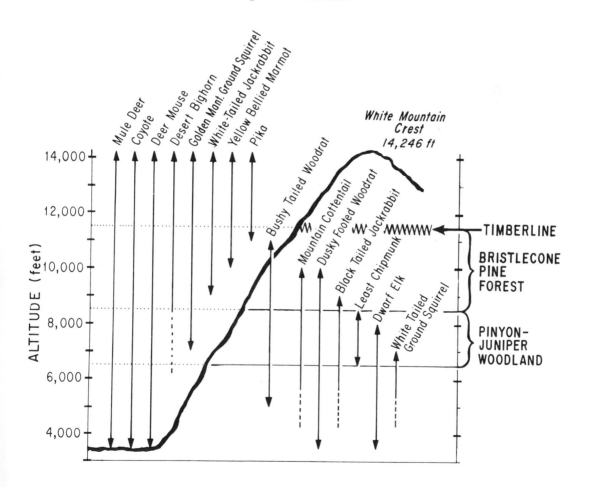

FIGURE 90. *Altitude and Mammalian Distribution.* A study of the vertical distribution of mammals, as depicted on this typical California peak, stimulates many unanswered questions for the student of mammalian environmental physiology. A series of experimental questions for the future are listed in the text.

tudes has been intensively studied by Hock.[425] Other intriguing species are: the golden-mantled ground squirrel, the bushy-tailed woodrat, the porcupine, and the shrews. More detailed studies of mammals have been made on Mount Evans, Colorado, making this area more suitable for comparison with the Arctic Slope of Alaska. The list of mammals in the two areas are:

samples listed, the arctic area seems to have a richer fauna.

Adaptations of Arctic and Alpine Species

It is now of interest to consider some sample adaptations to be found in the two environments; perhaps these adaptations

The Alpine Mammals of Mt. Evans, Colorado	The Arctic Tundra Mammals North of the Brooks Range
Whitetail Deer	Moose
Mule Deer	Caribou
Bighorn	Dall Sheep
Red Fox	Red Fox
Coyote	Coyote
Yellow-Bellied Marmot	Hoary Marmot
Rocky Mountain Goat	Pika
Pika	Collared Lemming
Deer Mouse	Brown Lemming
Cottontail	Tundra Hare
Porcupine	Porcupine
Marten	Wolverine
Longtailed Weasel	Ermine
Pocket Gopher	Least Weasel
Sorex c.	*Sorex c.*
Zapus	*Sorex o.*
Mountain Lion	*Sorex a.*
Black Bear	Black Bear
Bobcat	Lynx
Chipmunk	Red-backed Vole
Boreal Vole	Tundra Vole
Meadow Vole	Singing Vole
Mountain Vole	Mink
(Bison)	Otter (River)
(Gray Wolf)	Gray Wolf
	(Musk Ox)
	Arctic Ground Squirrel
	Grizzly Bear
	Arctic Fox

Here we have compared the fauna of two extremely rigorous environments: the arctic tundra, and the alpine meadows (which represent an area deficient in oxygen). The similarity in animal life is remarkable considering the distance which separates the alpine and tundra areas. Judging from the

might permit alpine and arctic species to be interchanged. A comparison of adaptations from the two areas is reasonable since there are many characteristics of the alpine area which are not concerned with a limited supply of oxygen.

The most conspicuous adaptation for

tundra life appears to be small body size. This is in contrast to an area like the African Veldt where there are numerous species which are of large size. Morrison [446] supports this view, reporting that 70% of the check list of 33 species for the Siberian tundra are under 1 kilogram, 60% are under 100 grams. A second generalization for adaptation to tundra life is an easy acclimatization which may not be lost in the summer.[446] A third characteristic is that of utilization of a low grade food. A fourth is an increased ability to mobilize bodily reserves such as glycogen in the liver. The next generalization applies to breeding: larger litters of young are frequently found in tundra mammals, although this does not apply to lemmings. In this regard Morrison points out that the reproduction occurs at a younger age, supporting the statement with an example of a northern subspecies of *Microtus* which breeds successfully at 10 to 12 days of age and produces offspring at 30 days. These observations may eventually be found to apply to small mammals in the "alpine islands" of North America, irrespective of the presence of a low partial pressure of oxygen.

Photoperiodic Responses. Another adaptation of arctic mammals which we may expect in alpine mammals is concerned with photoperiod. It is a generalization that arctic rodents synchronize their seasonal activities without conspicuous dependence on light. This would seem to be a necessary adaptation because of the long periods of continuous darkness (except for moonlight and northern lights) and the long period of continuous light. At Barrow, Alaska, these periods extend for approximately 82 days each. Since this extreme condition of a light environment does not usually apply to the alpine area, especially in the "lower 49 states", one would not expect to find an independence from photoperiod in mammals in the high mountains. Nevertheless there is some evidence that alpine mammals also are independent of photoperiod. For example, the Columbia ground squirrel (*Spermophilus columbianus*) hibernates for 7 months from mid-July to March. Because of the time at which it goes into

hibernation, one would have to postulate that it responds to a decreasing photoperiod of about 16.5 hours. This is an unusual photoperiod for rodents to respond to, and it seems more likely that the animal is relatively independent of the use of photoperiod as a clue for annual activities. Furthermore Pengelley and Fisher [389] have experimentally demonstrated that one of the ground squirrels already indicated as an important one in the present discussion, the golden-mantled ground squirrel, actually is independent of photoperiod in the laboratory environment. At first this consideration of this particular adaptation seems to result in a conspicuous similarity in arctic and alpine mammals; unfortunately the picture is complicated by the southern sea-level squirrel, the 13-lined ground squirrel (see Chapter 7) which also does not depend upon photoperiod.

Mammals With Special Adaptations For Arctic And Alpine Living

Porcupine. The North American porcupine should be considered next because of its unusual distribution. It is found at sea level across the United States (except in 17 southeastern states), and also at the summit of White Mountain, California, and the summit of Mount Evans in Colorado. Probably it may be called a common alpine form. More importantly it has been found at the tip of North America at Barrow, Alaska; one specimen has been collected on Point Barrow and another wandered through the Eskimo village of Barrow. It lives on the tundra by digging roots and sleeps in fox or wolf dens. One cannot help but ask whether the individual porcupines wandering on to the tundra would have survived the next winter; it does seem unlikely, however, that this type of animal could walk the 200 miles from the Brooks Range to Barrow Village in one short summer. Whatever the conditions of its being found on the tundra, it is apparent that this animal (although primarily a forest animal) is adapted for tundra living and alpine living. Because of its broad distribution and high vertical distribution, and its ability to live on varied food materials the study of this animal should prove particularly fruitful to the environmental physiologist; the physiological devices of acclimatization of this species may turn out to be conspicuous.

Pika. A small mammal which symbolizes the fauna of high mountain peaks is the Alaskan and the alpine pika. This is one of the most interesting animals to be found at high altitude because it lacks conspicuous physiological adaptations. Their rodent neighbors, the ground squirrels and marmots, combat the extreme environments by hibernation. Although the pika has the unusual adaptation of storing dried grass, as far as is known it has no physiological adaptations except a tolerance to very cold temperature. Dr. Viereck[446] has taken burrow temperatures in winter near Fairbanks, Alaska, where active pikas were found. These burrows were not protected by snow because this would not pack due to excessive wind; as a result burrow temperatures were near air temperatures, which were as low as —22°C. Probably many pikas in central and western United States live under very deep drifts of snow. Much more experimental work is needed with this especially interesting alpine resident.

Marmot. A comparison of two species of marmots will now be useful, one living in the subarctic and arctic and the other living in midwest United States in mountain alpine; these are the hoary marmot and the yellow-bellied marmot. The natural history of these two species will serve as an illustration of a partial answer to the question: does physiology control distribution? Another reason for detailed consideration is that the hoary marmot appears to be an exception to the statement by Schwartz[443] that there are no mammals of the tundra that have been preadapted for tundra life by alpine living; the arctic marmot does occur at sea level.[411] Normally in Alaska it is found in the high mountains of the Alaska Range, in Mount McKinley Park, and in the Brooks Range. It will be of interest to look for other species which have this vertical distribution and may be exceptions to the rule of Schwartz; perhaps

the pika is also an exception. If at first one is puzzled by the presence of the marmot in mountains up to possibly 15,000 feet and again at sea level on the Arctic Slope, on second thought one realizes that this is predictable. As long as the substratum is satisfactory the animal will in addition find alpine vegetation at sea level. For example there is a broad vertical distribution of the lichen which this animal prefers to eat. In spite of its distribution in the high latitudes the marmot's hibernation behavior is not similar to the hibernation behavior of the Columbian ground squirrel described earlier. The marmot is still active on the Arctic Slope even when the first snows fall in late August and September. In September it does go into hibernation (under a short photoperiod of approximately 11½ hours) and remains in hibernation until May or June.

Is the natural history of this species similar to that of the yellow-bellied marmot of the midwest and western mountains? If this southern marmot showed the same flexibility in vertical distribution of its northern counterpart, then we would have to consider it a dominant species such as the deer mouse and the porcupine.[346] One of the lowest altitude records of a yellow-bellied marmot colony is in the paper by Armatich on social behavior, a colony studied at 6,880 feet.[409] This species has not expanded its vertical range in the fashion of the hoary marmot. This is in spite of the fact that it does not appear to depend upon rock piles for protection to the same extent as the hoary marmot. Armatich reports animals living in burrows unprotected by rocks or logs. If the differences between the two species can be explained, they will help us understand the contribution made by physiological factors in determining the vertical distribution of such species.

Arctic Voles, Lemmings and Shrews. One question about adaptations of arctic and alpine mammals has not been considered, the substratum in which or on which they live. In the summer many small arctic mammals stay beneath the tundra mat. A word has been coined to describe such an existence, referred to as "subnivean". Another group of small mammals does not stay beneath the tundra mat. The same habits apply in the winter, the first group staying in burrows and under the snow and the second group running on the surface of the snow. In group one is found *Clethrionomys* (vole), *Lemmus* (lemming), and shrews. In the other, living on the surface of the mat and at times on the surface of the snow are *Microtus* (vole) and *Dicrostonyx* (lemming). It will be demonstrated later in a comparison of the physical environment of the two areas that those animals that stay beneath the tundra mat experience very little change in temperature during the winter and the summer.[446] Perhaps this explains the very broad distribution of two of the shrews which extend from North Alaska to a line across central United States. It is as if these shrews and the other species are "unaware" that they are in the arctic; in a sense they live in a temperate environment. In carrying this comparison over to the alpine area, as one might expect both Clethrionomys and shrews do occur there apparently living in a protected environment under the snow. The surface-living species must be true arctic species with successful adaptations for tolerating temperatures as low as —50°F. One of these species (*Dicrostonyx*) has been studied in detail and found to have very high fur insulation.[433] A reasonable question to ask is whether the subnivean lemming (Lemmus) has existed so long in a relatively constant environment, that it is not adapted to tolerate heat; this is the case—this species is heat-sensitive.

Jackrabbits. In the section above a comparison is found of two arctic species of closely related rodents living in different habitats and possessing marked physiological differences. There is no comparable information on alpine species; one pair (two species of jackrabbits) is worth considering since they have a range that slightly overlaps, and one of them has a vertical distribution including the alpine area. Hock [424] suggests that there are fairly conspicuous anatomical and physiological differences

between them; these differences would represent an illustration of Allen's Rule regarding protruding parts (see Appendix), if this rule can be applied to a species as well as to a race. Hock finds the following different characteristics of the species, some of them exaggerated as the cold season approaches:

White-Tailed Jackrabbit	Black-Tailed Jackrabbit
Thick fat layers	Less winter fat
Thicker fur	Thinner fur
Large body mass	Smaller mass
Shorter legs and ears	Longer legs and ears

A particular interesting study might be made on the white-tailed jackrabbit because of its large altitudinal distribution (up to 14,000 feet). With vertical distribution one should look within the race for a change in weight because of the decrease in ambient temperature with height; as phrased by Bergman (1847): [412] "body size increases in colder climates". Hock did not show this increase in weight of deer mice of the same species on White Mountain collected at colder climatic levels of the Mountain.[425] A checklist for other possible changes within the species (sampled from the alpine, and from the lowest point in its range toward sea level), would be: oxygen carrying capacity of blood, number of red cells, amount of hemoglobin, size of heart, size of lungs, and size of thorax. All of these factors might show a relative increase in the sample *taken* from altitude. It should be noted that Scholander contests the validity of both Allen's and Bergman's Rules.[422]

Physiological Control of Distribution of Mammals

Experimental work on altitude biology must be partially concerned with physiological control of animal distribution. Clearly the relationship between climate, geography, and physiological mechanisms are complicated. Bartholomew has emphasized that physiology helps to explain how mammals can live in their particular range but it rarely explains the exact limits of their distribution.[359] This comment of his has been ellucidated in more detail in an earlier chapter (Hibernation).

SUMMARY

This chapter has been concerned with the physiological expressions of the stress imposed by the rarified air at altitude. The resulting physiological strain is conspicuous in the circulatory system, the respiratory system, and the excretory system. Acclimatization to altitude consists of a partial correction of the deficits which are so evident in both the person and the domestic animal at high altitude; the term "partial-correction" is indicated because in actuality the oxygen-carrying capacity of even a native at high altitude is never the same as found in those individuals at sea-level. Even acclimatized athletes at altitude show more distress than do natives of that altitude. Gradually in man and domestic animals, with the exception of the domestic cat, the conspicuous evidences of altitude stress disappear, and fatigue is no longer apparent. Some of the characteristics of altitude acclimatization are evident in natives at high altitude. Some of them also are found in free-living mammals at high altitude, although some high-altitude mammals show no characteristics different from their counterparts at sea level. The point has been emphasized that there is acclimatization for each prolonged camp in a climb to high altitude; i.e., after physiological adjustments to a moderate altitude, the individuals concerned must next be acclimatized to more extreme altitudes. A detailed discussion is presented of the characteristics of the altitude environment which are not concerned with low oxygen pressure. If the factor of low oxygen pressure is disregarded (and there is justification for this) a reasonable comparison of the alpine area can be made with that of the arctic tundra. This comparison has been made in detail on the grounds that the comparative mammalian physiologist who wishes to work on alpine mammals will find it valuable to concern himself with the physiology of arctic mammals; for this reason, some background material on arctic mammals is included.

HIGH PRESSURE

FROM AIR AND WATER

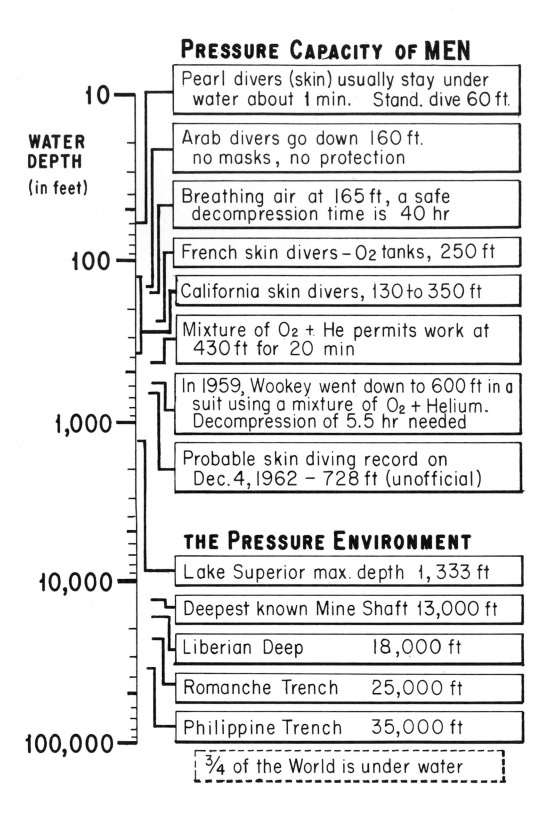

Pressure Capacity of MEN

WATER DEPTH (in feet)

10 — Pearl divers (skin) usually stay under water about 1 min.   Stand. dive 60 ft.

Arab divers go down 160 ft. no masks, no protection

Breathing air at 165 ft, a safe decompression time is 40 hr

100 — French skin divers – O₂ tanks, 250 ft

California skin divers, 130 to 350 ft

Mixture of O₂ + He permits work at 430 ft for 20 min

1,000 — In 1959, Wookey went down to 600 ft in a suit using a mixture of O₂ + Helium. Decompression of 5.5 hr needed

Probable skin diving record on Dec. 4, 1962 – 728 ft (unofficial)

The Pressure Environment

10,000 — Lake Superior max. depth 1,333 ft

Deepest known Mine Shaft 13,000 ft

Liberian Deep   18,000 ft

Romanche Trench   25,000 ft

100,000 — Philippine Trench   35,000 ft

¾ of the World is under water

240

Pressure Capacity of MAMMALS

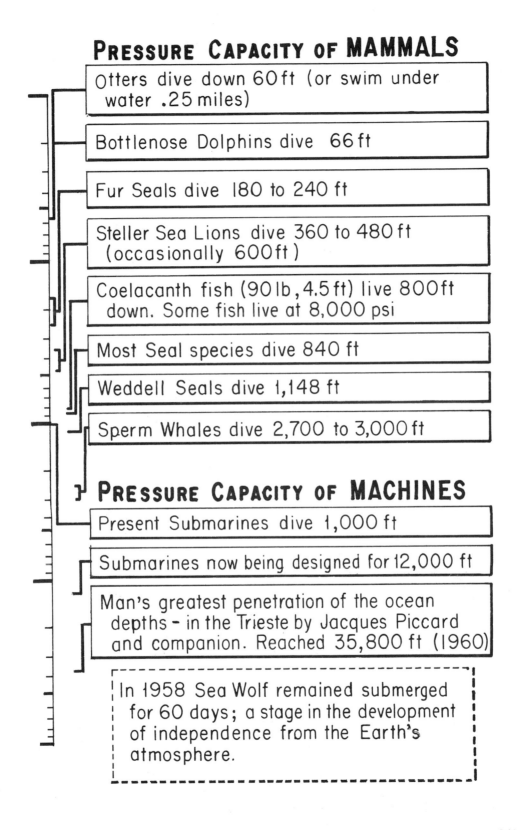

Otters dive down 60ft (or swim under water .25 miles)

Bottlenose Dolphins dive 66ft

Fur Seals dive 180 to 240 ft

Steller Sea Lions dive 360 to 480ft (occasionally 600ft)

Coelacanth fish (90lb, 4.5ft) live 800ft down. Some fish live at 8,000 psi

Most Seal species dive 840 ft

Weddell Seals dive 1,148 ft

Sperm Whales dive 2,700 to 3,000ft

Pressure Capacity of MACHINES

Present Submarines dive 1,000 ft

Submarines now being designed for 12,000 ft

Man's greatest penetration of the ocean depths – in the Trieste by Jacques Piccard and companion. Reached 35,800 ft (1960)

In 1958 Sea Wolf remained submerged for 60 days; a stage in the development of independence from the Earth's atmosphere.

High Pressure
From Air and Water

Mammals experience high pressure when they dive underwater. Men go to the bottom of deep mines and into high-pressure caissons where tunneling is done underneath large bodies of water. In a few hospitals surgery is performed in chambers maintained at 3 to 4 atmospheres of pressure.[450] In all of these cases there are four physiological factors which are detrimental to health, causing either discomfort or death at the end of an extended exposure. These factors are: the build up of carbon dioxide, the requirement for atmospheric oxygen, the large pressures especially on the thorax of the mammal, and at the end of exposure the effects of bubbles of nitrogen and air in the blood.

The pressure environment which can be tolerated depends on the mammal and the origin of the pressure: (1) pearl and sponge divers with held breath dive frequently to 60 feet, and one even to 200 feet; (2) construction workers tolerate pressures in caissons during tunnelling operations of 3 to 4 atmospheres; (3) mice can tolerate pressures in chambers of 90 atmospheres; and (4) one species of whale can dive to a depth of 3000 feet. Once we realize the gigantic capacity some animals have to tolerate high pressure, many obvious questions arise. How common are such pressures, where are they found, and what animal life can grow there? Do mammals which tolerate high pressure of water also tolerate anoxia? Is there acclimatization to pressure and to anoxia? How does man fit into this picture? What are the details of physiological adaptation to high

pressure? These questions are considered in this chapter. Appropriate physiological mechanisms are considered first.

PHYSIOLOGY OF HUMAN DIVERS

Many individuals still make their living by diving without any mechanical equipment. These groups include the sponge divers in the Arabian area, the pearl divers in the Australian area, and the Korean diving women.[468a] The record descent with held breath is that of the Greek sponge diver Stotti Georghios, who in 1913 swam down 200 feet to put a line on a lost anchor. Although man does not remain submerged as long as the other diving mammals (except Polar Bears), they do have some of the same adaptations as in lower mammals. Scholander et al.[474] reports a bradycardia during the dive of pearl divers; he also showed that systolic blood pressures remained at or near normal level, and there was no release of lactic acid into the blood until after the dive. It has been argued that this delay is also found after surface swimming and sprinting.[468] The advantage to the animal of bradycardia will be discussed in a later section. We must now consider in detail the major mechanisms which must be adapted for diving or high pressure. They are all respiratory mechanisms.

Respiratory Physiology

It will be helpful to review some baseline values of respiratory physiology. The atmosphere contains oxygen, carbon dioxide, nitrogen and water vapor. The inert gases helium, neon, and argon (1%) are customarily lumped with another abundant inert gas, nitrogen, and are called four-fifths of the atmosphere. CO_2 is scarcely measurable in air. The proportion of the three gases is extremely constant and remains the same from sea level to the highest mountains: oxygen 20.95%, carbon dioxide 0.03%, and nitrogen 79.02%.

The pressure of gases is expressed in millimeters of mercury (mm Hg). In a mixture of gases such as air the partial pressure of each component depends upon the proportionate number of molecules present. For example, if the normal atmospheric pressure is 760 mm Hg, and 21% of this is oxygen, then the partial pressure of oxygen in air or in water under the air is 21% of 760 mm or 159 mm Hg. The partial pressure of oxygen in the alveoli or in oxygenated blood leaving the lungs is 100 mm Hg; expressed in volumes percent (see chapter on Altitude) it is nearly 20 vols %. Let us now put this background to use in considering the first respiratory problem to face the diver, the disposal of carbon dioxide.

The Problem Of Carbon Dioxide Disposal. The most important single factor in human respiratory regulation is the sensitivity of the respiratory centers to the amount (tension) of carbon dioxide in the blood. If this tension increases only slightly, breathing immediately becomes deeper and faster, permitting more carbon dioxide to leave the blood until the tension has returned to normal. The regulation of CO_2 tension is so exact that the concentration in the lung always remains relatively constant. On the other hand, the respiratory center is quite insensitive to the oxygen concentration in the blood. If there is a serious decrease in oxygen concentration, then the chemoreceptors in the aorta and carotid arteries send impulses to the respiratory center causing an increase in respiration. To illustrate the influence of carbon dioxide on respiration, we may turn to some of the stories of submarine crews in World War II. At times the "carbon dioxide scrubbers" were faulty or saturated when submarines, for the sake of safety, had to remain submerged for exceptionally long periods. It was not uncommon to hear ex-members of crews describe how the CO_2 meters which read only to 4% were pressed hard off scale;[477] they described the violent and deep breathing which all members experienced.* This emphasizes that the regulation of respiration depends primarily upon the accumulation of carbon dioxide and not upon lack of oxygen. In the circumstances described and also in caissons and in mines, when the carbon dioxide increases to 3% (from 0.03%) the tidal air will increase from approximately 500 to 2000 ml. The diver will tolerate more of a buildup than this—up to breathing 10% carbon dioxide; in compensation his minute respiratory volume will increase up to a maximum of about 10-fold (50 to 60 liters per minute). Beyond the 10% level the situation becomes intolerable, and the cellular metabolism of the respiratory center becomes depressed rather than excited; the diver develops lethargy, narcosis, and finally, unconsciousness. McDonald and Simonson [463] tested subjects breathing 30% carbon dioxide; these high levels showed the narcotic effect and the subjects lost consciousness after 20 or 30 seconds. It is possible that white rats are more tolerant; Giaja states that carbon dioxide had to be raised to 50% before this atmosphere was fatal to these rodents.[456a] He did not report when they showed deep narcosis.

Why does a person take a series of deep breaths before swimming underwater? The increased ventilation of the lungs does not increase the oxygen content of the arterial blood, but it does remove more than the usual amount of carbon dioxide from the blood. Thus, it takes longer to build up carbon dioxide to the point where the respiratory center overrides the voluntary inhibition of breathing. Most professional divers can only stay underwater with held breath for about 1 minute, although a few train themselves to remain there 2.5 minutes. If man can only hold his breath that

---

* For further details see Ebersole.[454]

long, an explanation of why there are so many mammals that can remain underwater for 15 minutes certainly requires our attention. In the latter part of this chapter some of the adaptations for submersion for long periods underwater are reviewed.

When men swim underwater, there are three ways of handling the problem of CO_2: they retain it by breath holding; they use the dangerous closed-circuit oxygen lung which absorbs CO_2; they use the open-circuit system which releases CO_2 as bubbles.

The Supplying Of Oxygen. The pressure of the water around a diver has two important effects: it conditions the air delivered to him, and it compresses his air sacks (of all types) including lungs. To combat the influence of water pressure, a diver has approximately four choices of equipment: he can use an open-circuit system which automatically delivers air at the same pressure as the surrounding water and which expells CO_2 into the water; he can breathe from an oxygen-supplying, closed-circuit apparatus which is dangerous because it may produce oxygen poisoning; the diver can use an ordinary diving suit which means that water pressure is exerted against all parts of the body including the torso; or finally he may use a diving suit which is filled inside with compressed air. "Free" divers describe their equipment as "SCUBA" type, for "self-contained underwater breathing apparatus."[448]

Pressure Problems. As the diver goes down underwater the pressure will increase by 1 atmosphere for each 33 feet (10 meters) of submersion; this means that the weight of the atmosphere at sea level is essentially the same as a column of water approximately 33 feet high. If the diver then goes to 33 feet underwater, the pressure in his alveoli is 2 atmospheres instead of one; if he goes to 330 feet, then the pressure is 11 atmospheres. These pressures determine the volumes of air that must be pumped to a diver.

If 1 cubic foot of air is pumped to a diver who is under a pressure of 4 atmos-

pheres, this 1 cubic foot of air will be only ¼ cubic foot in the divers helmet. Therefore, a fixed amount more of air must flow from the helmet each minute in order to wash out the carbon dioxide from the helmet. The total quantity of air pumped to the diver must increase directly in proportion to the depth to which he descends.

On rapid descent damage can occur if there is an unequal difference of pressure where air is trapped in cavities such as the lungs, the nasal sinuses, and the middle ear. If a person descends without addition of gas to these cavities a painful reaction called "the squeeze" occurs. The smallest volume the lung can normally achieve is 1.5 liters; if a diver with held breath inspires a maximum breath, he can descend only to 100 feet before his chest begins to cave in. He must inspire additional air as he descends. Severe face damage occurs if air volume is lost from a helmet or the mask of a free diving apparatus. The first 33 feet of descent causes the greatest squeeze because this is a 2-fold pressure increase; if a person descends from 300 to 333 feet the pressure causes only a 10% reduction in volume. Rapid ascent if improperly performed can also cause severe damage. The opposite of "the squeeze" occurs if a person fails to expel air from his lungs on the way up. Above an alveolar pressure of 80 to 100 mm Hg, air is forced into capillaries. The result is air embolism, not to be confused with the "bends".

Oxygen Poisoning. There are harmful effects of high partial pressures of oxygen. These may be expressed as convulsions, which are similar to grand mal seizures; they stop as soon as excess oxygen is removed. If the sea level pressure (100 mm Hg) is increased to 1400 mm Hg, the amount of dissolved oxygen in the water of the blood (now 6.5 vols % instead of 0.2 vols %) plus a little from the hemoglobin is used by the tissues. This is the situation in about 30 feet of water if a diver wears an oxygen lung delivering 100% oxygen. If he goes deeper, the pressure is raised even higher, no oxygen is used from the

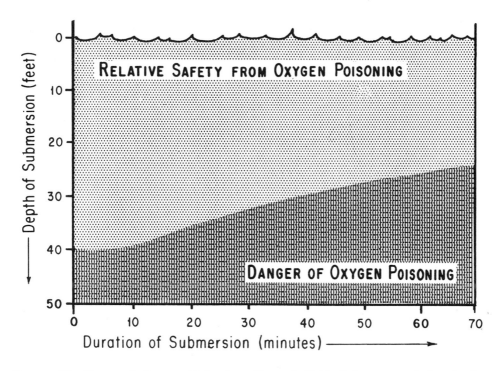

FIGURE 91. *Onset of Oxygen Poisoning.* Every individual is aware of the absolute necessity for rhythmic sipping of oxygen many times each minute. Only in recent years has it been realized that this essential ingredient for life can act as a poison as well as a benefit. The safe duration of submersion before pure oxygen acts as a poison is indicated in the diagram. From Duffner.[453]

hemoglobin, the tissues remain saturated, and oxygen convulsions may result (Fig. 91). To prevent this, the rule of thumb for the safety factor is that one should not increase the concentration of oxygen in the alveoli above approximately 7 times normal. The cause of the convulsions is the large amount of oxyhemoglobin leaving the brain. There is direct tissue damage due to the excess oxygen; also because of the Bohr effect, oxyhemoglobin has less capacity for carbon dioxide transport, and the diver suffers from excess tissue carbon dioxide. For further details see article by Capt. G. J. Duffner[453] and Guyton.[421]

If a diver is breathing only compressed air (21% oxygen), he can descend to about 200 feet and still be within the safe limit of 7 times normal oxygen in the alveoli. He can go further if special mixtures of helium and oxygen are used as long as

toxic amounts of helium are not absorbed.

Influence of Nitrogen and Helium. The nitrogen gas from the air is as important to the diver as oxygen and carbon dioxide. If the pressure of nitrogen reaches 7 times atmosphere, then there may be an anesthetic function on the central nervous system ganglia, and coma can result. The early stages are called nitrogen narcosis or "rapture of the deep". This state is so much like alcohol intoxication that one diver took off his mouthpiece and offered it to a passing fish. Each diver has his own nitrogen narcosis limit; for some it lies between 330 and 350 feet. There is a second type of damage from nitrogen; as it bubbles out of the blood during decompression, it causes the bends (see next section).

The breathing of helium is an experimental solution to the damage done by nitrogen at high atmospheric pressures. The experimenting with helium has been accelerated because during high altitude flight and space flight the formation of bubbles by nitrogen escaping during decompression is also a problem. Helium has a small molecule and diffuses through tissue 2.5 times faster than nitrogen; also helium is one-third as soluble in fluids as is nitrogen and has few noxious effects on the body. Because of its diffusability during decompression helium leaves the body fluids rapidly and easily.[462] Some very interesting experiments with helium have been done: on several occasions volunteer subjects have lived in space-cabin simulators for a long as 5 weeks in atmospheric mixtures of 56% helium and 44% oxygen at a simulated altitude of 18,000 feet. Under these circumstances the major influence on the subjects seemed to be a change in their method of speech (the Donald Duck effect). Different results were obtained when they breathed 85% helium and 15% oxygen by mask and at a pressure of 15 atmospheres or comparable to 642 feet of sea water. Although the subjects seemed to function and behave quite normally while respiring these mixtures, their performance and behavior deteriorated within 20 to 60 seconds following a return to air-breathing.

Decompression Sickness (Dysbarism)*

As a diver is decompressed, or the aviator ascends to 30,000 feet, the dissolved nitrogen in the blood begins to escape causing various degrees of damage (Fig. 92). Terms applied to this damage in the 19th century were bends, caisson disease, compressed air disease, and divers paralysis. Small bubbles of this nitrogen may cause pain or nerve block and large bubbles may cause air embolism, pulmonary edema, or brain damage. The pain in the arms, legs, and head is usually referred to

---

* The leader in understanding and treating this sickness is Capt. A. R. Behnke[449]. He has published on pressure physiology since 1931.

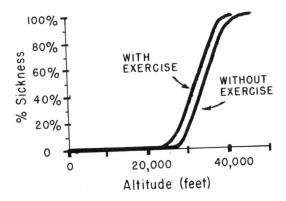

FIGURE 92. *Effect of Exercise on the Bends.* The range of resistance and susceptibility to the bends is indicated with and without exercise. It is of interest that the curves are parallel; one might predict that with exercise a higher percent would become sick at the same altitude. Although this diagram represents the bends at altitude, the principle of the effect of exercise on the bends also applies underwater. From Guyton.[421]

as the "bends"; if the bubbles block capillaries in the lungs, they cause a shortness of breath called the "chokes". The monograph by Adler of Brooks Air Force Base includes seven symptoms of which the "bends" and the "chokes" are the two most conspicuous.[447]

The first experiments involving the formation of bubbles by a change from high pressure to low pressure was done by Robert Boyle in 1670;[447] he exposed a viper (a snake) to a very low ambient pressure and reported seeing a bubble within the eye. He picked a very convenient animal for this experiment since snakes do not have eyelids. By 1850 the study of dysbarism became of practical importance to a French engineer, Triger, who at that time built the first caisson for tunnel work. Gradually many of these caissons were used during the last half of the 19th century resulting in a high death rate and extreme discomfort in the workers on the tunneling projects.[447]

The principles which control the formation of bubbles caused by a pressure change are as follows: the total nitrogen normally dissolved in all body fluids and in the body fat at one time is approximately 1 liter; if the person is under 2 atmospheres of pressure, then there will be 2 liters of nitrogen or if under 5 atmospheres, then 5 liters of nitrogen. The rate of nitrogen elimination is expressed in the rule which states that approximately one-half of the excess nitrogen is removed in the first 40 minutes of decompression and half of the remaining is removed in the next 40 minutes. There is 5 times as much nitrogen stored in the body fat as in body water and nitrogen leaves fat tissues very slowly. This is an obvious advantage for lean divers.

If the pressure on a diver is 5000 mm Hg, and the pressure of carbon dioxide and oxygen is in the normal range, then that of nitrogen will be 3918 mm Hg. If the diver has been at 2 atmospheres, there are 2 liters of nitrogen to be handled; one remains dissolved in the body fluid, while the other forms bubbles. A certain number of these bubbles are tolerated so that discomfort does not begin unless the total volume of nitrogen available for forming bubbles is more than 1.25 liters.

The rate at which a diver can be brought to the surface depends on two factors: the depth of the dive, and the amount of time spent there. If he remains at deep levels for only a short period, the body fluids will not become saturated and decompression time can be reduced. Because of the slow formation of bubbles, a flyer can avoid the bends if he does not spend too long over 25,000 feet. Exercise hastens the formation of bubbles during decompression because of increased motion of tissues (Fig. 92). As examples of decompression time, note that only 20 minutes at a depth of 300 feet requires over 2.5 hours decompression time; and 45 minutes at 300 feet requires over 5 hours. In Figure 93 it will be seen that submerging to 30 feet can be tolerated indefinitely without experiencing decompression sickness. However, when one exceeds a depth of 60 feet, the length of time necessary to produce the bends decreases sharply. One

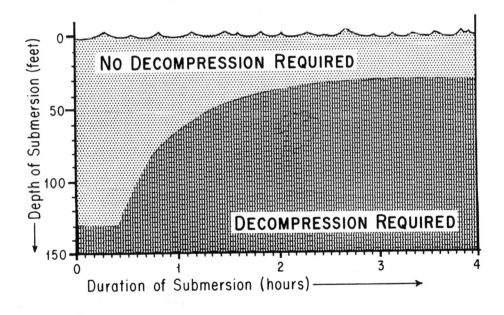

FIGURE 93. *Requirements for Decompression After Diving.* This diagram emphasizes that a diver must choose between going deep for a period of 25 minutes or remaining near the surface for a much longer period. From Duffner.[453]

can stay at 100 feet only about 30 minutes without absorbing so much nitrogen that slow decompression is essential. The onset of the bends is somewhat unpredictable. One Japanese diver went down to 192 feet 4 times consecutively for 1 hour each without getting decompression sickness, but the fifth time he had a very severe case. This is of course probably related to the speed of coming to the surface.

At high altitude the bends usually begin around 25,000 feet; this means that men on mountains similar to Mount Everest could experience the symptoms if they are rapidly transported.[457]

Concerning the question of acclimatization to diving, there is little information. Acclimatization to CO_2 does take place during prolonged training, allowing the diver to stay under water longer. Schaefer discusses some of the unfavorable consequences of this form of acclimatization.[470]

Modern Applications of Diving Theory

Navy teams of several nationalities have lived in submerged chambers at 200 feet for 3 weeks at a time, and are exploring the possibility of living at 300 to 600 feet down. They can move from 600 to 300 feet without decompressing. Their interest is to exploit the food and fresh water resources of the continental shelf. The submerged continents could provide 2 to 3 times the minerals and other resources that have been obtained from dry land. Such men will range out from their shelters in 2-man submarines.

Other topics on submarine physiology are reviewed by Miles[466] and Schaefer.[471, 472]

COMPARATIVE PHYSIOLOGY OF DIVING MAMMALS

There are limitless areas of the ocean still to be explored, inhabited by large and undescribed vertebrates. There are five canyons in the Pacific which are deeper than 34,000 feet. The deepest is the re-

cently discovered Cook Deep in the Philippine trench, 37,782 feet. These depths are of equal interest to physical scientists and biologists: Jacques Piccard and his companion at 35,800 feet saw shrimp and a foot-long fish; it is here that the giant squid live. Harold Edgerton's deep sea camera was lowered to 26,000 feet; his pictures revealed marine invertebrates living on the bottom. As far as we know, mammals have sampled very little of the deep water area. The ecological "niche" of the sperm whale extends only to 3000 feet.

The ability to tolerate great pressure is no more interesting than the ability to survive and move without atmospheric oxygen; in an informal experiment we placed four fresh water turtles (*Chrysemys*) in jars containing boiled water; these jars were sealed and placed under water at 22°C. After 37 to 93 hours, reflex responses were still obtained from the turtles; we took them out and all of them revived.[452] This chapter is primarily concerned with mammals and not reptiles, but the reasonable question can be asked: If a reptile can survive with such a large oxygen debt, why cannot a mammal?

We can divide the aquatic mammals roughly into two groups; the small freshwater types and the very large marine mammals. The fresh water types vary in size from the water shrew, muskrat, platypus, otter, and nutria, to the beaver. There is of course one very large fresh water mammal, the hippopotamus. Another one is the totally aquatic manatee that frequents both salt and fresh water. In the marine group size varies from harbor seals to the very large elephant seals; the largest of all mammals are the baleen whales, over 90 feet long. Some aquatic mammals seem to be holding their own very successfully against present day challenges of civilization. Temple-Perkins,[476] while on a short trip in Africa, observed a hippopotamus population of 1,000 individuals. The present day stock of seals, carefully estimated because of their fur value, is considered to be 26 million. Although whales are becoming increasingly scarce, and some species are threatened with extinction, none the less in recent times 30,000 baleen whales a year have been taken from arctic and antarctic waters. We are interested in the physiological adaptations of these numerous aquatic mammals; whether they are fresh water or marine, they are of equal interest. If one recalls the discomfort experienced when attempting to swim the length of a swimming pool underwater, then one is impressed with the ability of a beaver to stay underwater regularly for 20 minutes, or whales who remain submerged for periods up to 2 hours.*

Breath-Holding Capacities

Some specific figures for the length of time for breath-holding of various mammals will be of interest. The data fall into three groups: mammals, which ordinarily do not go under water, those which regularly depend upon specific adaptations to stay down for from 5 to 28 minutes, and those which can remain submerged for as long as 2 hours (Table 22).

---

* Several authors have recently reviewed mammalian pressure physiology: Slijper,[475] Hart and Fisher,[43] Norris,[467] Scholander,[473] and Harrison and Tomlinson.[458]

The interesting generalization about the data presented is that some of the mammals which have the most extreme modification or adaptations for aquatic life do not appear to have a particularly marked breath-holding ability; examples are sea otters and porpoises.

Types of Diving Adaptations

The whales and seals represent a contradiction in physiological terms; they are animals that usually depend very closely upon atmospheric air and live near the atmosphere at the surface of the water. Yet at least some species in the whale and the seal group have a fantastic ability to dive so deeply that it is remarkable that any physiological mechanism can tolerate the pressure and the metabolic strain: the sperm whale dives to 3,000 feet and the Weddell seal to 1,830 feet.

The "challenges" faced by diving mammals are those listed for man, including the possible build up of carbon dioxide, the effect of extreme pressure, the oxygen debt, and the possibility of decompression effects. The problem of carbon dioxide can be quickly dispensed with: the Russian

Table 22 Breath-Holding Capacities of Mammals*
(in minutes)

GROUP 1		GROUP 2	
Most men	1	Sea Otter	5
Polar Bears	1.5	Platypus	10
Pearl Divers (Human)	2.5	Muskrat	12
		Hippopotamus	15
GROUP 3		Sea Cow	16
Greenland whale	60	Beaver	20
Sperm whale	90	Porpoises	15
Bottlenose whale	120	Seals	15 to 28

* For additional species see Prosser and Brown[152] and Slijper.[475]

biologist, E. Krebs [475] in 1941 demonstrated that the central nervous system of diving animals is singularly unresponsive to carbonic acid.

The problem of extreme pressure is exemplified during the dive of a whale to 1,500 feet, where it undergoes a pressure of 50 atmospheres; when it reaches 3,000 feet, it experiences 100 atmospheres. Popular descriptions of diving in deep water emphasize the tremendous crushing force of such an experience; in actual fact, the mammalian body is almost entirely made up of solids and fluids, and the body is no more likely to be crushed than a bucket of water lowered into the depths. Damage can occur if there is an unequal difference of pressure where air is trapped, such as in the lungs, the nasal sinuses, and the middle ear. Sometimes there is gas in the intestine but this gives little trouble because the intestinal walls contract down to equalize the pressure. It is possible that deep-diving mammals control the volume of air in the lungs like the human diver (see earlier section). We have little knowledge of what happens to the volume of air in the lungs of a whale under 50 to 100 atmospheres of pressure and why his ribs are not crushed when the air is compressed. Scholander [473] states that the anatomy of the lungs must permit a complete collapse in deep diving.

There have been a number of hypotheses over the years on the question of decompression sickness in diving mammals. These theories were complicated and improbable until the simple and obvious solution became generally accepted. L. Hill [475] in 1935 showed that there is a basic difference between diving with held breath and diving with fresh air delivered to a helmet. In the diving helmet and from the tanks of an open-circuit apparatus there is a continuous supply of fresh air and thus of fresh nitrogen with which the blood can become saturated. The diving mammal takes down a fixed quantity of air so that despite the high pressure of water only a small quantity of nitrogen is available for solution in the blood.

The question of oxygen debt will be considered in a separate section.

Circulation

Diving mammals are able to sustain themselves under water under very deep pressure for prolonged periods by reducing their overall metabolism; this process has been variously described as "making themselves into smaller animals" or as "making themselves into a heart-lung-brain preparation". Apparently the blood flow to large muscle and skin areas is markedly reduced. The evidence for the redistributed blood flow and attendant metabolic changes are: (1) incisions into skin and muscles do not bleed, (2) elevated lactic acid does not appear in the blood until after ascent, suggesting that it is trapped and non-circulating during the dive, (3) the myoglobin oxygen is almost exhausted, while the blood remains 50% saturated with oxygen, (4) direct arterial tracings indicate increased peripheral resistance; part of the evidence is that the rate of fall of pressure during diastole is reduced. Associated with the reduced flow of blood is a marked bradycardia; all diving and non-diving animals when placed under water demonstrate this (Fig. 94). The development of this effect is gradual in most animals; in the seal, however, the frequency usually drops immediately to 1/10 of normal. This drop is abolished by atropine or vagotomy. The electrocardiogram during the dive showing initially a normal complex, tends to develop a prolongation of the Q-T interval and a peaked T wave which is sometimes inverted. The bradycardia is maintained while the animal is in its dive which lasts as long as 15 minutes. In most cases this bradycardia is of sinus origin, since the electrocardiogram exhibits a normal sinus rhythm. The effect upon central blood pressure is what one would predict with a greatly reduced blood flow: with the heart of the seal beating only 5 to 6 times per minute, it has been shown that the central blood pressure taken in the femoral artery is nevertheless maintained at a normal or even an elevated level. [461] The extent of the depression in

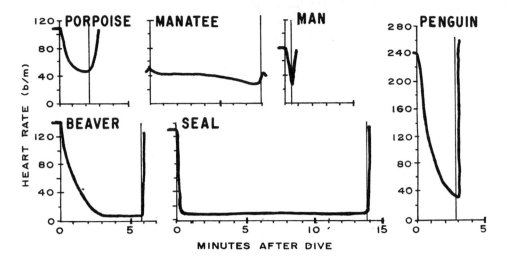

FIGURE 94. *Heart Rate Response to Diving.* One of the most consistent of physiological syndromes is the slowing of the heart during submergence both in non-diving mammals and in aquatic mammals and birds. Curiously the bradycardia during the dive is more marked in man, a non-aquatic mammal than in one which never leaves the water, the manatee. Also, one might predict a similarity in the response of porpoises and seals, but the latter markedly prolongs the bradycardia. From Irving *et al.*[460]

pulse rate may be from 10 to 50% of the surface rate; once developed it persists during physical activity and struggle.

Teamwork between electrical engineer and physiologist has produced recent confirmation of the theory of Irving and Scholander[473] of selective vasoconstriction during diving. Van Citters' group[478] completed an expedition to study cardiovascular adaptations to diving of the elephant seal in its habitat on Guadalupe Island, Mexico. A telemetry system was used for blood flow measurements in the iliac artery, the carotid artery, and the aorta. On these large animals resting heart rates averaged 36 beats per minute with marked sinus arrhythmia.* The blood pressure was similar to that of man. Bradycardia occurred with diving but the immediate response was much less than that commonly observed in smaller seals. Blood flow

changes varied with the duration of immersion, but with prolonged immersion iliac flow fell severely, while carotid flow was more adequately maintained. The overall changes in the pressure pulse were consistant with marked peripheral vasoconstriction to combine with the reduced iliac flow. Some of these measurements were repeated and confirmed in the beaver.[456]

Another study using radio-telemetry was done by Elsner[455] at the Scripps Institution of Oceanography. The radio-capsules were surgically implanted in two species of seals on the main pulmonary artery, the aorta, and the superior mesenteric and renal arteries. Heart rates as low as 10 beats per minute were commonly seen in harbor seals. Cardiac output decreased in proportion to heart rate with little change in stroke volume. Blood flow was reduced in all measured sites falling virtually to zero in mesenteric and renal arteries. Less reduction was noted in the common carotid and coronary arteries.

---

* We have also recorded sinus arrhythmia by telemetry in wolves, wolverines, and black bears.[7, 137, 138]

Respiration

Mammals which naturally submerge themselves repeatedly usually have a somewhat larger relative oxygen storage, since their relative blood volumes, myoglobin content, and lung volumes apparently exceed those of man.[459] A partial exception appears to be the lung volumes of the whale; if volumes are referred to body weight, then the lung capacity of whales are one-half that of terrestrial mammals. This apparently relates to the observation that whales dive deeper than any other aquatic mammals.

The breathing of whales is of particular interest since it is accomplished through the top of the skull through the blow hole. The pattern and type of spray formed when the whale spouts is of assistance in identifying the types of whales. Slijper[475] points out that one can determine by the spouting when a whale is panting; this happens when whales are chased and are moving at top speed and are alarmed. He has observed them change their normal resting respiration from 2 to 30 per minute. Their method of breathing has an important bearing upon their ability to dive; while the tidal air of man is a small fraction of the total lung volume, it is notable that especially whales, and porpoises to a certain extent, use a very large part of the total lung volume for their tidal air. The mechanism of breathing deeply with each respiration is attributed to the fact that whales expand and contract their thorax to the maximum; in related terms this maximum is 10% greater than it is in terrestrial mammals. As a result their relative volume of residual air is only half that of terrestrial animals. How does this basic information fit in with diving? Do whales and porpoises breath deeply while swimming quietly near the surface and also before they dive? A number of investigators have tried to get information on this; it appears that Grey Seals and sea elephants are known to make a point of exhaling before they dive. Whales do the reverse, and furthermore Scholander[473] gained the clear impression that they fill their lungs to ca-

pacity. It is difficult to explain such a breathing pattern. Because of the forces applied to the thorax during a deep dive, there seem to be advantages in exhaling before breathing; in a deep dive, however, obviously the oxygen stored in the lungs is of value. One reasonable explanation for the continuous deep breathing of the whales is that this pattern is of survival value because they must at times dive rapidly and no final gasp is needed before the quick dive.

We must next consider oxygen transport. In whales the hematocrit is much larger than that of man. In spite of this, the blood oxygen capacity of whales is not particularly striking. Mammals in general have a blood oxygen-carrying capacity varying from 11 to 24 vols %; that of the porpoise is 19 vols %, while that of the fin whale is only 14 vols %. The answer must be that for prolonged submersion whales depend more upon myoglobin; this is quite possible since some whales have 8 times as much of this material as terrestrial mammals. This shows that there are a variety of ways for the diving mammal to obtain a larger relative oxygen storage; for example, the seal has used a different technique: in spite of its increased myoglobin, the oxygen-carrying capacity of its blood alone is 29 vols %.

The oxygen supply, no matter how carried, also seems to be conserved by temporary metabolic changes which occur during the process of diving. To consider this we must recall the two phases of the chemical processes which supply the energy for muscle contraction. In the anaerobic phase the energy supply which is glycogen is broken down in the muscles into lactic acid without the intervention of oxygen. In the second phase, the aerobic part, some of this lactic acid is oxidized, while another part is resynthesized into glycogen. The theory of Irving and Scholender[473] is that during deep diving the mammal carrying out this difficult process is undergoing a metabolic phase in which the anaerobic part predominates. If this is accomplished, of course, there is a saving in the resources of oxygen. The basis for their hypothesis was obtained by experiments with rats, seals, and ducks which showed that during diving the lactic acid increases considerably in the muscles but does not accumulate in the blood until shortly after surfacing. Thus, it appears that during diving the muscles require very little oxygen and the blood is shunted primarily to the heart and brain.

What sort of blood can respond to the osmotic challenge of the ocean's 3.5% salt solution as well as have an oxygen-carrying capacity of 29 vols %? The blood chemistry of the bottlenose dolphin has been compared to that of dogs and horses. The components are very different from most mammals and have some characteristics of shark blood. Plasma sodium, plasma chloride, and serum albumin levels are higher, while globulin levels are lower than those found in dogs and horses. Blood urea seems to be considerably higher than that found in the land mammals.[464]

Small mammals (albino mice) have been tested for their ability to tolerate pressure-equivalent depths down to 914 meters of sea water. Because of their small size, they have a rapid uptake and later elimination of inert gases. Membery and Link estimated that mice attain gaseous equilibrium within 1 hour in a hyperbaric environment, while man requires 12 hours.[465] In a 0.65% oxygen mixture, with helium, mice tolerated 13 hours at 90 atmospheres of the gas, equivalent to 914 meters of sea water.

Thermal Environment of Marine Mammals

We find that the problem of carbon dioxide accumulation, oxygen debt, tremendous water pressure, and decompression effects have all been solved quite nicely by adaptations in the mammals which can accomplish deep diving. There still remain large numbers of questions about the physiology of these fascinating animals.

The challenges imposed upon them by their extreme environment are exaggerated by cold. For example the water about the Antarctic Continent near the Weddell Sea varies from —1.95° to +5°C all the year around.[451] Considering whales first, we realize that a high percent of them live in Arctic and Antarctic waters where they can consume great quantities of the biomass of plankton which is abundant there. In the Arctic, the whales avoid the extreme rigors of the winter by migration. Recall that although we have stressed in this chapter the capacity for deep and prolonged diving for some of the whales, there are many of them which seldom submerge for more than 30 minutes. The porpoises usually dive for only 4 to 15 minutes. Therefore sea ice can be an extremely serious barrier to whales and porpoises. The latter species often die in large numbers in the Baltic Ocean when the sea freezes over before they have migrated from it. Apparently there are more cases in the Antarctic of failing to solve this problem than in the Arctic; observers near Grahamland and Ross Island in the Antarctic observed three species of whales which were obviously cut off from the open water by frozen sea, especially the Little Piked Whales. These fairly numerous animals had breathing holes which eventually froze over. This situation is even more striking in the Arctic and Antarctic seals which do not migrate in the winter time. Seals can seldom remain submerged longer than 15 minutes, although the Weddell seal tolerates 43 minutes. This means they must keep breathing holes open all winter which is no small task when the temperature above the ice is —50° to —70°C.[469] The problem is not simply one of requirements for oxygen for whales and seals under the ice; one should recall that they are also living in continuous darkness during the winter season. It is a mystery as to how they select and obtain their food, and orient themselves during the food search so that they can return to breathing holes.

Chapter Ten

CONCLUDING REMARKS

Chapter Ten

Concluding Remarks

TOPICS NOT INCLUDED IN BOOK

Medical Biometeorology

The theme of this book has been *normal* Biometeorology (Environmental Physiology). We can conveniently group several other areas of the parent discipline under *Medical* Biometeorolgy. It is regrettable that space has not permitted the inclusion of this fascinating area: we have not been able to make use of the concept taught by A. Carlson: "Disease is nature's experiment." In a problem in Medical Biometeorology a number of types of influences upon man must be considered at the same time; as a result this field is a much more subtle, complicated, and difficult one than a study such as acclimation which can involve the influence of a single environmental factor in an environmental chamber. Sargent has recently listed three medical areas as being of especial interest to those working in Medical Biometeorology: air pollution, seasonal variation of illness, and regional variation of illness.[491] Several volumes have been compiled covering what is known in these areas: *Medical Biometerology* [22] and *Biometeorology*,[496] both edited by S. W. Tromp; *Medical Climatology* [296] edited by Sidney Licht.

Medical Geography. An illustration of the approach of the medical geographer is the study by Mills [488] who showed that Negroes who have moved from southern United States to colder areas in the North, such as near Chicago, have a higher incidence of diabetes than in the warmer climate. He points out that this might be due to endocrine inbalance, or living in a colder climate, or because of increased food intake due to the colder climate, or some other cause. Some Japanese workers have been particularly interested in seasonal variations of the optimum room temperature for light work.[489] There have been many similar papers in the United States describing seasonal changes in physiological indices which varied from urinary catecholamine determinations [481] to changes in fingernail growth.[483] Some workers have attempted to match physiological characteristics with the climatic preference of some individuals.[480] The relationships between heat and sickness are well handled in the books *Environmental Physiology in Arid Conditions*,[327] and *Physiological Responses to Hot Environments.*[299]

As a part of Medical Biometeorology one must study the modification of environment by man. As a result of the exponential growth of human populations, there is increased industrial, military, and agricultural activity which has given rise to chemical and radioactive pollution of air, soil, and water.[2, 296, 492]

Ecology of Malnutrition. Another approach to Medical Biometeorology stresses that analysis of the complete environment of man including the physical environment and the social impacts and changes. A series of volumes on the ecology of malnutrition in various countries has been helpful for analyzing the possibility of a future catastrophe created by the population explosion. As an illustration of the approach in these volumes the fourth in the series has the title: *Ecology of Malnutrition in Five Countries of Europe.*[486] A fifth volume, on Africa, outlines the conditions under which food is at present produced and consumed, and gives an outline of the future problems which are being created by the current transition from a mainly subsistance tribal way of life to a money-economy due to the emergence of Africa into the industrial revolution. One might also say that this approach overlaps that of the medical geographer.

Cross Acclimatization

Another area which has received little attention here is the consideration of the many concurrent factors of the environment. One experimental approach to this situation, which we must consider the most common or normal condition, is the use of cross exposures: two factors are studied for their influence upon an animal but they are applied separately instead of simultaneously. The experimental result is called cross acclimatization.[482, 487] It is quite apparent that the future of Environmental Physiology must include many more studies of multi-factor environmental influences upon the animal.

Artificial Environments

Two topics which have not been included are those of winged flight and rocket flight. Our emphasis has been upon environments which are considered natural, with the possible exception of altitude effects and deep pressure effects. High altitude is a natural environment for some individuals, since entire human populations have evolved there. When one considers high pressure, the justification is that somewhat primitive cultures for many generations have developed their capacity to dive with held breath and are still doing this today. Since many of the problems of men in diving equipment are similar to those of the pearl divers, and since many mammals in the free environment live by diving, is seemed reasonable to include this topic.

Winged Flight. The physiological challenges of winged flight are being solved in aeronautics and human engineering.[483a] A brief mention of the changes in airplanes over the past few years will emphasize the physiological problems which must arise from a change in design. From the modest planes of World War I there evolved the X-15 of the 1960's; in manned flight these aircraft travel nearly 70 miles high, and at a speed of 5,500 miles per hour or 1.5 miles per second (Fig. 95). More conservative but more common planes such as the "YF-12 A" travel at 80,000 feet at speeds of over 2,000 miles per hour. The engineers concerned expect to design planes which may achieve orbital speeds which can be controlled from 2,500 mph to as much as 17,000 mph (orbital speed refers to achieving escape velocity so that an airplane behaves like a satellite). What are the physiological challenges that go along with these engineering miracles? To parachute from the very slowest of these speeds which were mentioned would introduce a force of approximately 32 times that of gravity upon the pilots (32G). It is possible that slight changes in pattern of flight might introduce forces on man of 16 to 20 times the force of gravity. Such factors as these are in the area of biophysics; they are presented clearly in the recent text by Dr. Charles C. Wunder.[497]

We should not lose sight of other unnatural demands on the pilots. It has been tempting to emphasize the extreme physical stresses which face the pilot; in addition, routine demands of flying require exceptional individuals, who must be alert and prepared to watch and operate for long hours as many as 75 switches, levers, and dials on the panel in front of them.

Rocket Flight. The pioneer work on rocket propulsion in The United States was done by Dr. Robert Goddard, at Fort Devens, Ayer, Massachusetts during his modest experimental program between 1920 and 1930. Earlier Russian work was extensive enough to justify the designation of Tsiolkovskii as the father of astronautics.[479] Serious and substantial rocket research programs were not begun in the United States until 1942.[493] We have made

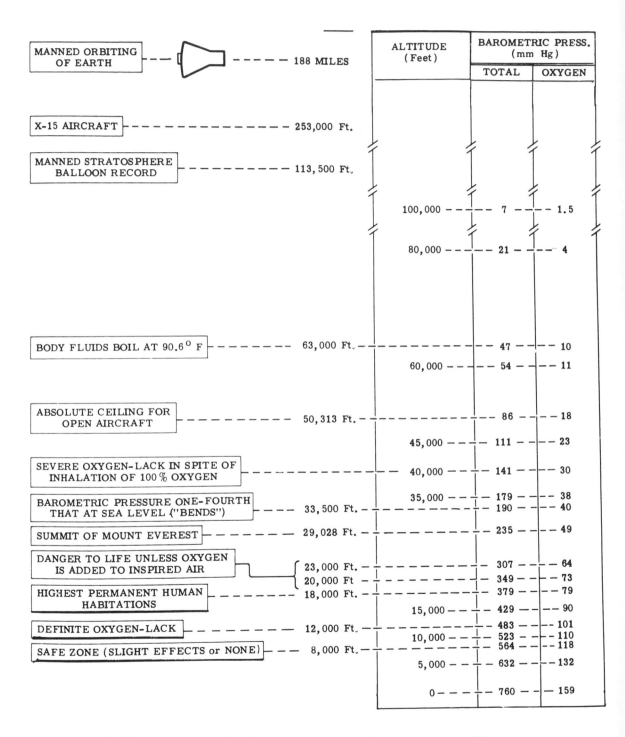

	ALTITUDE (Feet)	BAROMETRIC PRESS. (mm Hg)	
		TOTAL	OXYGEN

MANNED ORBITING OF EARTH — 188 MILES

X-15 AIRCRAFT — 253,000 Ft.

MANNED STRATOSPHERE BALLOON RECORD — 113,500 Ft.

| 100,000 | 7 | 1.5 |
| 80,000 | 21 | 4 |

BODY FLUIDS BOIL AT 90.6° F — 63,000 Ft.

| 63,000 | 47 | 10 |
| 60,000 | 54 | 11 |

ABSOLUTE CEILING FOR OPEN AIRCRAFT — 50,313 Ft.

| 50,313 | 86 | 18 |
| 45,000 | 111 | 23 |

SEVERE OXYGEN-LACK IN SPITE OF INHALATION OF 100% OXYGEN — 40,000

| 40,000 | 141 | 30 |
| 35,000 | 179 | 38 |

BAROMETRIC PRESSURE ONE-FOURTH THAT AT SEA LEVEL ("BENDS") — 33,500 Ft.

| 33,500 | 190 | 40 |

SUMMIT OF MOUNT EVEREST — 29,028 Ft.

| 29,028 | 235 | 49 |

DANGER TO LIFE UNLESS OXYGEN IS ADDED TO INSPIRED AIR

| 23,000 Ft. | 307 | 64 |
| 20,000 Ft | 349 | 73 |

HIGHEST PERMANENT HUMAN HABITATIONS — 18,000 Ft.

| 18,000 Ft. | 379 | 79 |
| 15,000 | 429 | 90 |

DEFINITE OXYGEN-LACK — 12,000 Ft.

| 12,000 Ft. | 483 | 101 |
| 10,000 | 523 | 110 |

SAFE ZONE (SLIGHT EFFECTS or NONE) — 8,000 Ft.

8,000 Ft.	564	118
5,000	632	132
0	760	159

FIGURE 95. *The Conquest of the Upper Atmosphere.* From Lambertson.[484a]

remarkable progress in 23 years. The three-stage Saturn Rocket delivers a first-stage thrust of 7,500,000 pounds. There is some impression that medical and physiological progress has lagged behind that of the engineer. There is much to be learned about the physiological conditioning of the astronaut so that he can tolerate his space ship.[485] The space race applies to physiological matters as well as missiles: Russian physiologists have studied some unusually hardy subjects who tolerated 120 days of hypokinesia (reduced exercise) in a high pressure chamber;[484] the United States' announcement of similar endurance will probably not be far behind.

The physiological problems of space flight are not much different from those of winged flight. The astronaut does have to tolerate higher G forces, intense vibration, and prolonged confinement. Apparently weightlessness *per se* does not have known physiological effects. Five articles on this topic by Lamb, in 1964 and 1965 in Aerospace Medicine, have been summarized by him: "Because all space flights to date appear to be associated with an alteration of many factors, it is impossible to prove that weightlessness has produced any adverse effects other than those which might be expected by a decrease in power requirement, thereby resulting in generalized physiological deconditioning."[484b]

Biochemical Approach and Statistics

Biochemical considerations have been left out of this volume except where a physiologist was using biochemical techniques. The interested reader is referred to Smith,[233, 494] and to the Symposium on Temperature Acclimation.[495] Statistical aspects have also not been covered, yet they are needed more in Biometeorology than in many other fields. Some commonly used formulas are in the Appendix; a section on statistical methods to be used in biometeorological research is found in *Medical Biometeorology*, pp 157-169.[22] Articles by F. Sargent "Physiological Variability in Young Men" and "Small Sample Statistics" are found in Consolazio *et al.*[450a]

TOPICS INCLUDED IN BOOK

Purpose

The purpose of this book was simple: I hope it guides and encourages some young physiologists toward Environmental Physiology. I hope all such people do not bury themselves in molecular biology; the gaps in our knowledge of tissue and organ physiology are still so obvious that we will continue to need a breed of physiologists who are willing and inspired to carry out an experiment such as this: to hike over a mountain to shoot a sleeping bear in his hibernating den, to measure its body temperature (it was 33°C); to measure its quantity of subcutaneous and abdominal fat (it was 40% of the total weight); and to take a portion of its sciatic nerve back to the laboratory (conduction at different temperatures was like the rat); and eventually to discuss and modify the equations which describe the physiological relationship between the winter bear and his cold environment.[386] I hope the potential environmentalist will read this book and will then turn for quantitative details to the *Handbook of Physiology, section 4 "Adaptation to the Environment"*.[2]

Comparative Mammalian Physiology

The foregoing chapters include that comparative mammalian physiology which relates to responses to a stressful environment. To make comparisons was not an organized goal; I simply set out to enjoy the discovery of some fascinating evolutionary adaptations for combating extreme environments. However, comparisons were automatic and obvious. I frankly expected to find larger differences in environmental responses from species to species; what this means is that the uncomfortable mammal of all sizes and shapes doggedly finds a way of becoming comfortable.

There is increasing interest in comparative mammalian physiology today. An outstanding leader in this field is Dr. C. Ladd Prosser who believes that when one makes comparisons, biological generalizations emerge which seem at first to be applicable to only one organism such as man but when more deeply analyzed, lead to "an understanding of a holistic biology." [490] Prosser states: "Comparative physiology puts man in his proper biological perspective." [490]

Principles of Environmental Physiology

Homeostasis and Climatic Extremes. One of the principles of Environmental Physiology is the familiar one of homeostasis. In a sense we reapply the principle under circumstances of climatic extremes where it is expressed in different terms and at different levels compared to those applying to the animal at room temperature under comfortable conditions. Homeostasis refers to the maintenance of the dynamic equilibrium of the body, so that its physiological state remains constant within narrow limits; examples of mechanisms which are controlled are acid-base balance, body weight, blood pressure and body temperature. If the condition of homeostasis does not hold and the animal's tissues become too cold, we find that this state imposes a limiting sluggishness on all energy yielding reactions. If the animal tissues become too hot, at about 40°C there are changes in proteins and lipids which render them useless for carrying out their normal activities in active cells. Sometimes extreme environments move the state of the animal close to the condition (or status) which could be lethal; homeostasis must still be carried out under these conditions.

Let us review some of the unusual levels of homeostasis. The first is concerned with the two daily "conditions" of homeostasis which are the double settings of biological daily rhythm. These two settings are actually different physiological equilibria which become visible as a daily physiological pattern-of-change. This rigid day-night pattern continues even in the extreme environment of continuous darkness or continuous light.

The second example is seen in the maintenance of body temperature by evaporative cooling. In the dehydrated mammal the necessary water for evaporative cooling in a hot environment is used just as lavishly as it is in the fully hydrated mammal.

Another example is concerned with acclimatization to heat; this new condition of homeostasis (*i.e.,* acclimatization) applys only to a particular environmental temperature. A man must acclimatize separately for an ambient temperature of 30° or 35° or 40°C.

A final illustration is seen in hibernation. The mammalian hibernator carries out a delicate regulation of body temperature which is maintained between safe limits at totally different ambient temperatures. In some species these ambient temperatures may vary from 15° to 1°C. The body temperature will be regulated about 1° above ambient temperature.

Because homeostasis can be set for a variety of temperatures, at times the environmental temperature which is considered optimal for the species is difficult to define. The optimal temperature is that environment where maximum growth, activity, and preference are demonstrated by the species. These temperatures tend to be several degrees below lethal values for the animal and on the high side of normally experienced temperatures;[152] this may represent a compromise between maximum metabolic activity and inactivation of essential proteins. Mammalian temperatures seem to be poised as high as is consistent with a margin of physiological safety.[152] Prosser points out that the margin between body temperature and death is the most narrow in birds.[152] To summarize, what I have searched for in the writing of this volume are the extreme limits at which homeokineses will still perform.

Acclimatization and Acclimation. A second principle of Environmental Physiology is that some animals demonstrate acclimatization or acclimation when they are exposed to extreme environments. It is not uncommon to see improvement either in the behavior or the comfort of animals after some time in a stressful environment. This is not always referred to as acclimatization but it may have something in common with it. For example when Smith and Andjus exposed mammals until their body temperature reached super-cooled levels, they found that when the animals were cooled several times, their recovery rate improved. Again, in two separate experiments on starved men and on starved pigs, two different authors found that when the experiments were repeated, the subjects tolerated the starvation with less evidence of discomfort or damage as the experiment progressed. Such results as these are not always detectable; in experiments where cats were exposed to hypothermia, and men were exposed to near-freezing water temperatures, no improvement was apparent with repeated exposures. It may be that the cats and the men were demonstrating habituation which was not easily recognized or measured. Also, there may have been biochemical changes which indicate improvement with different exposures which were not detected or measured. When improvement is clearly definable over a period of continuous exposure, it is called acclimation or acclimatization.

As defined in an earlier chapter, it is the development of higher capacity for activity in the extreme environment and less discomfort upon continued exposure; this state can be detected by measurable physiological changes day by day as exposure progresses. A major function of this volume has been to record those cases where acclimatization or acclimation have been observed. It should be made clear that some individual mammals do not demonstrate this phenomenon. An example is found in those vigorous mammals studied by Morrison [433] which showed an identical physiology when the measurements were made at altitude and at sea level and when environments were reversed. The mystery still remains as to whether these more vigorous species do not need to acclimatize or whether more sensitive test are required to determine the evidence of their gradual adjustment. Nevertheless it is apparent that other mammals exposed outdoors in extreme cold and heat do demonstrate specific physiological changes which have a reproducible time course and result in greater biological efficiency for the species. Such animals are then said to be acclimatized.

APPENDICES

Appendix A

CLASSIFICATION OF MAMMALIA*

Orders:

Monotremata:	egg-laying mammals
Marsupialia:	pouched mammals
Insectivora:	hedgehogs, moles, shrews
Dermoptera:	flying lemurs
Chiroptera:	bats
Primates:	monkey-like mammals, man
Edentata:	anteaters, sloths, armadillos
Pholidota:	scaly anteaters, pangolins
Lagomorpha:	hares, rabbits
Rodentia:	rodents
Cetacea:	whales, dolphins
Carnivora:	dogs, cats, weasel-like mammals, seals
Tubulidentata:	aardvarks
Proboscidea:	elephants
Hyracoidea:	conies
Sirenia:	manatees
Perissodactyla:	horse-type mammals, tapirs, rhinoceros
Artiodactyla:	pigs, goats, deer, cattle, giraffes, hippopotami, camels

---

* Simpson, G. G. (1945) *The Principles of Classification and a Classification Of Mammals.* Bulletin of the American Museum of Natural History. New York 85:xi.

Appendix B

TECHNICAL NAMES OF MAMMALS OF IMPORTANCE TO ENVIRONMENTAL PHYSIOLOGISTS

1. Pocket mouse   (Perognathus longimembris)
2. Golden Hamster   (Cricetus auratus)
3. European ground squirrel   (Citellus citellus)
4. Thirteen-lined ground squirrel   (Citellus tridecemlineatus)
5. Mohave ground squirrel   (Citellus mohavensis)
6. Golden-manteled ground squirrel   (Citellus lateralis)
7. California ground squirrel   (Citellus beecheyi)
8. Roundtail ground squirrel   (Citellus tereticaudus)
9. Jerboa   (Dipus aegyptius)
10. Woodchuck   (Marmota monax)
11. Muskrat   (Ondatra zibethica)
12. Beaver   (Castor canadensis)
13. Little brown bat   (Myotis lucifugus)
14. Big brown bat   (Eptesicus serotinus)
15. Aoudad or Barbary sheep   (Ammotragus lervia)
16. Himalayan tahr goat   (Hemitragus jemlaicus)
17. Guanaco or wild llama   (Lama guanicoe)
18. Harbor seal   (Phoca vitulina)
19. Bottlenose dolphin   (Tursiops truncatus)
20. Sperm whale   (Physeter macrocephalus)
21. Finback whale   (Balaenoptera physalus)

Appendix C

ADDITIONAL ECOLOGY TEXTBOOKS

Allee, W. C., O. Park, A. Emerson, T. Park, and K. P. Schmidt. 1949. *Principles of Animal Ecology.* Saunders: Philadelphia. 837 p.

Andrewartha, H. G. and L. C. Birch. 1954. *The Distribution and Abundance of Animals.* Univ. Chicago Press: Chicago. 782 p.

Baer, J. G. 1951. *Ecology of Animal Parasites.* Univ. Illinois Press: Urbana. 224 p.

Bates, M. 1960. *The Forest and the Sea;* A look at the economy of nature and the ecology of man. Random House: New York. 277 p.

Benton, A. H. and W. E. Werner. 1958. *Principles of Field Biology and Ecology.* McGraw-Hill: New York. 341 p.

Bodenheimer, F. S. 1958. *Animal Ecology Today.* W. Junk: Den Haag. 276 p. (Monographiae Biologicae, v. 6)

Bresler, J. B. 1966. *Human Ecology:* Collected readings. Addison-Wesley Publ.: Reading, Mass. 250 p.

Carpenter, J. R. (Comp.). 1938. *An Ecological Glossary.* Univ. Oklahoma Press: Norman. 306 p.

Chapman, R. N. 1931. *Animal Ecology,* with Special Reference to Insects. 1st Ed. McGraw-Hill: New York. 464 p.

Clarke, G. L. 1965. *Elements of Ecology.* 1st Ed., rev. with subject guide to new references. Contrib. 704 from the Woods Hole Oceanographic Instit. Wiley: New York. 534 p.

Clements, F. E. and V. E. Shelford. 1939. *Bio-ecology.* Wiley: New York. 425 p.

Consolazio, C. F., R. E. Johnson, and L. J. Pecora. 1963. Meteorological measurements. In *Physiological Measurements of Metabolic Functions in Man.* Blakiston Div., McGraw-Hill: New York. 505 p.

Cragg, J. B. (Ed.). 1962. *Advances in Ecological Research.* Vol. 1. Academic Press: New York. 203 p.

Dansereau, P. M. 1957. *Biogeography;* an ecological perspective. Ronald Press: New York. 394 p.

Dasmann, R. F. 1959. *Environmental Conservation.* Wiley: New York. 307 p.

Daubenmire, R. F. 1959. *Plants and Environment;* A Textbook of Plant Autecology. 2nd Ed. Wiley: New York. 422 p.

Davis, D. H. S. (Ed.). 1964. *Ecological Studies in Southern Africa.* W. Junk: Den Haag. 415 p. (Monographiae Biologicae, v. 14)

Davis, D. E. and F. B. Golley. 1963. *Principles in Mammalogy.* Reinhold: New York. 335 p.

Dice, L. R. 1952. *Natural Communities.* Univ. Michigan Press: Ann Arbor. 547 p.

Dowdeswell, W. H. 1961. *Animal Ecology.* 2nd Ed. Harper: New York. 209 p.

Elton, C. S. 1930. *Animal Ecology and Evolution.* Clarenden Press: Oxford; Milford: London. 96 p.

Elton, C. S. 1933. *The Ecology of Animals.* Methuen: London. 97 p.

Elton, C. S. 1956. *Animal Ecology.* Sedgwick & Jackson: London 209 p.

Appendix C (Continued)

Elton, C. S. 1958. *The Ecology of Invasion by Animals and Plants*. Methuen: London. 181 p.

Hedgpeth, J. W. (Ed.). 1957. *Treatise on Marine Ecology and Paleoecology*. Nat. Res. Counsil., Geological Soc. Amer. (Memoir 67). 1296 p.

Hess, R. 1951. *Ecological Animal Geography*. Based on his *Tiergeographie auf Oekologischer Grundlage*. 2nd Ed. by W. C. Allee and K. P. Schmidt. Wiley: New York 715 p.

Kendeigh, S. C. 1961. *Animal Ecology*. Prentice-Hall: Englewood Cliffs, N. J. 468 p.

Klopfer, P. H. 1962. *Behavioral Aspects of Ecology*. Prentice-Hall: Englewood Cliffs, N. J. 171 p.

Knight, C. B. 1965. *Basic Concepts of Ecology*. Macmillan: New York. 468 p.

Kormondy, E. J. (Ed.). 1965. *Readings in Ecology*. Prentice-Hall: New Jersey. 219 p. Contains articles by L. J. Henderson, G. L. Clark, T. H. Bullock, G. E. Hutchinson, J. Loeb, K. Lorenz, A. C. Redfield, N. Tinbergen, W. M. Wheeler.

Lemon, P. C. 1962. *Field and Laboratory Guide for Ecology*. Burgess: Minneapolis. 180 p.

Nikolskii, G. V. 1963. *The Ecology of Fishes*. (Trans. from Russian by L. Burkett). Academic Press: New York & London. 352 p.

Odum, E. P. 1959. *Fundamentals of Ecology*. (Written in collaboration with H. T. Odum). 2nd Ed. Saunders: Philadelphia. 546 p.

Pearse, A. P. 1939. *Animal Ecology*. 2nd Ed. McGraw-Hill: New York. 642 p.

Reid, G. K. 1961. *Ecology of Inland Waters and Estuaries*. Reinhold: New York. 375 p.

Shelford, V. E. 1929. *Laboratory and Field Ecology;* The responses of animals as indicators of correct working methods. Williams & Wilkins: Baltimore. 608 p.

Appendix D

THE BIOTIC COMMUNITIES OF NORTH AMERICA

as listed by Shelford: [*]

1. The Temperate Deciduous Forest Biome (Northern and Upland Regions)
2. The Temperate Deciduous Forest Biome (Southern and Lowland Regions)
3. Floodplain Forest Biotic Communities in the Deciduous Forest and Grassland Biomes
4. The Boreal Coniferous Forest
5. Montaine Coniferous Forest and Alpine Communities
6. The Tundra Biome
7. The Northern Pacific Coast Rainy Western Hemlock Forest Biome and Mountain Communities
8. The Summer Drought or Broad Sclerophyll-Grizzly Bear Community
9. Cold Desert and Semidesert Communities
10. Ecotone Woodland and Bushland Communities
11. The Marginal Contacts of the Temperate Grassland
12. The Northern Temperate Grassland
13. The Southern Temperate Grassland
14. The Hot Desert
15. The Tropical Rain Forest
16. The Tropical Deciduous Forest and Related Communities with a Dry Season
17. The Oak and Pine Forests, Cloud Forests, and Other Mountain Communities
18. The Communities of Southern Florida, Cuba, and the Shores of the Mainland

---

[*] Shelford, Victor E. 1964. *The Ecology of North America.* Univ. Illinois Press: Urbana.

Appendix E

AN IMPORTANT REFERENCE BOOK

ROBERT B. PLATT AND JOHN F. GRIFFITHS 1964
ENVIRONMENTAL MEASUREMENT & INTERPRETATION
Reinhold College Textbook Department 256 p.

Contents:

Appendix F

OTHER REFERENCES

Bailey, N. T. J. 1964. *The Elements of Stochastic Prosesses.* Oxford Univ. Press. 250 p.

Consolazio, C. F., R. E. Johnson, and L. J. Pecora. 1963. *Physiological Measurements of Metabolic Functions in Man.* McGraw-Hill: New York. 505 p.

Pennak, R. W. 1964. *Collegiate Dictionary of Zoology.* Ronald Press: New York. 583 p.

Hannon, J. P. and C. W. Harris. 1966. High altitude acclimatization of college women. Fed. Proc. 25: 399.

Appendix G

SOME BIOMETEOROLOGICAL OR ECOGEOGRAPHIC RULES

(1) *Gloger's Rule:* "In mammals and birds, races which inhabit warm and humid regions have more melanin pigmentation than races of the same species in cooler and drier regions; arid regions are characterized by accumulation of yellow and reddish-brown phaeomelanin pigmentation; in cold climate phaeomelanin is reduced, in extreme cases also the eumelanin (polar white)."

(2) *Bergmann's Rule:* "The smaller-sized geographic races of a species are found in the warmer parts of the ecological range, the larger-sized races in the cooler districts."

(3) *Allen's Rule:* "Protruding body-parts, such as tails, ears, bills, extremities, and so forth, are relatively shorter in the cooler parts of the range of the species than in the warmer parts."

Criticisms of these rules are discussed in the text.

Appendix H

SKIN TEMPERATURES AND THE PLACEMENT OF THERMOCOUPLES ON MEN

A. Placement of Thermocouples or Thermistors on the Belding Points

1. Inside and end (medial) of great toe on side.
2. Lateral side of calf.
3. Lateral mid-thigh.
4. Medial mid-thigh.
5. Below scapula at midpoint of lateral to midline.
6. On thorax below nipple on right side.
7. Insertion deltoid or lateral side upper arm.
8. Lateral lower arm.
9. Dorsum of hand on proximal end of 2nd metacarpal. Not on a large vein.
10. Center of forehead.
11. Medial, center, lateral-edge of sole.

B. Obtaining Mean Skin Values

It would be inaccurate to use an average of the above points to obtain the mean skin values. The temperatures for various body segments should be WEIGHTED as follows:

Feet	7%
Lower Leg	13%
Upper Leg	19%
Trunk	35%
Arms	14%
Hands	5%
Head	7%

C. Locations of Thermocouples for Foot Temperatures

If the temperature of the foot is to be recorded at five points, standardized placement is:

1. Tip of great toe.
2. Base of great toe on dorsum.
3. Tip of small toe.
4. Ball of foot.
5. Center on instep, not over vein or artery.

Appendix I

DATA FORM: STUDIES ON HEAT DISSIPATION
OF MEN UNDER HEAT STRESS

Preliminary Procedure:

1. Record:

Observer's Name
Subject's Name } always in *bound* Notebook
Date

2. Keep a detailed diary in Notebook.
   - What clothing worn.
   - Times of measurements.
   - Times of exercise.

3. Record subject's: attitude
   health
   amount of rest previous night } try to keep these constant
   time and content of last meal
   water intake

4. Have Subject urinate.
5. Have Subject drink 500 ml tap water, or 10 ml/kilo body weight.
6. Dress Subject for experiment and attach electrodes.
7. Take rectal temperature (usually after dressing).
8. Procedure must always be identical.

Sample Analysis (Hypothetical Figures).

Ambient Temp. $24 \pm 1.5°C$

Subject: J. D.   Weight: 61 kg   Height: 176 cm   Surface Area: 1.76 m²

RECTAL TEMPERATURE: Initial: 37.4°C (99.2°F)   Final: 38°C (100.5°F)

MEAN SKIN TEMPERATURE: Initial: 27.8°C (82°F)   Final: 30.5°C (87°F)

PULSE RATE: Initial: 82 beats/min   Final: 96 beats/min

MOISTURE UPTAKE OF CLOTHING: 445 gm / 30 min/ total body—less head & hands.

VENTILATION: 1000 liters/hr.   Use 500 1/30 min or 17 1/min.

OXYGEN CONSUMPTION: 36.1 liters/hr or 18.5 1/30 min or 100 Cals/m²/hr

SWEAT CALCULATION:

A. Correction for Saturation of Air in Lungs:

500 liters Vent. $\times$ 0.029 gm = 14.53 gm/30 min

B. Correction for Excess of CO_2 over O_2:

18.5 liters O_2/30 min $\times$ 0.3 gm = 5.6 gm/30 min

C. Calculation of evaporation from face, head and hands (or in some cases from just the face) (in gm/30 min):

Gross weight loss during experiment	975 gm
	—20
Corrected for loss from lungs (A + B)	955 gm
	—455
Corrected for moisture uptake	510 gm Evaporation

Appendix J

STATISTICS

The following formulas will prove useful.[*]

Mean:

A mean of a group of data is the arithmetic average. It is derived from the formula:

$$\bar{x} = \frac{\Sigma x}{n}$$

where: $\bar{x}$ = the mean
Σ = the sum of
x = a single measurement
n = the number of measurements

Range:

In a group of data the extent of the values from the smallest to the largest is termed the range.

Standard Deviation

The standard deviation is an indication of the variation of the data around the mean. It is calculated using the following formula:

$$S.D. = \sqrt{\frac{\Sigma(x - \bar{x})^2}{n}}$$

If n is less than 30, another formula is used:

$$S.D. = \sqrt{\frac{\Sigma(x - \bar{x})^2}{n - 1}}$$

Probable Error

Another index to the variation of the data around the mean is the probable error. If a distribution curve is normal, 50% of the measurements fall within plus and minus one probable error. It is calculated using the following:

$$P.E. = .6745 \ S.D.$$

Standard Error of the Mean:

The standard error of the mean is a measure of precision or spread of the mean:

$$S.E. = \frac{S.D.}{\sqrt{n - 1}}$$

Student's t Test:

Gosset, pseudonym Student, devised a test to evaluate the significance of the difference between two means:

$$t = \frac{\bar{x}_1 - \bar{x}_2}{\sqrt{(S.E._1)^2 + (S.E._2)^2}}$$

where: t = a value used to determine probability
$\bar{x}_1$ = the mean of one group of data
$\bar{x}_2$ = the mean of the second group of data
$S.E._1$ = the standard error of the mean of the first group
$S.E._2$ = the standard error of the mean of the second group

Using the t value in a table of *Student's t Distribution* one determines the probability, P. A P less than .05 is usually considered to be significant; this means that there are less than 5 chances out of 100 that a difference between the means of the indicated magnitude occurred by chance. Some examples are given in the table taken from Langley ($t = 0.386$ to 63.66).

---

[*] From L. L. Langley. 1965. *Outline of Physiology.* 2nd Ed. By permission of McGraw-Hill: New York. 532p.

to determine Probability (P)

n	.7	.2	.05	.01
1	.510	3.08	12.71	63.66
5	.408	1.48	2.57	4.03
10	.397	1.37	2.23	3.17
15	.393	1.34	2.13	2.95
20	.391	1.33	2.09	2.85
30	.389	1.31	2.04	2.75
120	.386	1.29	1.98	2.62

* More complete tables are found in a textbook of statistics.

"n" refers to the *degrees of freedom,* which equals $(n_1 - 1)$ $(n_2 - 1)$ where n has the usual connotation of the number of measurements in each sample.

Chi-Square Test:

If the date fits into the yes and no category, the chi-square test of significance is used. It would be used to detect whether a drug has a significant effect or not. The calculation is:

$$\text{Chi-square} = \underset{\text{First Group}}{\frac{(\text{Observed} - \text{Expected})^2}{\text{Expected}}} + \underset{\text{Second Group}}{\frac{(\text{Observed} - \text{Expected})^2}{\text{Expected}}} \ldots$$

The expected number is based on the null hypothesis that there is no difference between the two groups.

Langleys' explanation of use of the chi-square test is as follows:*

"If a coin is perfectly balanced, one may expect that with repeated tossings it will land heads 50% of the time and tails the other 50%. The coin is tossed, say, 50 times. It is anticipated, according to the null hypothesis, that the coin will land heads 25 times and tails the same number. Actually, it is observed that it lands heads 32 times and tails 18 times. Using the above equation, chi-square is calculated to be 3.92. A chi-square distribution table is consulted for the P value, that is, the Probability. Again, a P value of less than .05 is usually considered to be significant.

"A second example is the testing of a drug to determine its ability to combat fever. The drug is given to one group of patients; the control group receives an impotent substitute, a *placebo.* It is found, at the end of the treatment period, that 40% of the patients have no fever, 60% still have fever. Using the null hypothesis it is to be expected that 40% of the patients in each group would be without fever. This number is then compared with the observed number and chi-square calculated."

* From the 1960 edition.

Appendix K

CONVERSION FACTORS*

1 centimeter	=	0.39370 inches
1 meter	=	39.37 inches or 3.28 feet
1 kilometer	=	0.62137 mile
1 milliliter	=	0.03381 fluid ounces
1 liter	=	1.0567 U. S. quarts
1 cubic meter	=	1.3080 cubic yards
1 gram	=	15.4324 grains
1 kilogram	=	2.2046 pounds
1 foot candle	=	10 lux
1 fathom	=	6 feet

---

* From the United States Department of Commerce, Miscellaneous Publication 233.

BIBLIOGRAPHY

Bibliography

Preface and Chapter 1
What is Environmental Physiology

1 BUETTNER, K. J. K. 1957. Aim and purpose of symposium on Bioclimatology. Fed. Proc. *16*:607.

2 DILL, D. B. (Sec. Ed.). 1964. *Handbook of Physiology: sec 4, Adaptation to the Environment.* Amer. Physiol. Soc. (Publishers) 1056p.

3 DOTY, R. W. 1962. Behavioral aspects of Neurophysiology. Physiologist *15*:270–284.

4 DUBOS, R. 1964. Environmental Biology. BioScience *14*:11–14.

5 EAGAN, C. J. 1963. Introduction and terminology: Habituation and peripheral tissue adaptations. Fed. Proc. *22*:930–933.

6 EHRLICH, P. R., and R. W. HOLM. 1962. Patterns and populations. Science *137*:652–657.

7 FOLK, G. E., JR. 1964. The problem of electrodes for use with electrocardiograph radio capsules. Proc. 2nd Nat. Biomed. Sci. Instrumentation Symp. Plenum Press: New York.

8 FOLK, G. E., JR., and M. A. FOLK. 1964. Continuous physiological measurements of unrestrained arctic ground squirrels. Ann. Finn. Acad. of Sci. *71*:157–173.

9 GLASER, E. M., M. S. HALL, and G. C. WHITTOW. 1959. Habituation and adaptation. J. Physiol. *146*:152.

9a HARDY, J. D. (Ed.). 1963. *Temperature:Its Measurement and Control in Biology and Medicine.* Vol. 3. Reinhold: New York. 683 p.

10 HART, J. S. 1957. Climatic and temperature induced changes in the energetics of homeotherms. Rev. Canad. Biol. *16*:133-141.

11 HEISTAND, W. A., F. W. STEMLER and R. L. JASPER. 1955. Increased anoxic resistance resulting from short period heat adaptation. Proc. Soc. Exp. Biol. Med. *88*:94-97.

12 LEE, D. H. K. 1953. Physiological Climatology as a field of study. Ann. Assoc. Amer. Geogr. *43*:127.

12a LICHT, S. (Ed.). 1964. *Medical Climatology.* Elizabeth Licht, Publ.; New Haven, Conn. 753p.

12b LORENZ, K. L. 1957. *King Solomon's Ring.* Pan Books Ltd: London. 217p.

13 MONGE, C. 1942. Life in the Andes and chronic mountain sickness. Science *19*:79-80.

14 MURRAY, J. A. H., (Ed.). 1888. A *New English Dictionary.* Oxford Univ. Press, London.

15 PLATT, R. B. 1964. The importance of environment to life. BioScience *14*:25-29.

16 PROSSER, C. L. (Ed.). 1958. *Physiological Adaptation.* Amer. Physiol. Soc.: Washington, D.C. 180p.

17 RICHTER, C. P. 1927. Animal behavior and internal drives. Quart. Rev. Biol. *2*:307-343.

17a SARGENT, F., II. 1957. A prospectus of Bioclimatology: historical observations on its national and international growth. Fed. Proc. *16*:603.

18 SARGENT, F., II. 1963. A program for Biometerology. Int. J. Biometeorol. *7*:115-119.

19 SARGENT, F., II. 1963. The nature and nurture of Biometeorology. AIBS Bull. *13*:20–23.

20 SEALANDER, J. A., JR. 1951. Survival of *Peromyscus* in relation to environmental temperature and acclimation at high and low temperature. Amer. Midland Nat. *46*:257–263.

21 SELYE, H. 1950. *The Physiology and Pathology Of Exposure To Stress.* Acta: Montreal. 203p.

22 TROMP, S. W. (Ed.). 1963. *Medical Biometeorology.* Amer. Elsevier Press: New York. 991p.

23 TROMP, S. W. 1963. Human Biometeorology. Int. J. Biometeorol. 7:145–158.

Chapter 2

Influence of Visible Light Radiations

24 ASCHOFF, J. 1953. Tierische Periodik unter dem Einfluss von Zeitgebern. Z. Vergleich. Physiol. 35:159-166.

25 ASCHOFF, J. 1963. Comparative Physiology: diurnal rhythms. Ann. Rev. Physiol., *25*: 581–600.

26 BAKER, J. R., and J. BIRD. 1936. The seasons in a tropical rain-forest. Linn. Soc. Zool. 39:508–542.

27 BISSONETTE, T. H. 1938. Influence of light on the hypophysis. Endocrinology 22:92.

28 BISSONETTE, T. H. 1939. Sexual photoperiodicity in the blue jay. Wilson Bulletin *51*: 227–231.

29 BREDER, C. M., and P. RASQUIN. 1947. Comparative studies of the light sensitivity of blind characens from a series of Mexican caves. Bull. Amer. Mus. Natur. Hist. 89:319–329.

29a BRUCE, V. G., and C. S. PITTENDRIGH. 1956. Temperature independence in a unicellular "clock". Proc. Nat. Acad. Sci. *42*: 676-682.

30 CAJLACHJAN, M. C. 1936. On the mechanism of the photoperiodic reaction. Compt. Rend. (Doklady) Acad. Sci. URSS. *1*:89–93.

31 CHOW, K. L. 1957. Degeneration of retinal ganglion cells in infant chimpanzees reared in darkness. J. Comp. Neurol. *107*: 314–321.

32 EAYERS, J. L., and K. F. IRELAND. 1950. The effect of total darkness on the growth of the new-born albino rat. J. Endocrinal. 6:386–392.

33 FARNER, D. S. 1957. An essential compound in bird photoperiodicity. Physiologist *1*: 26.

34 FARNER, D. S. 1961. Photoperiodicity. Ann. Rev. Physiol. 23:71–96.

35 FARNER, D. S. 1964. Role of extreme changes in photoperiod in the annual cycles of birds and insects. Fed. Proc. 23:1215-1220.

36 FARNER, D. S. 1964. The Photoperiodic control of reproductive cycles in birds. Amer. Scientist, March. 137–156.

37 FISK, VIRGINIA M. 1965. Serotonin rhythm in the pineal organ: control by the sympathetic nervous system. Science *146*:253-254.

38 FOLK, G. E., JR. 1955. Modification by light and feeding of the 24-hour rhythm of activity in rodents. Proc. 5th Conf. on Biol. Rhythms, Stockholm.

39 FOLK, G. E., JR. 1959. Modification by light of 24-hour activity of white rats. Iowa Acad. Sci. *66*:399-406.

40 FOLK, G. E., JR. 1961. Observations on the daily rhythms of body temperature labile mammals. Ann. N. Y. Acad. Sci. 98:954–969.

41 GARDNER, W. W. and H. A. ALLARD. 1920. Effect of the relative length of day and night and other factors of the environment in growth and reproduction in plants. Agr. Res. *18*:553-605.

42 HALL, E. R. 1953. The distribution of mammals. Proc. Int. Cong. Zool. *14*:397.

42a HAMNER, K. C. 1940. Interrelation of light and darkness in photoperiodic induction. Bot. Gaz. *101*:658–687.

43 HART, J. S. and H. D. FISHER. 1964. The question of adaptations to polar envir-

onments in marine mammals. Fed. Proc. 23:1207–1214.

43a Harvey, H. E., and W. V. Macfarlane. 1958. The effects of day length upon the coat shedding cycles, body weight, and reproduction in the ferret. Australian J. Biol. Sci. 11:187.

44 Hendricks, S. B. 1956. Control of growth and reproduction by light and darkness. Amer. Scientist, July. 229–247.

45 Hoffman, R. A. and R. J. Reiter. 1965. Pineal gland: influence on gonads of male hamsters. Science 148:1609–1610.

46 Hollaender, A. (Ed.). 1956. Visable and near visible light; Vol. 3 in Radiation Biology. McGraw-Hill: New York. 765p.

47 Johnson, M. S. 1939. Effect of continuous light on periodic spontaneous activity of white-footed mice. J. Exp. Zöol. 82:315-321.

48 Lang, A. and G. Melchers. 1943. Die photoperiodische Reaktion von Hyoscyamus niger. Planta. 33:653–702.

49 Lisk, R. D., and L. R. Kannwischer. 1964. Light: evidence for its direct effect on hypothalamic neurons. Science 146:272-273.

50 Long, E. M. 1939. Photoperiodic induction as influenced by environmental factors. Bot. Gaz. 101:168–188.

51 Marshall, F. H. A. 1936. Sexual periodicity and the causes which determine it. Phil. Trans. B., 226:423-434.

52 Melchers, G. 1952. The Physiology of Flower Initiation. Lectures at Imperial College, London, 168p.

52a Odum, E. P. 1963. Ecology. Modern Biology Series. Holt, Rinehart and Winston, Inc. 152p.

53 Pittendrigh, C. S. 1960. Circadian Rhythms and Circadian Organization. Cold Spring Harbor Symposia 25:159-185.

54 Poulter, T. C. 1963. Sonar signals of the sea lion. Science 139:753-754.

54a Rawson, K. S. 1959. Experimental modification of mammalian endogenus activity rhythms, p. 791-800. In Photoperiodism, R. W. Withrow, (Ed.). Amer. Assoc. Adv. Sci. Publ. 55. Wash, D.C. 903p.

55 Riesen, A. H. 1960. Chimpanzees raised in darkness. Amer. J. Orthopsychiat. 30:23–25.

56 Swade, R. H. 1964. Circadian Rhythms in the Arctic. Thesis. University Microfilm, Inc., Ann Arbor, Michigan No. 64–9145. 305p.

57 Withrow, R. B. (Ed.). 1959. Photoperiodism and related phenomena in plants and animals. Proc. Conf. on Photoperiodism AAAS Publ. No. 55. 903p.

58 Wolfson, A. 1959. Role of light in the photoperiodic responses of migratory birds. Science 129:1425–1426

59 Wolfson, A. 1964. Animal photoperiodism, In Phytophysiology Vol. 2, A. C. Giescl, (Ed.), Academic Press. 531p.

60 Wurtman, R. J., J. Axelrod, S. H. Snyder and Elizabeth W. Chu. 1965. Changes in the enzymatic synthesis of Melatonin in the pineal during the estrous cycle. Endocrinology 76:798–800.

Chapter 3

Biological Rhythms

61 Andrews, R. V. and G. E. Folk, Jr. 1963. Circadian metabolic patterns in cultured hamster adrenals. J. Comp. Biochem. Physiol. 11:393–409.

62 Aschoff, J. 1952. Frequenzänderungen der Aktivitätsperiodik Bei Mäusen im Dauerlicht und Dauerdunkel. Pflüg. Arch. ges Physiol. 255:197.

63 Aschoff, J. 1955. Exogne and endogone Komponente de 24-Studen–Periodik bei Tier und Mensch. Naturwissenschaften 42:569.

64 Aschoff, J. (Ed.). 1964. Circadian Clocks North-Holland Publishing Co. 500p.

65 Aschoff, J. 1965. Circadian Rhythms in Man. Science 148:1427-1432.

66 Beck, S. D. 1963. Animal Photoperiodism.

Holt, Rinehart and Winston, Inc., New York. 124p.

67 BROWN, F. A., JR. 1957. Responses of a living organism, under "constant conditions" including pressure, to a barometric-pressure-correlated, cyclic, external variable. Biol. Bull. *112*:288–304.

68 BROWN, F. A., JR. 1958. Comparisons of some fluctuations in cosmic radiation and in organismic activity during 1954, 1955 and 1956. Amer. J. Physiol. *195*:237-243.

69 BROWN, F. A. JR. 1959. Biological Chronometry. Amer. Natur. *91*:129-133.

70 BROWN, F. A., JR. 1962. Extrinsic rhythmicity, a reference frame for biological rhythms under so-called constant conditions. Ann. N.Y. Acad. Sci. *98*:775-787.

71 BROWN, F. A., JR. 1963. An orientational response to weak gamma radiation. Biol. Bull. *125*:206–225.

72 BRETT, W. J. 1955. Persistent diurnal rhythmicity in *Drosophilia* emergence. Ann. Ent. Soc. Amer. *48*:119–131.

73 BUNNING, E. 1964. *The Physiological Clock.* Academic Press: London. 145p.

74 CANNON, W. B. 1918. The physiological basis of thirst. Proc. Roy. Soc. Lond. *90*:283-294.

75 CLAYTON, D. L. 1964. Effect of torpor on activity rhythms in the pocket mouse (*Perognatus*). Bull. Ecol. Soc. Amer. *45*:105.

76 CLOUDSLEY-THOMPSON, J. L. 1961. *Rhythmic Activity in Animal Physiology and Behavior.* Academic Press, London. 236p.

76a DILL, D. B. 1960. Fatigue and Physical Fitness. p. 384-402. In *Science and Medicine of Exercise and Sports.* W. R. Johnson (Ed.). Harper: New York. 740p.

77 DILL, D. B., et al. 1932. Factors limiting capacity for work: Studies in muscular activity. J. Physiol. 77:49–62.

78 FLINK, E. B., and R. P. DOE. 1959. Effect of sudden time displacement by air travel on synchronization of adrenal function. Proc. Soc. Exp. Biol. and Med. *100*:498–501.

79 FOLK, G. E., JR. 1960. Day-night rhythms and hibernation. In *Mammalian Hibernation.* Bull. Mus. Comp. Zöol., Harvard College, *124*:209–232.

80 FOLK, G. E., JR. 1961. Circadian aspects of the circulation. p86-88. In *Circadian Systems.* Proc. 39th Ross Conf. on Pediatric Res.

81 FOLK, G. E., JR., W. ASHLOCK, and E. M. BAKER. 1965. Daily physiological rhythms of unrestrained monkeys. Physiologist 8:165.

82 FOLK, G. E., JR., R. E. GRINDELAND, and M. R. MELTZER. 1958. A mammalian biological rhythm independent of temperature. Nature *181*:1598–1600.

83 FOLK, G. E., JR., R. R. SCHELLINGER and D. SNYDER. 1961. Day-night changes after exercise in body temperatures and heart rates of hamsters. Proc. Iowa Acad. Sci. *68*:594–602.

84 FOMON, S. (Ed.). 1961. *Circadian Systems* Proc. 39th Ross Conf. on Pediatric Res. 91p.

85 GOULD, E. 1957. Orientation in box turtles. Biol. Bull. *112*:336–348.

86 HALBERG, F. 1964. 17– Ketosteroid and volume of human urine. Minnesota Medicine 47:916–925.

87 HALBERG, F., C. P. BARNUM, R. SILBER, and J. J. BITTNER. 1958. 24-hour rhythms at different levels of integration in the mouse, and the lighting regimen. Proc. Soc. Exp. Biol. and Med. 97:879–900.

88 HARKER, J. E. 1958. Diurnal rhythms in the animal kingdom. Biol. Rev. *33*:1–52.

89 HARKER, J. E. 1964. *The Physiology of Diurnal Rhythms.* Cambridge University Press: New York. 114p.

90 HASLER, A. D. 1958. Sun-orientation and homing in fishes. Limnol. and Oceanogr. 3:353-361.

91 HASTINGS, J. W. 1959. Unicellular clocks, Ann. Rev. Microbiol. *13*:297-312.

92 HENDRICKS, S. B. 1963. Metabolic control of timing. Science *141*:21-27.

93 HOFFMAN, K. 1960. Experimental manipulation of the orientational clock in birds. Cold Spring Harbor Symp. *25*:379-389.

94 KALMUS, H. 1956. Sun navigation of Apis mellifica L. in the Southern hemisphere. J. Exp. Biol. 33:554–565.

95 KLEITMAN, N. 1963. *Sleep and Wakefulness* 2nd ed. Univ. of Chicago Press. 552p.

96 LEWIS, H. E. 1963. Nutritional research in the polar regions. Nutrition Rev. *21*: 353–356.

97 LEWIS, P. R., and M. C. LOBBAN. 1957. Dissociation of diurnal rhythms in human subjects on abnormal time routines. Quart. J. Exp. Physiol. *42*:371-386.

98 LORAND, A. 1925. *Old Age Deferred*. F. A. Davis Co: Philadelphia. 436p.

99 MENAKER, M. 1959. Endogenous rhythms of body temperature in hibernating bats. Nature *184*:1251–1252.

100 MENZEL, W. 1962. *Menschliche-Tag-Nacht-Rhythmik und Schichtarbeit*. Schwabe: Stuttgart. 192p.

101 PITTENDRIGH, C. S. 1954. On temperature independence in the clock system controlling emergence in *Drosophila*. Proc. Nat. Acad. Sci. *40*:1018–1029.

102 PITTENDRIGH, C. S. 1957. Perspectives in the study of biological clocks, p. 235-261. In *Perspectives in Marine Biology*. Univ. Calif. Press. 282p.

103 PITTENDRIGH, C. S., and G. V. BRUCE. 1957. An oscillator model for biological clocks, p. 75-109. In *Rhythmic and Systemic Prosesses in Growth*. Princeton Univ. Press. 345p.

104 PITTENDRIGH, C. S. 1964. The entrainment of circadian oscillations by skeleton photoperiods. Science *144*:565-566.

105 PRECHT, H. 1958. Concepts of the temperature adaption of unchanging reaction systems of cold-blooded animals, p. 50-78. In *Physiological Adaptation*. C. L. Prosser (Ed.). Amer. Physiol Soc. Publ. Wash. D.C. 185p.

105a RAWSON, K. S. 1960. Effects of tissue temperature on mammalian activity rhythms. Cold Spring Harbor Symp. on Quant. Biol. *25*:105-115.

106 RAY, J. T., O. E. MARTIN, JR., and E. A. ALLUISI. 1961. Human performance as a function of the work-rest cycle. Nat. Acad. Sci.-Nat. Res. Council. Wash. D.C. *882*:1-32.

107 REINBERG, A., and J. GHATA. 1964. *Biological Rhythms*. Walker: New York. 138p.

108 SASAKI, TAKASHI. 1963. Effects of rapid transportation around the earth on diurnal variation in body temperature. Proc. Soc. Exp. Biol. Med. *115*:1129-1131.

109 SLUCKIN, W. 1965. *Imprinting and Early Learning*. Aldine Publishing Co: Chicago. 150p.

110 SOLLBERGER, A. 1965. *Biological Rhythm Research*. Amer. Elsevier Press: New York. 461p.

111 STEVENS, G. C. 1962. Circadian melanophore rhythms of the fiddler crab: interaction between animals. *In Rhythmic functions in the living systems*. Wm. Wolf (Ed.). Ann. N. Y. Acad. Sci. *98*:926-939.

112 STIER, T. J. B. 1930. Spontaneous activity of mice. J. Gen. Psychol. *4*:67.

113 STIER, T. J. B. 1933. On the temperature-regulating function of spontaneous activity in the mouse. Proc. Nat. Acad. Sci., Wash., *19*:725.

114 STRUGHOLD, H. 1963. The physiological clock in aeronautics and astronautics. Lectures in Aerospace Medicine. U.S.A.F. School of Aerospace Medicine, Brooks A.F.B., Texas. p. 387-400.

115 STRUGHOLD, H. 1964. The solved and unsolved problems. p. 298-310. Lectures in Aerospace Medicine. U.S.A.F. School of Aerospace Medicine. Brooks A.F.B., Texas.

116 SUDA, I., K. KOIZUMI, and C. M. BROOKS. 1956. Effects of cooling on central nervous system responses. Fed. Proc. *15*:182.

117 SWARTZ, M. N., N. O. KAPLAN and M. E. FRECH. 1956. Significance of 'heat activated' enzymes. Science. *123*:50-53.

118 SWEENEY, B., and J. W. HASTINGS. 1960. Effects of temperature upon diurnal rhythms. Cold Spring Harbor Symp. *25*: 87-105.

119 THARP, GERALD D. and G. EDGAR FOLK, JR., 1964. Rhythmic changes in rate of the mammalian heart and heart cells during prolonged isolation. J. Comp. Biochem. Physiol. *14*:255-273.

120 TIMMERMAN, J. C., G. E. FOLK, JR., and S. M. HORVATH. 1959. Day-night differences of body temperature and heart rate after exercise. Quart. J. Exp. Physiol. *44*:258-263.

121 WEBB, H. M. and F. A. BROWN, JR. 1959. Timing long-cycle physiological rhythms. Physiol. Rev. *39*:127-161.

122 WELLS, G. P. 1955. *The Sources of Animal Behavior* H. K. Lewis: London. 20p.

123 WELSH, J. A. 1938. Diurnal rhythms. Quart. Rev. Biol. *13*:123-129.

124 WILKINS, H. 1960. The effect of light on plant rhythms. Cold Spring Harbor Symp. 25:115-131.

125 WOLF, E. 1930. Die activität der japonischen tanzmaus und ihre rhythmische verteilung. Z. vergl. Physiol. *II*:321.

126 WOLF, W. (Conf. Ed.). 1962. *Rhymic Function in the Living System.* Ann. N. Y. Acad. Sci. 98:753-1326.

Chapter 4

Principles of Temperature Regulation

127 BARTHOLOMEW, G. A., P. LEITNER, J. E. NELSON. 1964. Body temperature, O_2 consumption and heart rate in 3 species of Australian flying fox. Physiol. Zöol. 37: 179-198.

128 BELDING, H. S., H. D. RUSSELL, R. C. DARLING, and G. E. FOLK. 1947. Analysis of factors concerned in maintaining energy balance for dressed men in extreme cold. Amer. J. Physiol. *149*:223-239.

129 BELDING, H. S., H. D. RUSSELL, R. C. DARLING, and G. E. FOLK. 1947. Thermal responses and efficiency of sweating when men are dressed in arctic clothing and exposed to extreme cold. Amer. J. Physiol. *149*:204-222.

130 BENZINGER, T. H. 1961. The diminution of thermoregulatory sweating during cold reception at the skin. Proc. Nat. Acad. Sci. *47*:1683.

131 BENZINGER, T. H., and G. W. TAYLOR. 1963. Cranial measurement of internal temperature in man. p. 111-120. In *Temperature: Its Measurement and Control in Biology and Medicine.* Vol. 3. J. D. Hardy, (Ed.). Reinhold: New York. 683p.

132 CARLSON, L. D. 1964. Physiology of exposure to cold. Physiology For Physicians 2:1-7.

133 CENA, K. 1964. Thermoregulation in the hippopotamus. Int. J. Biometeorol. 8:57-60.

133a COOPER, K. E., W. I. CRANSTON, and E. S. SNELL. 1964. Temperature in the external auditory meatus. J. Appl. Physiol. *19*:1032-1035.

134 DILL, D. B. 1938. *Life, Heat, and Attitude.* Harvard Univ. Press. Cambridge, Mass. 211p.

135 ERIKSON, H. and J. KROG. 1956. Critical temperature in naked man. Acta Physiol. Scand. *37*:35-39.

136 FINLAY, J. D. 1963. Acclimatization to heat in sheep and cattle. Fed. Proc. *22*:688-692.

137 FOLK, G. E., JR. 1964. Daily physiology rhythms of carnivores exposed to extreme changes in arctic daylight. Fed. Proc. 23:1221-1228.

138 FOLK, G. E., JR. 1966. Physiological observations on bears under winter den conditions. Proc. 3rd Symp. Mammal. Hibernation. Oliver and Boyd: Edinburgh. 530p.

139 GREEN, J. H. 1963. *An Introduction to Human Physiology.* Oxford University Press: London. 153p.

140 HAFEZ, E. S. E. 1964. Behavioral thermoregulation in mammals and birds (a review). Int. J. Biometeorol. 7:231-239.

141 HAIDER, M., and D. B. LINDSLEY. 1964. Microvibrations in man and dolphin. Science *146*:1181-1183.

142 HARDY, J. D. 1961. Physiology of temperature regulation. Physiol. Rev. *41*:521-554.

143 HENDERSON, L. J. 1958. *The Fitness of The Environment.* Beacon Paperback. BP68. Beacon Press: Boston. 317p.

144 HERTZMAN, A. B., W. C. RANDALL, C. N., PEISS, and R. J. SECKENDORF. 1952. Regional rates of evaporation from the skin at various environmental temperatures. J. Appl. Physiol. 5:153-156.

145 HUDSON, J. W., and A. H. BRUSH. 1964. A comparative study of the cardiac and metabolic performance of the dove, and the quail. Comp. Biochem. Physiol. *12*: 157-170.

146 KUNO, Y. 1956. *Human Perspiration.* Thomas: Springfield, Ill. 268p.

147 LUCK, C. P., and P. G. WRIGHT. 1962. Aspects of the body temperature and habitat

of large animals. p. 334-338. In *Bio-meteorology (a Symposium)*. Proc. 2nd Int. Bioclimatol. Congr. Pergamon Press. 687p.

148 MINARD, D., L. COPMAN, and A. R. DASLER. 1964. Elevation of body temperature in health. Ann. N. Y. Acad. Sci. *121*:12-25.

149 MORRISON, P. R. 1946. Temperature regulation of marsupials and bats. J. Cell. Comp. Physiol. 27:125-137.

150 NEWBURGH, L. H. (Ed.). 1949. *Physiology of Heat Regulation and the Science of Clothing*. Saunders Co.: Philadelphia. 457p.

151 PEMBREY, M. S. 1898. *Schafer's Textbook of Physiology. Vol. I*, 838p.

152 PROSSER, C. L., and F. A. BROWN, JR. 1961. *Comparative Animal Physiology* 2nd ed. Saunders, Philadelphia. 688p.

152a RAMANATHAN, N. L. 1964. A new weighting system for mean surface temperature (human). J. Appl. Physiol. *19*:531-533.

153 RIEDESEL, M. L. 1965. Personal Communication.

154 SCHMIDT-NIELSEN, K. 1964. *Desert Animals: Physiological Problems of Heat and Water*. Oxford Univ. Press, London. 277p.

155 SCHOLANDER, P. F., R. HOCK, V. WALTERS, L. IRVING. 1950. Heat regulation in some arctic and tropical mammals and birds. Biol. Bull. 99:237-258.

155a STRYDOM, N. B., H. C. WYNDHAM, C. G. WILLIAMS, and J. F. MORRISON. 1965. Oral/Rectal temperature differences during work in heat. J. Appl. Physiol. *20*: 283-288.

156 TUTTLE, W. W., and B. A. SCHOTTELIUS. 1961. *Textbook of Physiology*. 14th Ed. C. V. Mosby Co. St. Louis. 547p.

157 WHIPPLE, H. E. (Ed.). 1964. Thermography and its clinical applications. Ann. N. Y. Acad. Sci. *121*:1-304.

Chapter 5

Responses to a Cold Environment

158 ADOLPH, E. F. 1950. Oxygen consumption of hypothermic rats and acclimatization to cold. Amer. J. Physiol. *161*:359-373.

159 ADOLPH, E. F. 1959. Hypothermia. Ann. N. Y. Acad. Sci. *80*:332-337.

160 ANDERSEN, K. L. 1963. Comparison of Lapps, fishermen, and Indians. Fed. Proc. *22*: 834-840.

161 ANDJUS, R. K. and A. U. SMITH. 1955. Reanimation of adult rats from body temperatures between 0° and 2°C. J. Physiol. *128*:446-472.

162 BASS, D. E., P. F. IAMPIETRO, and E. R. BUSWICK. 1959. Blood components in different races of men. J. Appl. Physiol. *14*: 801-805.

163 BECKMAN, E. L. 1963. Thermal protection during emersion in cold water. Proc. 2nd Symp. Underwater Physiol., Nat. Acad. Sci., Pub. No. 1181.

164 BERNARD, C. 1876. *Leçons sur la Chaleur Animale*. Baillière, Tindall, & Cox: London. 125p.

165 BLAIR, E. 1965. *Clinical Hypothermia*. McGraw-Hill, New York. 272p.

166 BLAIR, J. R. 1951. In the discussion in Acclimatization Chapter. Proc. 1st Conf. on Cold Injury. J. Macy, Jr. Found.: New York.

167 BURTON, A. C. 1951. Discussion, p. 201. First Conference on Cold Injury Josiah Macy, Jr. Foundation: New York.

168 BURTON, A. C., and O. G. EDHOLM. 1955. *Man In A Cold Environment*. Edward Arnold (Publishers) Ltd., London. 273p.

169 BUSS, I. O. and A. WALLNER. 1965. Body temperature of the African elephant. J. Mammal. *46*:104-107.

170 CHATFIELD, P. O., C. P. LYMAN, and L. IRVING. 1963. Physiological adaptation to cold of peripheral nerve of herring gull. Amer. J. Physiol. *172*:639-644.

171 COVINO, B. G. 1957. Some observations on ventricular fibrillation in acute hypothermia. p. 135-160. 5th Conf. on Cold Injury; J. Macy Found. 341p.

172 COVINO, B. G. and W. R. BEAVERS. 1957. Cardiovascular response to hypothermia. Amer. J. Physiol. *191*:153-156.

173 DARWIN, C. R. 1845. *Voyage of the Beagle*. John Murray: London. 525p.

174 DAWE, R. A., and P. R. MORRISON. 1955. The hibernating heart. Amer. Heart J. 49:367-376.

175 DAWSON, W. 1963. Personal Communication.

176 DOG MUSHERS' MAGAZINE. 1965. Alaska Dog Mushers' Association, Box 1212, Fairbanks, Alaska. 37p.

177 DRIPPS, R. D. (Ed.). 1956. *The Physiology of Induced Hypothermia.* (A Symposium). Nat. Acad. Sci. and Nat. Res. Council. Publication 451. 446p.

178 DURRER, J. L., and J. P. HANNON. 1962. Seasonal variations in caloric intake of dogs living in an arctic environment. Amer. J. Physiol. 202:375-378.

179 EAGAN, C. J. 1963. Local vascular adaptations to cold in man. Fed. Proc. 22:947-951.

180 EAGAN, C. J., J. L. DURRER, and W. M. MILLARD. 1963. Rectal temperature of the working sled dog. Technical Report 63-40, Arctic Aeromedical Laboratory, Fort Wainwright. 8p.

181 EAGAN, C. J., and E. EVONUK. 1964. Retention of resistance to cooling by Alaskan natives in a temperate climate. Fed. Proc. 23:367.

182 EAGAN, C. J., E. EVONUK, and R. A. BOSTER. 1964. Behavioral temperature regulation in the working sled dog. Proc. 15th Alaska Science Conf. AAAS. 15:12.

183 ELSNER, R. W. 1963. Comparison of Australian Aborigines, Alacaluf Indians, and Andean Indians. Fed. Proc. 22:840-843.

184 ESSLER, W. O., and G. E. FOLK, JR. 1960. The determination of 24-hour physiological rhythms of unrestrained animals by radio telemetry. Nature 190:90-91.

185 EVONUK, E., and J. P. HANNON. 1963. Cardiovascular function and norepinephrine-thermogenesis in cold-acclimatized rats. Amer. J. Physiol. 204:888-894.

186 FARRAND, R. L. 1959. Cold acclimatization in the golden hamster. Univ. Iowa, Studies in Natur. Hist. 22:3-29.

187 FOLK, G. E., JR., R. R. SCHELLINGER, and D. SNYDER. 1961. Day-night changes after exercise in body temperatures and heart rates of hamsters. Proc. Iowa Acad. Sci. 68:594-602.

188 FOX, R. H. 1961. Local Cooling in Man. Brit. Med. Bull. 17:14-18.

189 GIAJA, J. 1940. Etat semblable à la torpeur des hibernants obtenu chez le rat par la dépression barométrique. Bull. Acad. Beograd 6:65-79.

190 GLASER, E. M., and J. P. GRIFFIN. 1962. Habituation of rats to repeated cooling. J. Physiol. 160:429-432.

191 GLASER, E. M., and G. C. WHITTOW. 1957. The cold pressor response. J. Physiol. 136:98-102.

192 GOLLAN, F. 1954. Cardiac arrest of one hour duration in dogs during hypothermia of 0°C followed by survival. Fed. Proc. 166:75-91.

193 HAMMEL, H. T. 1963. Effect of race on response to cold. Fed. Proc. 22:795-800.

194 HAMMEL, H. T. 1963. Summary of comparative thermal patterns in man. Fed. Proc. 22:846-847.

195 HAMMEL, H. T. 1965. One Method For Assessing Cold Tolerance. Tech. Report: AF 41(609)-1970. Arctic Aeromedical Laboratory; Fort Wainwright, Alaska.

196 HANNON, J. P., and ELEANOR VIERECK (Eds.). 1962. Comparative Physiology of Temperature Regulation. Proc. 2nd Symp. Arctic Biol. and Med. Arctic Aeromedical Lab. Ft. Wainwright, Alaska. 2:1-455.

197 HART, J. S. 1961. Physiological Effects of Continued Cold on Animals and Man. Brit. Med Bull. 17:19-23.

198 HEMINGWAY, A. 1957. *Nervous control of shivering.* Tech. Report: TN-40. Arctic Aeromedical Laboratory, Fort Wainwright, Alaska. 11p.

199 HENSHAW, R. E., and G. E. FOLK, JR., 1966. Thermoregulation and microclimate selection in bats. Physiol. Zool. 38: in press.

200 HEROUX, O., F. DEPOCAS, and J. S. HART. 1959. Comparison between seasonal and thermal acclimation in white rats. Canad. J. Biochem. Physiol. 37:473-479.

201 HERRING, P. T. 1905. Effect of cold narcosis on reflex action in warm-blooded animals. J. Physiol. 32:305-311.

202 HIEBEL, G. and C. KAYSER. 1950. Recherches electrocardiographiques sur le reveil de hibernants. J. de Physiol. 42:606-612.

203 HILDES, J. A. 1963. Comparison of coastal Eskimos and Kalahari Bushmen. Fed. Proc. 22:843-845.

204 Hong, Suk Ki. 1963. Comparison of diving and nondiving women of Korea. Int. Symp. Temperature Acclimation. Fed. Proc. 22:831-833.

205 Horvath, A. 1881. Einfluss verschiedener temperaturen auf die wintershläfer. Verh. phys.-med. Ges. 15:187-219.

206 Irving, L. 1957. Animal adaptation to cold. 5th Conf. on Cold Injury, Josiah Macy, Jr. Found. p. 11-59.

207 Johnson, H. M. 1951. Microclimatic measurements at Fairbanks, Alaska. Proc. 2nd Alaska Sci. Conf., Washington, D.C. AAAS. 2:125.

208 Kayser, C. 1957. Effet de la température, sur la durée de différents accidents de l'electrodiogramme chez quelques mammifères homéothermes et deux hibernants refroidis. Arch. Sci. Physiol. 11:7-27.

209 Kayser, C., E. Coraboeuf, and Y. Gargori. 1956. Recherches sur la repolarization de myocarde chez différents mammifères homéotherms et hibernant en hypothermie. Comp. Rend. Soc. Biol. 150:1789-1792.

210 Lewis, F. J. 1956. Clinical application of hypothermia during heart surgery. pp. 305-329. Proc. 4th Conf. on Cold Injury. J. Macy, Jr. Found. N.Y.

211 Lewis, T. 1930. Vasodilitation in response to strong cooling. Heart 15:177-181.

212 Lewis, H. E., and J. P. Masterton. 1963. Polar Physiology: its development in Britain. Lancet, May 11. pp. 1009-1014.

213 Lipp, J. A., and G. E. Folk, Jr. 1960. Cardiac response to cold of two species of mammalian hibernators. Ecology 41:377-378.

214 Lipp, J. A., J. R. Knott, and G. E. Folk, Jr. 1960. EEG and heart rates of hypothermic cats. Fed. Proc. 19:179 and Dissertation Abstract: Jan 1961 Vol XXI No. 7.

214a Luyet, B. J. 1965. Human encounters with cold, from early primitive reactions to modern experimental modes of approach. Cryobiology 1:4-11.

215 Lyman, C. P., and P. O. Chatfield. 1956. Physiology of hibernation in mammals. pp. 80-124. In Physiology of Induced Hypothermia. R. D. Dripps (Ed.). Nat. Acad. Sci.-Nat. Res. Council Pub. No. 451. 446p.

216 Meehan, J. P., Jr. 1955. Basal metabolic rate of Eskimos. J. Appl. Physiol. 7:537-540.

217 Meehan, J. P. 1957. Animal Adaptation to Cold, pp. 18-59. 5th Conf. on Cold Injury. J. Macy, Jr. Found. New York.

218 Miller, L. K., and L. Irving. 1964. Peripheral nerve conduction at low temperature. Proc. 15th Alaska Science Conf. AAAS. 15:29.

219 Morrison, P. R. 1957. Body temperatures in aboriginals. Fed. Proc. 16:90.

220 Nagasaka, T., and L. O. Carlson. 1965. Responses of cold- and warm-adapted dogs to infused noradrenalin and acute body cooling. Amer. J. Physiol. 209:227-230.

221 Negovskii, V. A. 1959. Pathophysiologie und Therapie der Agonie und des Klinischen Todes. Berlin: Akademe-Verlag. 223p.

222 Popovic, P. and V. Popovic. 1963. Survival of newborn ground squirrels after supercooling or freezing. Amer. J. Physiol. 204:949-952.

223 Popovic, V. 1964. Cardiac output in hibernating ground squirrels. Amer. J. Physiol. 207:1345-1349.

224 Pugh, L. G. C., and O. G. Edholm. 1955. Physiology of Channel Swimmers. Laucet, 2:761-768.

225 Scholander, P. F. 1958. Studies of man exposed to cold. Fed. Proc. 17:1054-1057.

226 Scholander, P. F., and W. F. Schville. 1955. Counter-current vascular heat exchange. J. Appl. Physiol. 8:279-282.

227 Scholander, P. F., L. van Dam, J. W. Kanwischer, H. T. Hammel, and M. S. Gordon. 1957. Supercooling and osmoregulation in arctic fish. J. Cell. Comp. Physiol. 49:5-24.

228 Scholander, P. F., V. Walters, R. Hock, and L. Irving. 1950. Body insulation of some arctic and tropical mammals and birds. Biol. Bull. 99:225-236.

229 Simpson, S. 1902. Temperature range of monkeys in ether anesthesia. J. Physiol. (proceedings) 28:37-40.

230 Smith, A. U. 1959. Viability of supercooled and frozen mammals. Ann. N.Y. Acad. Sci. 80:291-300.

231 Smith, A. U. 1961. Biological Effects of Freezing and Supercooling. Edward Arnold Ltd. London. 462p.

232 SMITH, L. W. and T. FAY. 1940. Observations on human beings with cancer maintained at reduced temperatures of 75° to 90°F. Amer. J. Clin. Path. *10*:1-11.

233 SMITH, R. E., and D. J. HOIJER. 1962. Metabolism and cellular function in cold acclimation. Physiol. Rev. *42*:60-142.

234 SPURR, G. B., B. K. HUTT, and S. M. HORVATH. 1954. Responses of dogs to hypothermia. Amer. J. Physiol. *179*:139-145.

235 STEFANSSON, V. 1960. Tropical winter life of the polar eskimo. Chapters XII, XIII in *Cancer: Disease of Civilization*. Macmillan: New York. 426p.

236 SWAN, H. 1956. The use of hypothermia in cardiac surgery. pp. 402-412. In *Physiology of Induced Hypothermia*. R. D. Dripps (Ed.). Nat. Acad. Sci.-Nat. Res. Council Pub. No. 451. 446p.

237 TOMILIN, A. G. 1950. Notes on Siberian white-sided dolphin. Rybnoe Khozaistvo *26*:50-53.

238 TREGEAR, R. T. 1965. Hair density, wind speed, and heat loss in mammals. J. Appl. Physiol. *20*:796-801.

239 U.S. GOVERNMENT PRINTING OFFICE. 1964. Temperature and wind chill index. U.S. Army Aviation Digest. p. 48.

240 VAUGHN, L. (Ed.). 1965. *Nutritional Requirements in Cold*. Proc. 5th Symp. Arctic Med. and Biology. Arctic Aeromedical Lab. Fort Wainwright, Alaska (in Press).

241 VIERECK, E. G. (Ed.). 1964. *Frostbite*. Proc. 4th Symp. Arctic Med. and Biology. Arctic Aeromedical Lab. Fort Wainwright, Alaska. 457p.

242 WALTHER, A. 1862. Beiträge Zur Lehre von der Thierischen Wärme. Virchow's Arch. 25:414-417.

242a WEIHE, W. H. (Ed.). 1964. *The Physiological Effects of High Altitude*, Macmillan. 351p.

243 WOODCOCK, A. H. 1955. Possible interpretation of damp penetrating cold. Amer. J. Physiol. *183*:675-678.

244 WYNDHAM, C. H. and J. F. MORRISSON. 1958. Adjustment to cold of bushmen in the Kalahari Desert. J. Appl. Physiol. *13*: 219-225.

Chapter 6

Responses to a Hot Environment

245 ADOLPH, E. F. 1947. *Physiology of Man In The Desert*. Interscience: New York. 357p.

246 ANDERSSON, B. and S. M. MCCANN. 1955. A further study of polydipsia evoked by hypothalamic stimulation in the goat. Acta Physiol. Scand. 33:333-346.

247 AOKI, T., and M. WADA. 1951. Functional activity of the sweat glands in the hairy skin of the dog. Science *114*:123-124.

248 ASCHER, R. 1965. Recognizing the emergence of man. Science *147*:243-250.

249 BARTHOLOMEW, G. A., and F. WILKE. 1956. Body temperature of fur seal. J. Mammal. 37:327-337.

250 BARTLETT, R. G., JR., and F. H. QUIMBY. 1958. Heat balance in restraint (emotionally) induced hypothermia. Amer. J. Physiol. *193*:557-559.

251 BELDING, H. S., and T. F. HATCH. 1955. Index for evaluating heat stress in terms of resulting physiological strains. Heat., Pip. Air Condit. 27:129-136.

252 BELL, C. R., and R. F. HELLON. 1965. Safe exposure of men to severe heat. J. Appl. Physiol. *20*:288-293.

252a BENTLEY, P. J. and K. SCHMIDT-NIELSEN. 1966. Cutaneous water loss in reptiles. Science *151*:1547-1549.

253 BLAGDEN, C. 1775. Further experiments and observations in a heated room. Phil. Trans. Roy. Soc. Lond. 65:484-494.

254 BLAIR, J. R., and A. D. KELLER. 1941. Calibration studies of the regulation of body temperature in normal dogs. Amer. J. Physiol. *133*:215-216.

255 BLOCKLEY, W. V. 1963. Heat storage rate and tolerance time. Fed. Proc. *22*:887-890.

256 BUETTNER, K. J. K. 1959. Diffusion of liquid water through human skin. J. Appl. Physiol. *14*:261-265.

257. BULLOCK, T. H., and F. P. DIECKE. 1956. Anatomy and physiology of infrared sense organs in facial pit of pit vipers. J. Physiol. *134*:47-87.

258 CALVERY, H. O., J. H. DRAIZE, and E. P. LANG. 1946. The metabolism and permeability of normal skin. Physiol. Rev. *26*: 495-503.

259 CLOUDSLEY-THOMPSON, J. L. 1963 The mechanism of heat death. New Scientist (London) *18*:330-332.

260 COLIN, J. and Y. HOUDAS. 1965. Initiation of sweating in man after abrupt rise in environmental temperature. J. Appl. Physiol. *20*:984-990.

261 CONSOLAZIO, C. F., R. SHAPIRO, J. E. MASTERSON and P. S. L. McKINZIE. 1961. Energy requirements of men in extreme heat. J. Nutrition *73*:126-134.

262 DICKE, R. H. 1962. The earth and cosmology. Science *138*:653-664.

263 DOWLING, D. F. 1959. The Significance of the coat in heat tolerance of cattle. Australian J. Agr. Res. *10*:736.

264 EASTWOOD, F. R. 1960. Sports and medicine. Scope *5*:15.

265 EDWARDS, H. T., and D. B. DILL. 1935. Temperature effect on blood of gila monster and chuckwalla. J. Cell. Comp. Physiol. *6*:21-35.

266 EICHNA, L. W., W. F. ASHE, W. B. BEAN, and W. B. SHELLEY. 1945. The upper limits of environmental heat and humidity tolerated by acclimatized men working in hot environment. J. Indust. Hygiene & Toxicol. *27*:59-84.

267 EISENBERG, J. F. 1962. Behavioral evolution in the rodentia. Amer. Zool. *2*:520-521.

268 ELLIS, F. P., H. M. FERRES, A. R. LIND, and P. S. B. NEWLING. 1960. The upper limits of tolerance of environmental stress. pp. 158-179. In *Physiological Responses To Hot Environments*. Spec. Report, Series No. 298. Med. Res. Council. London. 323p.

269 FOLK, G. E., JR., and R. E. PEARY. 1951. Penetration of water into the human foot. QM Climatic Res. Lab. Rep. No. 181. 45p.

270 FRANKEL, H. M. 1958. *Tolerance to High Temperature in Small Mammals*. Thesis. Microfilm 58-5819. 128p. Dissertation Abstracts. Jan. 1959. *19(7)*.

271 FRANKEL, H. M. 1959. Effects of restraint on rats exposed to high temperature. J. Appl. Physiol. *14*:997-999.

272 FRANKEL, H. M., G. E. FOLK, JR., and F. N. CRAIG. 1957. Effects of type of restraint upon heat tolerance in monkeys. Proc. Exp. Biol. and Med. 97:339-341.

273 FRINGS, H., A. ANTHONY and M. W. SCHEIN. 1958. Salt excretion by nasal gland of Laysan and Blackfooted Albatrosses. Science *128*:1572.

274 GERMAN, A. L. 1961. The degree of resistance to thirst of some murine rodents of the steppe zone. Zool. Zhur. (in Russian) *40*:914-921.

275 GILES, E. 1889. *Australia Twice Traversed*. Low, Maston, Searle and Rivington: London. 2 vols.

276 HALDANE, J. S. 1929. Salt depletion by sweating. Brit. Med. J. *2*:469.

277 HALE, H. B., and R. B. MEFFERD, JR. 1963. Thermal spectrum analysis of thyroid-independent phases of nitrogen and mineral metabolism. Fed. Proc. *22*:766-771.

278 HARRISON, G. A. 1963. Temperature adaptation as evidenced by growth of mice. Fed. Proc. *22*:691-697.

279 HENSCHEL, A., and H. S. McPHILIMY. 1963. Field test methods. p. 315-345. In *Environmental Physiology and Psychology in Arid Conditions. Reviews of Research*—XXII. Unesco, Paris. 345p.

280 HENSHAW, R. E. 1965. *Physiology of Hibernation and Acclimatization in Two Species of Bats (Myotis lucifugus and Myotis sodalis)*. Ph.D. Thesis. Univ. of Iowa, Iowa City, Iowa. 143p.

281 HERTIG, B. A., M. L. RIEDESEL, and H. S. BELDING. 1961. Sweating in hot baths. J. Appl. Physiol. *16*:647-651.

282 HERTIG, B. A., and F. SARGENT II. 1963. Acclimatization of women during work in hot environments. Fed. Proc. *22*:810-813.

283 HOCK, R. J. 1951. The metabolic rates and body temperatures of bats. Biol. Bull. *101*:289-299.

284 HOOTEN, E. 1942. *Man's Poor Relations*. Doubleday, Doran: New York. 412p.

285 Hudson, J. W. 1964. Water metabolism in desert mammals. pp 211-235. Proc. 1st Int. Symp. *Thirst in Reg. Body Water.* Pergamon. New York. 308p.

286 Iampierto, P. F. 1963. Heat induced tetany. Fed. Proc. *22*:884-886.

287 Johnson, H. D., C. S. Cheng, and A. C. Ragsdale. 1958. Environmental physiology and shelter engineering with special reference to domestic animals. XLVI. Comparison of effect of environmental temperature on rabbits and cattle. Part 2. Influence of rising environmental temperature on the physiological reactions of rabbits and cattle. Univ. Mo. Agric. Exp. Sta. Res. Bull. No. 648. 27p.

288 Kanter, G. S. 1959. Cause of hypoglycemia in dogs exposed to heat. Amer. J. Physiol. *196*:619-622.

289 Keeton, R. W. 1924. The peripheral water loss in rabbits as a factor in heat regulation. Amer. J. Physiol. *69*:307-317.

290 Kirmiz, J. P. 1962. *Adaptation To Desert Environment—a Study on the Jeroba, Rat, and Man.* Butterworth & Co. Washington, D.C. 154p.

291 Ladell, W. S. S. 1945. Thermal sweating. Brit. Med. Bull. *3*:175-179.

292 Ladell, W. S. S. 1949. The changes in water and chloride distribution during heavy sweating. J. Physiol. *108*:440-450.

293 Ladell, W. S. S., J. C. Waterlow, and M. F. Hudson. 1944. Desert climate: physiological and clinical observations. Lancet *2*:491-497.

294 Lee, D. H. K., K. Robinson, and H. J. G. Hines. 1941. Reactions of the rabbit to hot atmospheres. Proc. Roy. Soc. Queensland *53*:129-144.

295 Lamaire, R. 1960. Considérations physiologiques sur la climatisation en mileaŭ désertique. *In* Journéis d'Inf. Med. Soc. Sahariennes. pp 101-112. Paris PRHUZA. A.M.G.

296 Licht, S. (Ed.). 1964. *Medical Climatology.* Elizabeth Licht, Publisher. New Haven, Conn. 753p.

297 Lyman, C. P. 1963. Hibernation in mammals and birds. Amer. Scientist *51*:127-138.

298 Macfarlane, W. V., K. Robertson, B. Howard, and R. Kinne. 1958. Heat, salt, and hormones in panting and sweating animals. Nature *182*:672-673.

299 Macpherson, R. K. (Compiler). 1960. *Physiological Responses To Hot Environments.* Spec. Report Series No. 298. Med. Res. Council. London. 323p.

300 McGee, W. J. 1906. Desert thirst as disease. Interstate Med. J. *13*:279-300.

301 Minard, D. 1959. Heat stress in tropical climates. Symposium on medical operations and research in climatic and environmental extremes. U.S. Naval Medical School. Bethesda, Md.

302 ·Mining Survey. P.R.D. Series 13. 36p. Chamber of Mines, P.O. Box 809, Johannesburg, South Africa.

303 Monod, Theodore. 1958. Majâbat al-Koubrâ. Contribution à l'étude de l' "Empty Quarter" Ouést-Saharien. Memoires Inst. Franc. d'Afrique Noire. No. 52, IFAN-Dakar. 407p.

304 Moss, K. N. 1924. Some effects of high air temperatures and muscular exertion upon colliers. Proc. Roy. Soc. Lond., B. *95*: 181-200.

305 Murray, R. H. and J. C. Ross. 1965. Cardiovascular effects of brief, intense thermal pulses in man. Fed. Proc. *24*:280.

306 Nielsen, M. 1938. Die Regulation der Körpertemperatur bei Muskelarbeit. Skand. Arch. f. Physiol. *79*:193-230.

307 Peiss, C. N., and W. C. Randall. 1957. The effect of vapor impermeable gloves on evaporation and sweat suppression in the hand. J. Invest. Derm. *28*:435-439.

308 Pilters-Gauthier, Hilde. 1961. Observations sur l'écologie du dromadaire dans le Sahara nordoccidental'. Mammalia *25*: 195-280.

309 Reeder, W. G. and R. B. Cowles. 1951. Aspects of thermoregulation in bats. J. Mammal. *32*:389-403.

310 Robinson, S., S. O. Gerking, E. S. Turrell, and R. K. Kincaid. 1950. Effects of skin temperature on salt concentration in sweat. J. Appl. Physiol. *2*:654-662.

311 Robinson, S., F. R. Meyer, and J. L. Newton. 1965. Relations between sweating, cutaneous blood flow, and body temperature. J. Appl. Physiol. *20*:575-583.

312 Rosenmann, M. and P. R. Morrison. 1963. The physiological response to heat and dehydration in the guanaco. Physiol. Zool. 36:45-51.

313 Schmidt-Nielsen, B. 1965. Comparative morphology and physiology of excretion. p. 393-425. In *Ideas In Modern Biology*. John A. Moore, (Ed.). Proc. 16th Int. Cong. Zöol. Vol. 6. The Natural History Press. Garden City, N. Y. 562p.

314 Schmidt-Nielsen, B. and K. Schmidt-Nielsen. 1950. Do kangaroo rats thrive when drinking sea water? Amer. J. Physiol. 162:31-36.

315 Schmidt-Nielsen, B. and K. Schmidt-Nielsen. 1951. A complete account of the water metabolism in kangaroo rats and an experimental verification. J. Cell. Comp. Physiol. 38:165-182.

316 Schmidt-Nielsen, B., K. Schmidt-Nielsen, T. R. Houpt, and S. A. Jarnum. 1956. Water balance of the camel. Amer. J. Physiol. 185:185-194.

317 Schmidt-Nielsen, K. 1954. Heat regulation in small and large desert mammals. pp. 182-187. In *Biology of Deserts*, J. L. Cloudsley-Thompson, Ed., Institute of Biology, London.

318 Schmidt-Nielsen, K., and R. Fange. 1958. The function of the salt gland in the Brown Pelican. Auk 75:282-289.

319 Schmidt-Nielsen, K., S. A. Jarnum, and T. R. Houpt. 1957. Body temperature of the camel and its relation to water economy. Amer. J. Physiol. 188:103-112.

320 Shelley, W. B., and A. Hemingway. 1940. The effects of thermal polypnea on the energy metabolism, respiratory quotient and water loss of dogs. Amer. J. Physiol. 129:623-630.

321 Smith, H. and H. Silvette. 1928. Note on the nitrogen excretion of camels. J. Biol. Chem. 78:409-411.

322 Sperber, I. 1944. Studies on the mammalian kidney. Zool. Bidrag Fran Upsala 22:249-431.

323 Strydom, N. B. and C. H. Wyndham. 1963. Effect of heat on work performance. Fed. Proc. 22:893-896.

324 Szczesniak, A. S., H. Sherman, and R. S. Harris. 1951. The percutaneous absorption of water. Science 113:293-295.

325 Taylor, C. 1951. Personal communication.

326 Unesco. 1958. *Climatology*. Arid Zone Research. Reviews of Research—X. Unesco: Paris. 190p.

327 Unesco. 1963. *Environmental Physiology and Physchology in Arid Conditions*. Arid Zone Research. Reviews of Research—XXII. Unesco-Paris 345p.

328 Weese, A. O. 1917. Thermal reactions of Phrynosoma. Biol. Bull. 32:98-116.

329 Wyndham, C. H., J. F. Morrisson and C. G. Williams. 1965. Heat reactions of male and female caucasians. J. Appl. Physiol. 20:357-364.

330 Wyndham, C. H., N. B. Strydom, J. S. Ward and J. F. Morrisson. 1964. Physiological reactions to heat of Bushmen. J. Appl. Physiol. 19:885-889.

331 Yaglou, C. P. 1947. Methods for improving the effective temperature index. Trans. Am. Soc. Heat. Vent. Engrs. 53:307-309.

332 Yaglou, C. P. and A. M. Baetjer. 1950. Thermal standards in industry. Amer. J. Publ. Hlth., Supplement Part II. 40:131-143.

333 Yokoi, Y. 1964. Vascular counter-current heat exchanger. Proc. Soc. Expt. Biol. Med. 115:1014-1017.

334 Yoshimura, H., K. Ogata, and S. Itoh. 1960. *Essential Problems in Climatic Physiology*. Kyoto. 299p.

Chapter 7

Hibernation

335 Aristotle (384-322 B.C.) 1783. *Histoire des Animaux*. Traduction francaise par M. Camus. Vol. I Desaint: Paris. 759p.

336 Bartholomew, G. A. and T. J. Cade. 1957. Temperature regulation, hibernation, and aestivation in the little pocket mouse. J. Mammal. 38:60-72.

337 BARTHOLOMEW, G. A., T. R. HOWELL, and T. J. CADE. 1957. Torpidity in the white-throated swift, anna hummingbird, and poor-will. The Condor 59:145-155.

338 BARTHOLOMEW, G. A. and J. W. HUDSON. 1960. Aestivation in the Mohave ground squirrel, *Citellus mohavensis*. Proc. 1st Int. Symp. Mammalian Hibernation; Bull. Mus. Comp. Zool. *124*:193-209.

339 BARTHOLOMEW, G. A. and F. WILKE. 1956. Body temperature in the northern fur seal, *Callorhinus ursinus*. J. Mammal. *37*:327-337.

340 BENEDICT, F. G. 1938. *Vital Energetics in Comparative Metabolism*. Carnegie Inst., Wash., D.C., Publ. No. 503. 215p.

341 BERT, W. H., and R. P. GROSSENHEIDER. 1952. A *Field Guide to the Mammals*. Houghton Mifflin Co. Boston. 200p.

342 BOGERT, C. M. 1959. How reptiles regulate their body temperature. Sci. Amer. *200*:105-120.

343 BOULOUARD, R. 1963. Effects of cold and starvation on adrenocortical activity of rats. Fed. Proc. *22*:750.

344 CASSUTO, Y. and R. R. J. CHAFFEE. 1963. The thermogenic role of the liver in the heat-acclimated hamster, (*Mesocricetus auratus*). Canada J. Biochem. and Physiol. *41*:1840-1842.

345 CHATFIELD, P. O. and C. P. LYMAN. 1954. Subcortical electrical activity in the golden hamster during arousal from hibernation. EEG Clin. Neurophysiol. *6*:403-409.

346 DARLINGTON, P. J. 1957. *Zoogeography: The Geographical Distribution of Animals*. John Wiley, New York 675p.

347 FISHER, K. C. and F. E. SOUTH (Eds.). 1966. *Mammalian Hibernation* Proc. 3rd Int. Symp. Nat. Mammal. Hiber. Oliver and Boyd: Edinburgh. 530p.

348 FOLK, G. E., JR. 1957. Twenty-four hour rhythms of mammals in a cold environment. Amer. Naturalist *91*:153-166.

349 FOLK, G. E., JR. 1960. Climate and hibernation, p. 703-714. In *Medical Biometerology*. Elsevier: Holland 991p.

350 FOLK, G. E., JR. and R. S. HEDGE. 1964. Comparative physiology of heart rate of unrestrained mammals. Amer. Zool. *4*:297.

351 FONTAINE, M. 1953. De l'hibernation naturelle á "l'hibernation expérimentale". Rev. Path. Comp. 52:53-64.

351a GRIFFIN, D. R. and H. B. HITCHCOCK. 1965. Probable 24-year longevity records for *Myotis lucifugus*. J. Mammal. *46*:332.

352 HALL, M. 1832. On hibernation. Trans. Roy. Soc. (London), B. *122*:335-360.

353 HART, J. S. 1964. Geography and Season: Mammals and Birds. p. 295-322. In *Handbook of Physiology Sec. 4 Adaptation to the Environment*. D. B. Dill (Sec. Ed.). Amer Physiol. Soc. (Publishers) 1056p.

354 HERREID, C. F., JR. 1963. Temperature regulation and metabolism in Mexican free-tail bats. Science *142*:1573-1574.

355 HOCK, R. 1957. Hibernation. 5th Conf. on Cold Injury, J. Macy Found. p. 61-135.

356 HOCK, R. J. 1960. Seasonal variations in physiologic functions of arctic ground squirrels and black bears. Proc. 1st Int. Symp. Nat. Hibernation. Bull. Mus. Comp. Zool. *124*:155-173.

357 HOFFMAN, R. A. 1964. Terrestrial animals in cold: hibernators. p. 379-403. In *Handbook of Physiology, Sec. 4. Adaptation to the Environment*. D. B. Dill, Sec. Ed. Amer. Physiol. Soc. (Publishers) 1056p.

358 HOFFMAN, R. A., R. J. HESTER and C. TOWNS. 1965. Effect of light and temperature on the endocrine system of the golden hamster. Comp. Biochem. Physiol. *15*:525-533.

359 HUBBS, C. L. (Ed.). 1958. *Zoogeography*. Am. Assoc. Adv. Sci., (Publ.); Washington D. C. 336p.

360 HUDSON, J. W. 1965. Temperature regulation and torpidity in the pygmy mouse, *Baiomys taylori*. Physiol. Zool. *38*:243-254.

361 HUDSON, J. W. and G. A. BARTHOLOMEW. 1964. Terrestrial animals in dry heat: estivators. p. 541-550. In *Handbook of Physiology, Sec. 4 Adaptation to the Environment* D. B. Dill (Sec. Ed.). 1056p.

362 JOHANSEN, K. 1961. Distribution of blood in the arousing hamster. Acta Physiol. Scand. 52:379-386.

363 JOHANSEN, K. and J. KROG. 1959. Diurnal body temperature variations and hibernation in the birchmouse, *Sicista betulina.* Amer. J. Physiol. *196*:1200-1204.

364 JOHANSSON, B. 1960. Brown fat and its possible significance for hibernation. Proc. 1st Int. Symp. on Natural Hibernation. Bull. Mus. Comp. Zool. *124*:232-243.

365 JOHNSON, G. E. 1929. The fall in temperature in ground squirrels going into hibernation. Anat. Record *44*:199-208.

366 KAYSER, CH. 1953. L'hibernation des mammifères. Ann Biol. *29*:109-150.

367 KAYSER, C. 1955. Hibernation et hypothermie experimentate. Rapports J. Med. France et Union Française—Strasbourg June 16-20.

368 KAYSER, CH. 1957. Le sommeil hivernal problème de thermorégulation. Rev. Canad. Biol. *16*:303-389.

369 KAYSER, CH. 1960. Hibernation versus hypothermia. p. 9-29. In Proc. 1st Inter. Symp. on Nat. Mamm. Hibernation. C. P. Lyman and A. R. Dawe (Eds.). Bull. Mus. Comp. Zool. Harvard. Vol. 124. 549p.

370 KAYSER, CH. 1965. Hibernation. chapter 3. p. 179-296. In *Physiological Mammalogy Vol. II.* W. Mayer & R. Van Gelder, (Eds.). Academic Press: New York. 298p.

371 KAYSER, CH., and M. ARON. 1939. Modifications structurales de la médullosurrénales dans l'adaptation thermique des hibernants. Comp. Rend. Soc. Biol. *130*:397-400.

372 KEHL, T. H., and P. MORRISON. 1960. Peripheral nerve function and hibernation in the 13-lined ground squirrel. p. 388-402. Proc. 1st. Internat. Symp. Nat. Mammalian Hiber. C. Lyman and A. Dawe (Eds.). Bull. Museum Comp. Zöol. Harvard Univ. Press. No. 124. 547p.

373 KRISTOFFERSSON, R. and SOIVIO, A. 1964. *Hibernation in the hedgehog (Erinaceus europæns l.).* Ann. Acad. Sci. Fennicæ. Series A. IV Biologica. No. 82. 16p.

374 LANDAU, B. R. and A. R. DAWE. 1958. Respiration in the hibernation of the 13-lined ground squirrel. Amer. J. Physiol. *194*:75-82.

375 LASIEWSKI, R. C. 1963. Oxygen consumption of torpid, resting, active, and flying hummingbirds. Physiol. Zool. *36*:122-140.

376 LEITNER, P. 1962. Body temperature regulation in the California Mastiff Bat, *Eumops peroitis.* (Abst.) Amer. Zool. 2:535.

377 LUYET, B. J. and R. J. WILLIAMS. 1964. Comparative study of freezing injury on a hibernator and a nonhibernator. AAL-TDR-63-30. Arctic Aeromed. Lab. Fort Wainwright, Alaska.

378 LYMAN, C. P. 1958. Oxygen consumption, body temperature, and heart rate of woodchucks entering hibernation. Amer. J. Physiol. *194*:83-91.

379 LYMAN, C. P. 1961. Hibernation in Mammals. Circulation *24*:434-445.

380 LYMAN, C. P. 1963. Hibernation in mammals and birds. Amer. Scientist *51*:127-138.

381 LYMAN, C. P. and P. O. CHATFIELD. 1955. Physiology of Hibernation in Mammals. Physiol. Rev. 35:403-425.

382 LYMAN, C. P. and A. R. DAWE (Eds.). 1960. *Mammalian Hibernation.* Proc. 1st Inter. Symp. Nat. Mammal. Hibernation. Bull. Mus. Comp. Zool. No. 124. Harvard Univ. Press 547p.

383 LYMAN, C. P. and R. C. O'BRIEN. 1963. Autonomic control of circulation during the hibernating cycle in ground squirrels. J. Physiol. *168*:477-499.

384 MENAKER, M. 1962. Hibernation hypothermia: an annual cycle of response to low temperature in the bat *Myotis lucifugus.* J. Cell. Comp. Physiol. 59:163-174.

385 MORRIS, L. and P. R. MORRISON. 1964. Cyclic responses in dormice (Glis glis) and ground squirrels (Spermophillis tridecemlineatus) exposed to normal and reversed yearly light schedules. p. 55. Proc. 15th Alaska Sci. Conf. AAAS.

386 MORRISON, P. R. 1960. Some interrelations between weight and hibernation function. p. 75-91. Proc. 1st Int. Symp. Nat. Mammal. Hibernation. Bull. Mus. Comp. Zool. 124. Harvard Univ. Press.

387 MORRISON, P. R. 1962. Modification of body temperature by activity in Brazilian hummingbirds. The Condor *64*:315-323.

388 PEARSON, O. P. 1960. Torpidity in birds. p. 93-104. 1st Int. Symp. Mammal. Hibernation. Bull. Mus. Comp. Zool. 124. Harvard Univ. Press. 547p.

389 PENGELLEY, E. T. and K. C. FISHER. 1961. Rhythmical arousal from hibernation in the golden-mantled ground squirrel. Canad. J. Zool. 39:105-120.

390 POHL, H. 1965. Temperature regulation and cold acclimation in the golden hamster. J. Appl. Physiol. 20:405-410.

391 POHL, H. and J. S. HART. 1965. Thermoregulation and cold acclimation in a hibernator, Citellus tridecemlineatus. J. Appl. Physiol. 20:398-404.

392 POPOVIC, V. 1959. Lethargic hypothermia in hibernators and non-hibernators. Ann. N. Y. Acad. Sci. 80:320-331.

392a RAUSCH, R. L. 1961. Notes on the black bear Ursus americanus pallus, in Alaska. Zeitschrift fur Saugetierkunde 26:65-128.

393 RIEDESEL, M. L. and G. E. FOLK, JR. 1958. Serum electrolyte levels in hibernating mammals. Amer. Natur. 92:307-312.

394 SMALLEY, R. and R. DRYER. 1966. Metabolism of fat and thermogenesis in hibernation. Proc. 3rd. Symp. Mammal. Hibernation. Oliver and Boyd. Edinburgh. 530p.

395 SMITH, R. E. 1964. Thermoregulatory and adaptive behavior of brown adipose tissue. Science 146:1686-1689.

396 SOUTH, F. E. 1960. Some metabolic specializations in tissues of hibernating mammals. Mus. Comp. Zool. Bull. 124:475-492.

397 STONES, R. C. and J. E. WIEBERS. 1965. A Review of Temperature Regulation in Bats (Chiroptera) Amer. Midland Natur. 74:155-177.

398 STRUMWASSER, F. 1959. Electrical activity of brain and temperature of brain in hibernation (Citellus) Amer. J. Physiol. 196:8-30.

399 STRUMWASSER, F. 1960. Some physiological principles governing hibernation in Citellus beecheyi. Proc. 1st Int. Symp. Nat. Hib. Bull. Mus. Comp. Zool. 124:285-320.

400 SUOMALAINEN, P. (Ed.). 1964. Mammalian Hibernation II: Proc. 2nd Int. Symp. Natur. Mammal. Hibernation. Ann. Acad. Sci. Fenn. Ser. A IV. 453p.

401 SUOMALAINEN, P. and E. KARPPANEN. 1956. Einflus des Winterschlafes auf das Albumin-Globulinverhältniss des Igelserums. Suomen Kemistilehti 29:74-75.

402 TUCKER, V. A. 1965. Oxygen consumption, thermal conductance, and torpor in the California pocket mouse Perognathus californicus. J. Cell. and Comp. Physiol. 65:393-404.

403 WILBUR, C. G. 1957. Physiological regulations and the origin of human types. Human Biol. 29:329-336.

404 WILLIS, J. S. 1964. Potassium and sodium content of tissues of hamsters and ground squirrels during hibernation. Science 146:546-547.

405 WIMSATT, W. A. 1962. Responses of captive common vampires to cold and warm environments. J. Mammal. 43:185-191.

406 YELVERTON, J. 1964. The water bath as a tool in evaluating responses of small mammals to thermal stress. M. S. Thesis, Univ. of New Mexico, Dept. of Biology.

407 ZIMNY, M. L. 1964. Enzyme activities during hibernation and arousal in the ground squirrel Citellus tridecemlineatus. Ann. Acad. Sci. Fenn. Ser. A: IV 71/33, p. 443-454.

408 ZIRM, K. L. 1956. Ein Beitrag zur Kenntnis des Natürlichen Winterschlafes und seines regulierenden Wirksloffes II. Zschr. Naturforsch. 116:535-538.

Chapter 8

Low Pressure from Terrestrial Altitude

409 ARMATICH, K. B. 1965. Vernal behaviour of the yellow-bellied marmot (Marmota flaviventris) Anim. Behavior 13:59-68.

410 BARCROFT, J., R. H. E. ELLIOT, L. B. FLEXNER, F. G. HALL, W. HERKEL, E. F. MCCARTHY, T. MCCLURKIN, and M. TATAAT. 1935. The affinity for oxygen of fetal blood of the goat. J. Physiol. 83: 192-196.

411 BEE, J. W. and E. R. HALL. 1956. Mammals of Northern Alaska. Univ. Kansas Mus. Nat. History, Misc. Pub. No. 8. Allen Press: Lawrence, Kansas 309p.

412 BERGMANN, C. 1847. Uber die verhaltnisse der warmeokonomie der theiere zu ihrer grosse. Gottinger Studien *1*:595-708.

413 BERT, P. 1878. *La Pression Barométrique.* Paris: Masson. 1168p.

414 BLISS, L. C. 1962. Adaptations of arctic and alpine plants to environmental conditions. Arctic *15*:117-145.

415 CORNELIUS, C. E., and J. J. KANEKO. 1962. Erythrocyte life span in the Guanaco. Science *137*:673-674.

416 CURREY, D. R. 1965. Ancient Bristlecone pine stand in Nevada. Ecology *46*:564-566.

417 DILL, D. B. 1963. Reunion at high altitude. Physiologist *6*:40-43.

418 DILL, D. B., S. ROBINSON, B. BALKE, and J. L. NEWTON. 1964. Work tolerance, age, and altitude. J. Appl. Physiol. *19*:483-488.

419 EHRLICH, P. R. and R. W. HOLM. 1962. Patterns and populations. Science *137*:652-657.

420 GLAISHER, J., C. FLAMMARION, W. DEFONVIELLE, and G. TIASSANDIER. 1871. *Travels in the Air.* Lippincott: Philadelphia. 398p.

421 GUYTON, A. C. 1961. *Textbook of Medical Physiology.* 2nd ed. Saunders, Philadelphia. 1181 p.

422 HIGHMAN, B. and P. D. ALTLAND. 1949. Acclimatization responses and pathologic changes in rats at an altitude of 25,000 feet. Arch. Path. *48*:503-515.

423 HITCHOCK, F. A. 1964. Animals in high altitudes: Early balloon flights p. 869-876. In *Handbook of Physiology Sec. 4: Adaption to the Environment.* D. B. Dill. (Sec. Ed.) 1056p.

424 HOCK, R. J. 1962. Mammals and Birds, p. 149-159. In *Deepest Valley*, G. Schumacher, Ed. Sierra Club, San Francisco. Vail-Ballou Press, Inc. 208p.

425 HOCK, R. J. 1964. Physiological responses of deer mice to various native altitudes p. 59-73. In *The Physiological Effects Of High Altitude.* W. H. Weihe, Ed. Pergemon Press, New York. 351p.

426 HOLMSTROM, F. M. G. 1965. Personal communication.

427 HUMBOLT, A. 1850. *Aspects of Nature.* (Trans. A. Sabin) Lea and Blanchard: Philadelphia. 475p.

428 HURTADO, A. 1964. Animals in high altitudes: resident man. p. 843-860. In *Handbook of Physiology, Sec. 4: Adaptation to the Environment.* D. B. Dill (Sec. Ed.). 1056p.

429 HURTADO, A., A. ROTTA, C. MERINO and J. PONS. 1937. Studies of myohemoglobin at high altitudes. Amer. J. Med. Sci. *194*: 708-713.

430 KALABUKOV, N. J. 1937. Some physiological adaptations of the mountain and plain forms of the wood mouse (Apodemus sylvaticua) and of other species of mouse-like rodents. J. Anim. Ecol. *6*:254-274.

431 MONGE, C. 1928. *La enfermedad de los Andes.* Lima: Facultad de Medicina. 150p.

432 MONGE, C. 1960. *Aclimatácion en los Andes.* Lima: Facultad de Medicina. 165p.

433 MORRISON, P. R. 1962. Temperature regulation in animals native to tropical and high altitude environments p. 381-413. In *Comparative Physiology of Temperature Regulation.* Proc. 2nd Symp. Arctic Biol. and Med. J. P. Hannon and E. Viereck (Eds.) 455p.

434 MORRISON, P. R. 1964. The adaptation of small mammals to the arctic. Fed Proc. *23*:1202-1206.

435 MORRISON, P. R., K. KERST, and M. ROSENMANN. 1963. Hematocrit and hemoglobin levels in some Chilean rodents from high and low altitude. Int. J. Biometeorol. 7: 45-50.

436 MOSSO, A. 1898. *Life of Man On The High Alps.* Inwin: London. 342p.

437 NEVISON, T. O., JR. 1965. Nutrition and fluid balance above 19,000 feet. Proc. 6th Symp. Arctic Biol. and Med., Arctic Aeromed. Lab., Ft. Wainwright, Alaska.

437a PACE, NELLO. 1961. Man at altitude, p. 53-70. In *The Air We Breathe.* S. M. Farber and R. H. L. Wilson, Eds. Charles C. Thomas: Springfield, Ill. 414p.

438 PEARSON, G. H. and P. NEWILL. 1962. *My Life of High Adventure.* Prentice-Hall: Englewood Cliffs, N. J. 234p.

439 PUGH, L. G. C. E. 1964. Animals in high altitudes: man above 5000 meters—moun-

tain exploration, page 861-868. In *Handbook of Physiology, Sec. 4: Adaptation to the Environment.* D. B. Dill (Sec. Ed.) 1056p.

440 REYNAFARJE, B. 1962. Myoglobin content and enzymatic activity of muscle and altitude adaptation. J. Appl. Physiol. *17*: 301-305.

441 SCHMIDT-NIELSEN, K. 1960. *Animal Physiology.* Found. Mod. Biol. Ser. Prentice-Hall, Inc., New Jersey. 118p.

442 SCHOLANDER, P. F. 1955. Evolution of climatic adaptation in homeotherms. Evolution *9*:15-26.

443 SCHWARTZ, S. S. 1963. Methods of adaptation of terrestrial vertebrates to conditions of existence in the sub-arctic. Vol. I. *Mammals,* Akad. Nauk SSSR Ural Filial Trudy Inst. Biol. (Trans. by E. R. Morrison) 331p.

444 SCOTT, R. W. 1917. CO_2 intake and volume of inspired air. Amer. J. Physiol. *44*:18-21.

445 TIMIRAS, P., A. A. KRUM, and N. PACE. 1957. Body and organ weights of rats during acclimatization to an altitude of 12,470 feet. Amer. J. Physiol., *191*:598-604.

446 VIERECK, ELEANOR G. 1964. Personal communication.

Chapter 9

High Pressure from Air and Water

447 ADLER, H. F. 1964. Dysbarism (Review p. 1-64) U.S.A.F. School of Aerospace Medicine. Brooks A.F.B., Texas. 165p.

448 BASCOM, W. N. and R. R. Revelle. 1953. Free Diving: a new exploratory tool. Amer. Scientist *41*:624-627.

449 BEHNKE, A. R. 1955. Decompression sickness. Military Med. *117*:257-262.

450 BOEREMA, L. (Ed.). 1964. *Clinical Applications of Hyperbaric Oxygen.* Elsevier: New York. 427p.

450a CONSOLAZIO, C. F., R. E. JOHNSON, and L. J. PECORA. 1963. *Physiological Measurements of Metabolic Functions in Man.* Blakiston Div., McGraw-Hill: New York. 505p.

451 DE WITT, H. H. 1965. Antarctic Ichthyology. BioScience *15*:290-293.

452 DODGE, C. H., and G. E. FOLK, JR. 1963. Notes on comparative tolerance of some Iowa turtles to oxygen deficiency (hypoxia). Iowa Acad. Sci. *70*:438-441.

453 DUFFNER, G. J. 1958. Medical problems involved in underwater compression and decompression. Ciba Clin. Symp. *10*:99-117.

454 EBERSOLE, J. H. 1960. The new dimensions of submarine medicine. New England J. Med. *262*:599-610.

455 ELSNER, R. W., D. FRANKLIN, R. VAN CITTERS, and N. WATSON. 1964. Circulatory adaptations in diving mammals. 15th Alaskan Sci. Conf. Alaska Div. AAAS Abstract No. 30.

456 FERRANTE, F. L., and H. N. FRANKEL. 1965. Cardiovascular responses during protracted apnea in a non-diving mammal. Fed. Proc. *24*:704.

456a GIAJA, J. and L. MARKOVIC. 1953. L'hypothermie et la toxicité du gaz carbonique. Compt. rend. Acad. sc. *236*:2437-2440.

457 GRAY, J. S., and R. L. MASLAND. 1946. Studies on altitude decompression sickness; effects of altitude and of exercise. J. Aviation Med. *17*:483-491.

458 HARRISON, R. L. and J. D. W. TOMLINSON. 1963. Anatomical and physiological adaptations in diving mammals. p 115. In *Viewpoints in Biology.* Carthy and Duddington (Eds.). Butterworths: London.

459 IRVING, L. 1939. Respiration in diving mammals. Physiol. Rev. *19*:112-132.

460 IRVING, L., P. F. SCHOLANDER, and S. W. GRINNELL. 1941. The respiration of the porpoise. J. Cell. Comp. Physiol *17*:145-168.

461 IRVING, L., P. F. SCHOLANDER, and S. W. GRINNELL. 1942. The regulation of arterial blood pressure in the seal during diving. Amer. J. Physiol. *135*:557-566.

462 LAMBERTSEN, C. J., and L. J. GREENBAUM, JR. (Eds.). 1963. Proc. 2nd Symp. Un-

derwater Physiol. Nat. Acad. Sci.-Nat. Res. Council Publ. 1181. 298p.

463 McDonald, F. and E. Simonson. 1953. Human electrocardiograms during and after inhalation of 30% carbon dioxide. J. Appl. Physiol. *6*:304-307.

464 Medway, W., and J. R. Geraci. 1965. Blood chemistry of the bottlenose dolphin (Tursiops truncatus). Amer. J. Physiol. *209*: 169-172.

465 Membery, J. H., and E. A. Link. 1964. Hyperbaric exposure of mice to pressures of 60 to 90 atmospheres. Science *144*:1241-1242.

466 Miles, S. 1962. *Underwater Medicine.* Lippincott: Philadelphia. 328p.

467 Norris, K. S., and J. H. Prescott. 1961. Whales, Dolphins and Porpoises. Univ Calif. Pub. Zool. *63*:291-401.

468 Peterson, L. H. 1963. Cardiovascular performance under water, p 267-269. Proc. 2nd Symp. Underwater Physiol. Nat. Acad. Sci. Publ. 1181.

468a Rahn, H. (Ed.). 1965. *Physiology of Breathhold Diving and The Ama of Japan.* Nat. Acad. Sci.-Nat. Res. Council, Pub. 1340.

469 Ray, C. and D. O. Lavallee. 1964. Self-contained diving operations in McMurdo Sound, Antarctica: Observations of the sub-ice environment of the Weddell seal, *Leptonychotes weddelli* (Lesson). Zoologica *49*:121-139.

470 Schaefer, K. E. 1963. Effect of prolonged diving training, p. 271-278. Proc. 2nd Symp. Underwater Physiol. Nat. Acad. Sci. Pub. 1181.

471 Schaefer, K. E. 1963. *Environmental Effects Upon Consciousness.* Macmillan: New York. 150p.

472 Schaefer, K. E. 1963. *Man's Dependence Upon the Earthly Atmosphere.* Macmillan: New York. 415p.

473 Scholander, P. F. 1964. Animals in aquatic environments: diving mammals and birds, p 729-741. In *Handbook of Physiology, Sec 4, Adaptation To The Environment.* D. B. Dill (Sec. Ed.). 1056p.

474 Scholander, P. H., H. T. Hammel, H. Le Messurier, E. Hemmingsen, and W. Gary. 1962. Circulatory adjustment in pearl divers. J. Appl. Physiol. *17*:184-190.

475 Slijper, E. J. 1962.*Whales.* Basic Books Publ. Co., Inc., New York. 475p.

476 Temple-Perkins, E. A. 1955. *Kingdom of the Elephant.* Andrew Melrose: Stratford Place. London. 271p.

477 Tonndorf, J. Personal communication.

478 Van Citters, R. L., O. A. Smith, N. W. Watson, D. L. Franklin, and R. W. Elsner. 1964. Cardiovascular responses of elephant seals during diving studied by blood flow telemetry. 15th Alaska Sci. Conf. Alaska Div. AAAS Abstract No. 106.

Chapter 10

Concluding Remarks

479 Buchheim, R. W. and Rand Corp. Staff. 1959. *Space Handbook: Astronautics and its applications.* Modern Library Paperbacks, Random House, New York. 330p.

480 Driver, A. F. M. 1958. Physiological characteristics in relation to climatic preference. J. Appl. Physiol. *13*:430-434.

481 Feller, R. P. and H. B. Hale. 1963. Human sympathoadrenal responsiveness in autumn, winter and spring. Report TDR 63-46 from School of Aerospace Medicine, Brooks A. F. Base, Texas. 3p.

482 Fleischner, J. R. and Sargent, F., II 1959.

Cross sensitization of rats to heat and cold. Amer. J. Physiol. *14*:789-797.

483 Geoghegan, B., D. F. Roberts, and M. R. Sampford. 1958. A possible climatic effect in nail growth. J. Appl. Physiol. *13*: 135-137.

483a Gillies, J. A. (Ed.). 1966. *Textbook of Aviation Physiology.* Pergamon: N. Y. 1232p.

484 Groundwork for New Journeys Into Outer Space. 1964. Aviation and Astronautics. *11*:24-31. (Trans. from Russian by Joint Publ. Res. Serv., U.S. Dept. Commerce. No. 29,069. 1965.)

484a LAMBERTSEN, C. J. 1961. Anoxia, Altitude and Acclimatization, p. 691-710. In *Medical Physiology*. 11th Ed. P. B. Bard (Ed.). Mosby: St. Louis. 1339p.

484b LAMB, L. E. 1965. Circulatory aspects of manned space flight, p. 343. In *Bioastronautics and The Exploration of Space*. T. C. Bedwell and H. Strughold (Eds.). Aerospace Medical Division, Brooks AFB, Texas. 642p.

485 LANSBERG, M. D. 1960. *A Primer of Space Medicine*. Elsevier Pub. Co., Holland. 165p.

486 MAY, J. M. 1964. *The Ecology of Malnutrition in Five Countries of Eastern and Central Europe. Vol. 4. Studies in Medical Geography*. Hafner: N.Y. 312p.

487 MEFFERD, R. B., and H. B. HALE. 1958. *Studies on Cross-Adaptation*. No. 58-106. School of Aviation Medicine, Randolph AF Base, Texas. 18p.

488 MILLS, C. A. 1939. *Medical Climatology: Climatic and Weather Influences in Health and Disease*. Charles C. Thomas: Springfield, Ill. 296p.

489 MIURA, T. and A. AKUTSU. 1963. Seasonal variation of the optimum room temperature for light work. Reports Inst. Sci. and Labour (Tokyo) *61*:22-32.

490 PROSSER, C. L. 1964. Comparative physiology and biochemistry: status and prospects. Comp. Biochem. Physiol. *11*:1-7.

491 SARGENT, F., II and S. ITOH. 1965. Bioclimatology. Science *147*:761-764.

492 SARGENT, F., II and S. ITOH. 1965. Broader generalizations of the medical biometeorologist. BioScience May p. 371-372.

493 SCHAEFER, K. E. (Ed.). 1964. *Bioastronautics*. Macmillan: New York, 406p.

494 SMITH, R. E. 1962. Cold acclimation—an altered steady state. J. Amer. Med. Assoc. *179*:948-954.

495 SMITH, R. E. (Ed.). 1963. *International Symposium on Temperature Acclimation*. Fed. Proc. *22*:687-960.

496 TROMP, S. W. (Ed.). 1962. *Biometeorology* (a symposium). Proc. 2nd Int. Bioclimatol. Congr. Pergamon Press. 687p.

497 WUNDER, C. C. 1965. *Life Into Space: An Introduction to Space Biology*. F. A. Davis: Philadelphia 400p.

INDEX

DATE DUE

Dec 72			
AG 15 73			

University of Pittsburgh at Bradford

WEIGHT SCALES

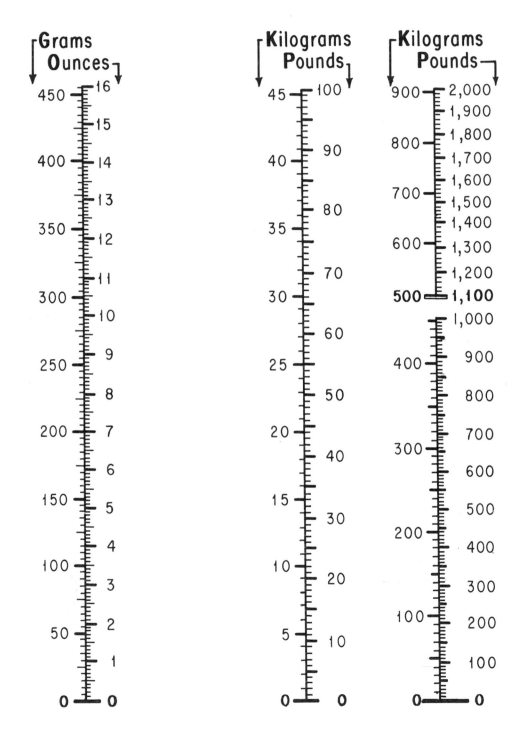

ALTITUDE and
BAROMETRIC PRESSURE

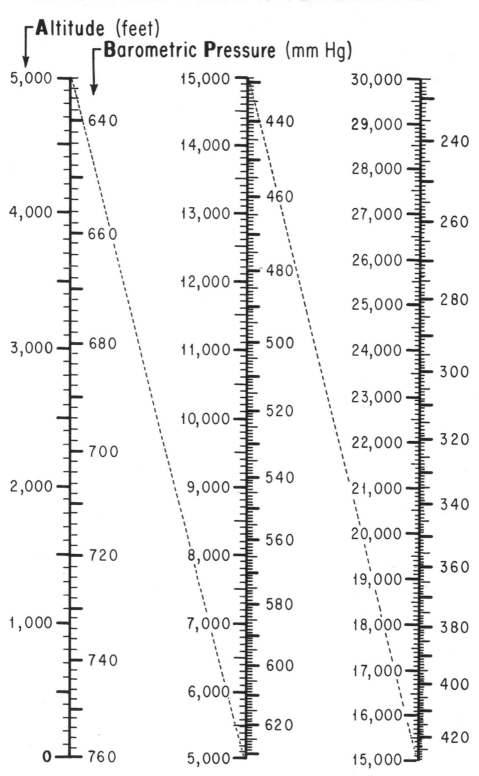

LENGTH SCALES

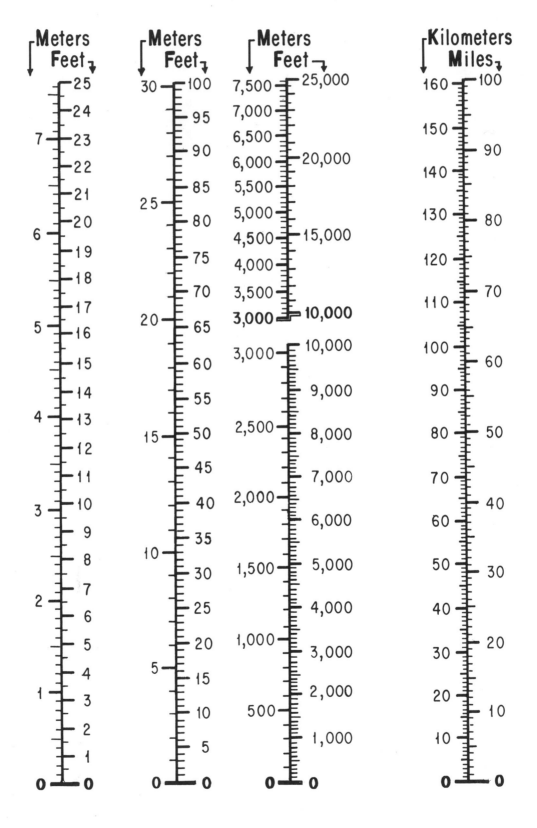